D0868962

PRINCIPLES OF STELLAR DYNAMICS

Mount Wilson Observatory

TYPES OF NEBULAE: NORMAL AND BARRED SPIRALS

PRINCIPLES OF STELLAR DYNAMICS

BY

S. CHANDRASEKHAR

Morton D. Hull Distinguished Service Professor

University of Chicago

Enlarged Edition

DOVER PUBLICATIONS, INC.

NEW YORK NEW YORK

Copyright © 1942 by S. Chandrasekhar

Copyright © 1943 by The New York Academy of Sciences

All rights reserved under Pan American and International Copyright Conventions.

Published in the United Kingdom by Constable and Company, 10 Orange Street, London, W.C. 2.

521.1
C 45 P
112993

Bibliographical Note

This new Dover edition, first published in 1960, is an unabridged and unaltered republication of *Principles of Stellar Dynamics* as originally published in 1942 by the University of Chicago Press. The following articles are also included and are unabridged and unaltered:

Dynamical Friction, Parts I and II, as originally published in 1943 by *The Astrophysical Journal*, Volume 97, No. 2.

Dynamical Friction, Part III, as originally published in 1943 by *The Astrophysical Journal*, Volume 98, No. 1.

New Methods in Stellar Dynamics as originally published in 1943 by the *Annals of the New York Academy of Sciences*, Volume XLV, Article 3. It is reprinted by the kind permission of the New York Academy of Sciences.

Library of Congress Catalog Card Number: 60-50050

Manufactured in the United States of America

Dover Publications, Inc.

180 Varick Street

New York 14, N. Y.

PREFACE

In this monograph an attempt has been made to present the theory of stellar dynamics as a branch of classical dynamics—a discipline in the same general category as celestial mechanics. Such an attempt clearly runs the risk of making idealizations (as in chap. i) which in the light of later developments may prove unwarranted. But the advantages gained for clarifying the fundamental issues involved and the underlying motivations of the theory are such as to outweigh, in the author's opinion, the disadvantages from which the method may otherwise suffer. Particularly, in stellar dynamics the deductive method has seemed appropriate, since we are thus enabled to formulate certain abstract problems (as in § 3.4, p. 89) which appear to have an interest for general dynamical theory even apart from the practical context in which they arise. Indeed, several of the problems of modern stellar dynamical theory are so severely classical that it is difficult to believe that they are not already discussed, for example, in Jacobi's *Vorlesungen.* But, in spite of the purely classical nature of the problems presented, progress in recent years has been recorded along only two principal directions.

The first is in relation to the group of problems in which the question of the time of relaxation of a stellar system occupies the central position and in which the method consists in analyzing the effects of stellar encounters in terms of the two-body problem of classical dynamics (chap. ii). It is now believed that this theory finds its most fruitful applications in the dynamics of star clusters (chap. v). In the second group of problems discussion centers around Liouville's theorem and the solutions of the equation of continuity; here the principal problem is to discover the dynamical implications of the existence of a field of differential motions which appears to be the most striking kinematical feature of the Galaxy and the extragalactic systems (chaps. iii and iv). While these methods have contributed substantially toward the clarification of the peculiarly characteristic aspects of stellar dynamics, an impartial survey of the ground already traversed suggests that we are perhaps still very far from having constructed an adequate theoretical framework in which the physical problems can be discussed satisfactorily. In any case we can expect that the near future will see the initiation of further methods of attack on the problems of stellar dynamics. As an example of such newer methods, reference may be made to the recent statistical theory of stellar encounters which has been developed by S. Chandrasekhar and J. von Neumann since the writing of this monograph. This statistical theory is still so very much in the early stages of its development that it has not been possible to include an account of it in this monograph. But it promises to make fresh starts on a variety of problems, and it is possible that it is along such lines that the final physical theory of stellar dynamics will be evolved. Meantime, it is perhaps of some value to present in a coherent and, as far as possible, a logical form the theories already available, as the present monograph attempts to do.

It remains only to record my indebtedness to Dr. E. Hubble, who provided five of the plates (Pls. I–IV and VI) which illustrate this volume; to Dr. R. C. Williams for Plate V; to Dr. N. U. Mayall for allowing me to quote some of his unpublished results; and, finally, to the University of Chicago Press for their invariable courtesy and consideration.

S. C.

YERKES OBSERVATORY
April 1942

TABLE OF CONTENTS

CHAPTER I

KINEMATICS

Stellar dynamics deals with the distribution of matter and motion in stellar systems. Under the term "stellar system" we shall include any physically significant aggregation of stars. Thus the study of the motions in our Galaxy, in the external galaxies, and in star clusters all come within the scope of stellar dynamics. Specifically, in stellar dynamics the emphasis is on the interpretation of the characteristic features of a stellar system in terms of the forces which govern the motions of the individual stars in the system. Consequently, a kinematical analysis of the state of motions in stellar systems is a necessary preliminary for the study of stellar dynamics. In this chapter we shall therefore attempt to bring together and describe the essential kinematical features of the observed state of motions in stellar systems.

1.1. *The fundamental standard of rest.*—In a general way it appears that the most convenient method of describing the state of motions in a stellar system is by specifying an appropriate distribution function $\Psi(x, y, z; U, V, W; t)$, which gives the number of stars dN in the element of volume $dxdydz$ at (x, y, z) and with velocities in the range $(U, U + dU; V, V + dV; W, W + dW)$ and at a certain instant of time t. Thus,

$$dN = \Psi(x, y, z; U, V, W; t)\, dxdydzdUdVdW . \quad (1.11)$$

It should be noted that in equation (1.11) U, V, and W represent the components of the velocity of an individual star in some *fixed* frame of reference. We shall refer to this fixed frame of reference as the *fundamental frame of reference* or as the *fundamental standard of rest.* From a theoretical point of view it is a matter of indifference how this fundamental standard of rest is chosen, as long as it is fixed. However, for a stellar system in a *steady state* the fundamental standard of rest is best so chosen as to coincide with the centroid of the motions of all the stars in the system, i.e., in such a way that in the chosen frame of reference

$$\Sigma U = \Sigma V = \Sigma W = 0 \,, \tag{1.12}$$

where the summation is extended over all the stars in the system. On the other hand, for a stellar system in a nonsteady state it can happen that the centroid of the motions in the system depends on the time; consequently, the standard of rest defined according to equation (1.12) is not always suitable for general theoretical discussions.

We may add here a few remarks concerning the manner in which the centroid of the motions in our Galaxy is determined. At the outset it is clear that we cannot adopt any direct method for determining the true centroid, since we do not have detailed information of *all* the motions in the system. Recourse must therefore be had to some other, indirect method. Now, from the general space distribution of the globular clusters it appears that they are symmetrically distributed about a plane perpendicular to the Galaxy and passing through the sun in the direction of galactic longitude $325° \pm 2°$, with the same number on each side of the central plane and arranged in an approximately spheroidal form. This symmetry suggests that the system of the globular clusters and the system of the stars are probably concentric. This suggestion appears highly probable when it is further noted that galactic longitude 325° is in the direction of Sagittarius, where the star clouds are richest. Quantitatively, the distribution of the faint stars at great distance from the galactic plane[1] indicates a maximum concentration of the stars in the direction $324° \pm 3°$. On the strength of this evidence, it is now generally agreed that in the system of the globular clusters we have a fair sample of objects which are symmetrically distributed about the center of the Galaxy. It therefore appears reasonable to conclude that the globular clusters will also determine the true centroid of all the motions in the Galaxy. The practical problem thus reduces to one of solving for the *solar motion* with respect to the system of the globular clusters. Let X, Y, and Z denote the components of the velocity of a globular cluster relative to the sun. If $(U_\odot, V_\odot, W_\odot)$

[1] Stars away from the galactic plane are used in this discussion to avoid complications arising from irregular absorption in the plane of the Milky Way.

represents the motion of the sun in the fundamental standard of rest, defined according to equation (1.12), then, according to our assumption,

$$\Sigma (X + U_{\odot}) = \Sigma (Y + V_{\odot}) = \Sigma (Z + W_{\odot}) = 0\,, \qquad (1.13)$$

where the summation is to be extended over all the globular clusters. In practice, only the radial velocities of 43 globular clusters are known. But it is clear that we should be able to determine ($U_{\odot}$, $V_{\odot}$, $W_{\odot}$) by the method of least squares, using (1.13) as the equations of condition. The most recent determination of the solar motion with respect to the system of the globular clusters is due to Mayall,[2] who finds that (in km/sec)

$$U_{\odot} = 129 \pm 19\,; \qquad V_{\odot} = 153 \pm 33\,; \qquad W_{\odot} = 34 \pm 30 \qquad (1.14)$$

in a galactic system of Cartesian co-ordinates.

1.2. *The local standard of rest.*—When we consider "extended" stellar systems like the Galaxy, it appears that it is possible to define a *unique local standard of rest* for describing the motions in a given relatively small region of space. We shall first formulate this notion quite abstractly.

Consider the motions in a small region of space, σ, surrounding the point (x, y, z). The stars in the element of volume σ will define a certain standard of rest. We assume that, as we make σ tend to zero, we shall obtain in the limit a standard of rest which is independent of the manner (i.e., the sequence of shapes) in which we may let σ tend to zero. The standard of rest thus uniquely defined at the point (x, y, z) may properly be called the local standard of rest at (x, y, z). More explicitly, let $U_0(\sigma)$, $V_0(\sigma)$, and $W_0(\sigma)$ be such that

$$\left.\begin{aligned} \sum_{\sigma} \{ U - U_0(\sigma) \} &= \sum_{\sigma} \{ V - V_0(\sigma) \} \\ &= \sum_{\sigma} \{ W - W_0(\sigma) \} = 0\,, \end{aligned}\right\} \qquad (1.21)$$

where the summation is extended over all the stars in the element

[2] The author is indebted to Dr. Mayall for providing this information in advance of publication. But Dr. Mayall wishes to emphasize that the values (1.14) have been derived after a preliminary discussion of the available data and should therefore be regarded as only provisional.

of volume σ. In words, $[U_0(\sigma), V_0(\sigma), W_0(\sigma)]$ represents the velocity of the centroid of the motions in the element of volume σ in the fundamental frame of reference. Our assumption is that $[U_0(\sigma), V_0(\sigma), W_0(\sigma)]$ tends to a unique limit as $\sigma \to 0$. We can thus write

$$\lim_{\sigma \to 0} [U_0(\sigma), V_0(\sigma), W_0(\sigma)] = (U_0, V_0, W_0) . \quad (1.22)$$

It is clear from the manner in which we have derived them that U_0, V_0, and W_0 will in general be functions of position and time.

In the preceding paragraph we have formulated the idealized abstraction which underlies the notion of the local standard of rest. We shall now examine the implications involved in this notion. It should first be noted that in introducing the distribution function $\Psi(x, y, z; U, V, W; t)$ the assumption is implicitly made that a stellar system can be treated by methods strictly applicable to continuous media. It is, however, clear that this idealization of a stellar system to a continuous medium must necessarily break down for sufficiently small elements of volume. Consequently, we cannot strictly carry out the limiting process implied in our definition of U_0, V_0, and W_0. In practice we contemplate a dependence of $U_0(\sigma)$, $V_0(\sigma)$, and $W_0(\sigma)$ on σ somewhat like that indicated in Figure 1. It is thus seen that the possibility of our being able to set up local standards of rest at different points of the system (and at different instants of time) implies that in the neighborhood of every point in the system we can find elements of volumes containing numbers of stars large enough for the notion of a local standard of rest to be significant but small enough to be able to neglect the variation of U_0, V_0, and W_0 over the spatial extent of the elements of volumes considered. It is difficult to formulate the conditions thus implied in

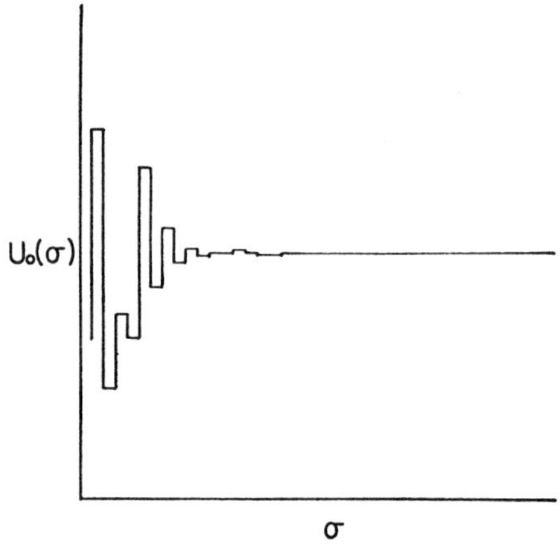

FIG. 1.—Illustrating the circumstances under which a local standard of rest can be defined.

a rigorous manner because of the necessarily discontinuous nature of $[U_0(\sigma), V_0(\sigma), W_0(\sigma)]$, which is particularly serious as σ tends to zero (see Fig. 1). However, the general implications are clear enough. Thus it is fairly obvious that the notion of a local standard of rest will not be of any special significance under the circumstances envisaged in Figure 2. We cannot, of course, draw a sharp line of demarcation between the extreme cases indicated in Figures 1 and 2. On the other hand, it appears reasonable that we should be able to define local standards of rest in stellar systems like our Galaxy. Similarly, the notion of the local standard of rest is probably of no importance for the discussion of relatively small clusters of stars.

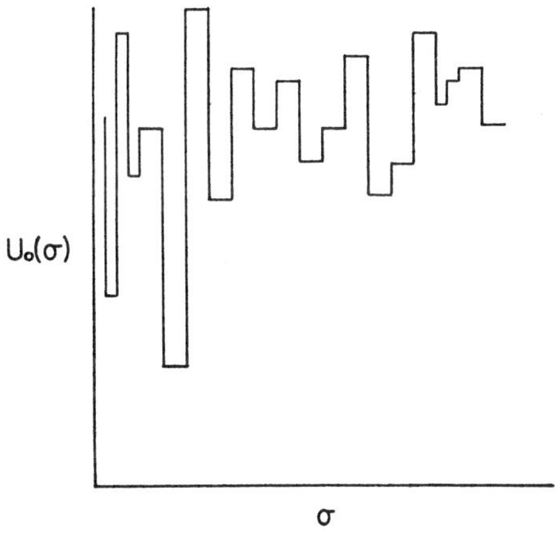

FIG. 2.—Illustrating the circumstances under which a local standard of rest cannot be unambiguously defined.

The determination of the local standard of rest in the neighborhood of the sun in our Galaxy is clearly equivalent to solving for the solar motion with respect to the "near-by" stars. Let (X, Y, Z) denote the velocity of a near-by star relative to the sun. Further, let $(u_\odot, v_\odot, w_\odot)$ be the velocity of the sun in the frame of reference defined by its own immediate neighborhood; in other words, $(u_\odot, v_\odot, w_\odot)$ represents the *local solar motion*. Then, according to our definition of the local standard of rest,

$$\Sigma (X + u_\odot) = \Sigma (Y + v_\odot) = \Sigma (Z + w_\odot) = 0 \,, \qquad (1.23)$$

where the summation should strictly be effected over all the motions in a sufficiently small volume of space (say, a sphere of radius 100 parsecs) about the sun. In practice the local solar motion is determined by the method of least squares, using the proper motions and/or the radial velocities of the near-by stars and employing equations (1.23) as the appropriate equations of condition. It is found that the magnitude of the local solar motion is 19.6 km/sec. The components of this motion along the three principal directions in the galactic system of co-ordinates are (in km/sec)

$$u_{\odot} = 16.6 \; ; \qquad v_{\odot} = 7.2 \; ; \qquad w_{\odot} = 7.2 \; . \qquad (1.24)$$

So far we have spoken only of the centroid of the motions and not of the center of mass. Thus, the components U_0, V_0, and W_0 of the motion of the local standard of rest in the fundamental frame of reference are defined in such a manner that

$$\Sigma \, (U - U_0) = \Sigma \, (V - V_0) = \Sigma \, (W - W_0) = 0 \; , \qquad (1.25)$$

where the summation is extended over all stars in a sufficiently small volume of space surrounding the point considered. In an analogous manner we can define the motion (U_0^*, V_0^*, W_0^*) of the *local center of mass* such that

$$\Sigma m \, (U - U_0^*) = \Sigma m \, (V - V_0^*) = \Sigma m \, (W - W_0^*) = 0 \; , \qquad (1.26)$$

where m denotes the mass of the star. In equation (1.26) the summation is to be effected over all the stars in a sufficiently small volume of space surrounding the point considered. Actually, the two motions, (U_0, V_0, W_0) and (U_0^*, V_0^*, W_0^*), need not be the same. However, as we shall see later in chapter iii, the centroid of the motions is a more significant notion for stellar dynamics than is the center of mass.

From the point of view of our present discussion it is seen that we can divide stellar systems into two kinds: those for which the notion of the local standard of rest is of significance and those for which it is not. In the former case the kinematical description of a stellar system divides itself into two parts: first, the specification of the distribution function

$$\Psi = \Psi \, (x, y, z; u, v, w; t) \; , \qquad (1.27)$$

where (u, v, w) denotes the *residual velocity*

$$u = U - U_0 \; ; \qquad v = V - V_0 \; ; \qquad w = W - W_0 \; ; \qquad (1.28)$$

and, second, the characterization of the functions U_0, V_0, and W_0 in their dependence on position and time. The quantities U_0, V_0, and W_0 may be said to define a *field of differential motions*. Thus, the state of motions in a stellar system like our Galaxy is completely described in terms of the distribution of the residual velocities, on the one hand, and the field of differential motions, on the other. For stellar systems for which the notion of the local standard of rest has no physical validity, the kinematical description will consist simply in the specification of the distribution function Ψ as a function of the seven variables x, y, z, U, V, W, and t.

Finally, we may briefly note how the ideas underlying the notion of a local standard of rest can be further generalized. It will sometimes be necessary to consider a stellar system as consisting of two or more distinct *subsystems*, each of which is described by its own characteristic distribution function (cf. § 1.5). Under such circumstances it would be natural to suppose that in any given small region of space the different subsystems will define local standards of rest which will not all be the same. In other words, each constituent subsystem should be considered as defining its own appropriate local standard of rest. It is thus seen that there is no formal difficulty in considering a stellar system as resulting from the superposition of two or more subsystems. From the physical point of view this is, of course, of importance inasmuch as the possibility that a stellar system can be considered as consisting of two or more subsystems assures us of a certain measure of freedom in interpreting the observational material. From the theoretical point of view, on the other hand, the resulting generalization is of a relatively formal nature. Consequently, for the sake of brevity, we shall, in general, restrict ourselves to a consideration of simple stellar systems and refer to systems formed by superposition only if any particular physical situation demands it (cf. § 1.5).

1.3. *The distribution of the residual velocities. Schwarzschild's law.* —From our discussion in § 1.2 it is apparent that an important part of the kinematics of motions in a system like our Galaxy consists in the specification of the distribution of the residual velocities. As we should expect, stellar motions in the neighborhood of the sun provide us with practically the only source of information we have concerning this matter. The parallaxes, the proper motions, and the radial velocities of the near-by stars represent, of course, the basic observational material for this discussion. An analysis of this extensive material, which is now available, has shown that the distribution of the residual velocities, (u, v, w), is characterized by (i) *randomness*, i.e., in any given direction the number of positive velocities in any given range equals the number of negative velocities in an equal range, and (ii) the mean residual speed in a given direction depends on the direction specified. This latter property of the distribution of the residual velocities implies that the mean residual speed has a maximum value in some determinate direction. This direction of maximum mean residual speed defines a certain preferential direction of motion or, as it is more commonly called, *the direction or the vertex of star streaming.*

Quantitatively, it is found that the distribution of the velocities in any given direction is Gaussian in character, i.e., the number of stars with velocities in the range $(\rho, \rho + d\rho)$ in a given direction can be expressed in terms of the frequency function

$$\frac{j}{\pi^{1/2}} e^{-j^2\rho^2} . \tag{1.301}$$

According to this, the mean residual speed in the direction considered is

$$\bar{\rho} = \frac{2j}{\pi^{1/2}} \int_0^\infty e^{-j^2\rho^2} \rho d\rho = \frac{1}{\pi^{1/2} j} . \tag{1.302}$$ [3]

Since the mean speed is a function of direction, it follows that j is also a function of direction. In particular, j has its minimum value in the direction of star streaming; in any other direction the dispersion of the residual velocities is less. These features of the distribution of the residual velocities, in the neighborhood of the sun, are clearly illustrated in Figures 3 and 4, in which the distribution of the radial velocities in the direction of the vertex (right ascension, $\alpha = 18^h16^m$; declination, $\delta = -12^\circ$) and in a direction at right angles to it ($\alpha = 22^h$, $\delta = +55^\circ$) are shown.[4] The appropriate Gaussian curves which fit the observed distribution of the velocities are also indicated. These diagrams exhibit in an explicit manner

[3] Strictly speaking, we should write $|\rho|$. However, it is convenient to omit the sign for absolute value in writing expressions or equations involving this quantity.

[4] I am indebted to Mr. Ralph E. Williamson for collecting the necessary material and preparing these diagrams (see *Ap. J.*, **93**, 511, 1941).

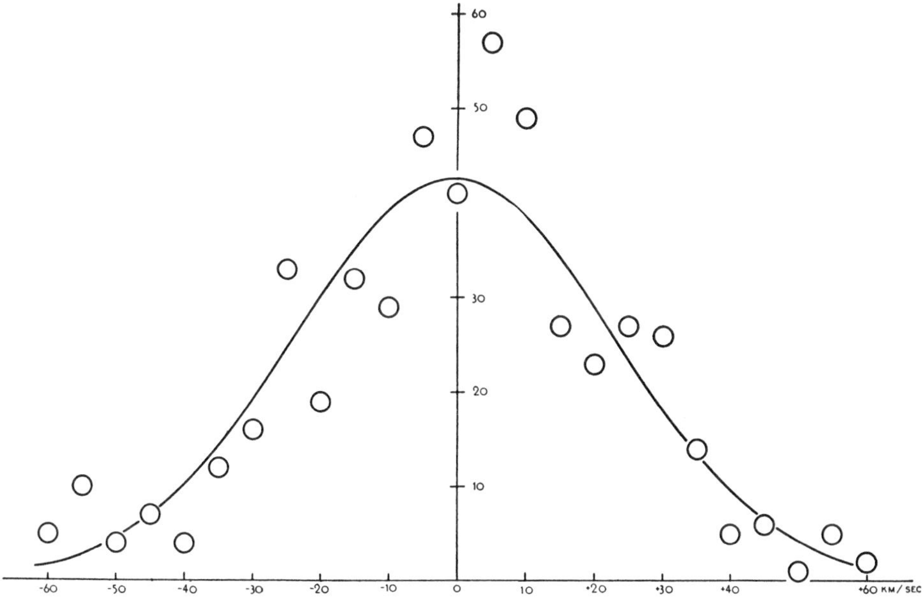

FIG. 3.—The distribution of the radial components of the peculiar velocities of stars near the vertex of star streaming ($\alpha = 18^h16^m$; $\delta = -12°$). The full-line curve represents a Gaussian curve with the same first and second moments as the observed distribution. It is found that the first and the second moments are -0.3 and 23.4 km/sec, respectively; the latter gives the dispersion of the velocities in the direction considered (Williamson, *Ap. J.*, **93**, 511, 1941).

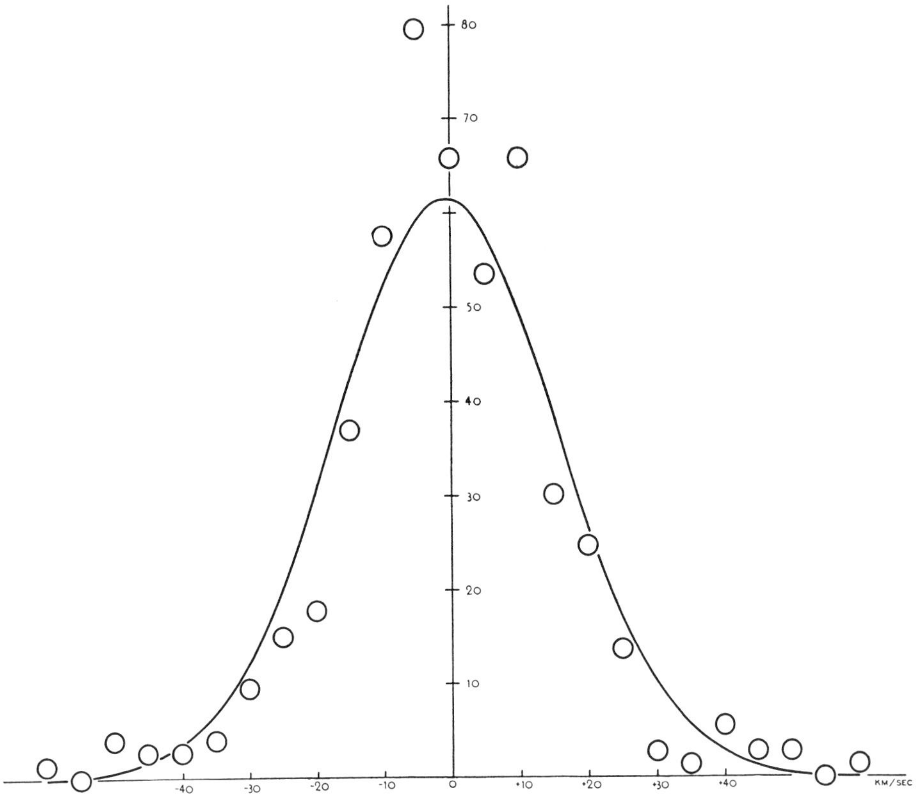

FIG. 4.—The distribution of the radial components of the peculiar velocities of stars approximately 90° from the vertex of star streaming and in the galactic plane ($\alpha = 22^h$; $\delta = +55°$). The full-line curve represents a Gaussian curve with the same first and second moments as the observed distribution. It is found that the first and the second moments are -0.7 and 16.3 km/sec, respectively; the latter gives the dispersion of the velocities in the direction considered (Williamson, *Ap. J.*, **93**, 511, 1941).

the essential physical characteristics of the observed distribution of the residual velocities.

Again, since $\bar{\rho}$ is a function of direction, there must be a determinate direction in which $\bar{\rho}$ has its minimum value. From general considerations of symmetry we should expect this direction of minimum mean speed to be at right angles to the direction of star streaming.[5] To consider more generally the dependence of j or $\bar{\rho}$ on the direction, we shall first set up a system of co-ordinates (u_1, v_1, w_1) such that the u_1 and w_1 axes are along the directions of maximum and minimum values of $\bar{\rho}$, respectively. Let the values of j along the three principal directions be j_1, j_2, and j_3. Accordingly, the distribution of the velocities in these three directions will be given in terms of the frequency functions

$$\frac{j_1}{\pi^{1/2}}\, e^{-j_1^2 u_1^2}\,, \qquad \frac{j_2}{\pi^{1/2}}\, e^{-j_2^2 v_1^2}\,, \qquad \text{and} \qquad \frac{j_3}{\pi^{1/2}}\, e^{-j_3^2 w_1^2}\,. \tag{1.303}$$

Consider, now, some arbitrary direction which has the direction cosines l_1, m_1, and n_1. The value of $\bar{\rho}$ for this direction will naturally depend on l_1, m_1, and n_1; in other words, $\bar{\rho} = \bar{\rho}(l_1, m_1, n_1)$. It is clear that, quite generally, $\bar{\rho}(l_1, m_1, n_1)$ must be an even function of l_1, m_1, and n_1. Further, it is evident that

$$\bar{\rho}\,(1, 0, 0) = \bar{u}_1\,; \quad \bar{\rho}\,(0, 1, 0) = \bar{v}_1\,; \quad \bar{\rho}\,(0, 0, 1) = \bar{w}_1\,. \tag{1.304}$$

A simple formula for $\bar{\rho}(l_1, m_1, n_1)$, which satisfies these requirements, is

$$[\,\bar{\rho}\,(l_1, m_1, n_1)\,]^2 = l_1^2\bar{u}_1^2 + m_1^2\bar{v}_1^2 + n_1^2\bar{w}_1^2\,. \tag{1.305}$$

From our present point of view the foregoing formula for $\bar{\rho}(l_1, m_1, n_1)$ has been written down purely from considerations of simplicity. However, detailed comparisons with the data of observations which have been carried out by Charlier and others have amply confirmed the adequacy of the formula (1.305) for the mean residual speed in any given direction. Table 1*a* summarizes the results of this analysis by Charlier and his associates. Further in Table 1*b* we give the results of a more recent discussion by Nordström based on radial velocities.

[5] Actually, it is known that the direction of star streaming is approximately *an axis of symmetry*, i.e., j (or $\bar{\rho}$) depends only on the angle which the specified direction makes with the vertex of star streaming.

TABLE 1*a*

CONSTANTS OF THE VELOCITY ELLIPSOID

	RADIAL VELOCITIES	SPACE MOTIONS	PROPER MOTIONS
NUMBER OF STARS	1986	646	4182
$1/\sqrt{2j_1}$	19.9 km/sec	27.9 km/sec	23.4 km/sec
l_1	341°.2	341°.3	339°.0
b_1	− 5°.7	+ 2°.8	− 3°.9
$1/\sqrt{2j_2}$	13.4 km/sec	19.4 km/sec	15.1 km/sec
l_2	69°.6	71°.4	70°.0
b_2	+ 16°.2	+ 7°.6	− 13°.4
$1/\sqrt{2j_3}$	15.6 km/sec	16.1 km/sec	12.1 km/sec
l_3	270°.0	233°.1	232°.9
b_3	72°.8	83°.1	+ 75°.8

TABLE 1*b*

THE AXES OF THE VELOCITY ELLIPSOID (IN KM/SEC) AND THE DIRECTION OF THE VERTEX (NORDSTRÖM)

Spectral Class	Average Absolute Magnitude	$\frac{1}{\sqrt{2j_1}}$	$\frac{1}{\sqrt{2j_2}}$	$\frac{1}{\sqrt{2j_3}}$	l_1
A	+0.3	16	12	10	357° ± 10°
A	+1.5	19	9	11	356 ± 5
F	−0.6	20	13	8	321 ± 12
F	+2.1	21	17	13	312 ± 15
F	+3.8	27	17	15	350 ± 8
gG	−0.4	18	14	16	341 ± 20
gG	+1.4	22	16	16	329 ± 17
dG	+3.8	43	29	20	324 ± 12
dG	+5.5	49	32	13	353 ± 10
gK	−1.3	17	12	15	343 ± 14
gK	−0.3	23	15	18	339 ± 11
gK	+0.4	26	18	19	333 ± 9
gK	+1.7	34	18	20	340 ± 7
dK	+6.4	40	28	21	336 ± 14

Now, a general distribution function which will predict, first, a Gaussian distribution of the velocities in any given direction and, second, a formula similar to (1.305) for the dispersion of the velocities as a function of direction is *Schwarzschild's law of ellipsoidal distribution of velocities:*

$$dN = N \frac{j_1 j_2 j_3}{\pi^{3/2}} e^{-j_1^2 u_1^2 - j_2^2 v_1^2 - j_3^2 w_1^2} du_1 dv_1 dw_1 , \qquad (1.306)$$

where N stands for the number of stars considered. We shall now show that this ellipsoidal law (1.306) does, in fact, satisfy the two requirements we have stated.

Our problem is to determine the law of distribution of velocities in some specified direction (l_1, m_1, n_1). For this purpose consider two other directions (l_2, m_2, n_2) and (l_3, m_3, n_3), which together with (l_1, m_1, n_1) form a new Cartesian system of co-ordinates. Let the velocities along these three directions be denoted by u, v, and w. The transformation from the system (u_1, v_1, w_1) to the system (u, v, w) corresponds to a simple rotation, and it is readily verified that in the new system the distribution law (1.306) becomes

$$dN = N \frac{j_1 j_2 j_3}{\pi^{3/2}} e^{-Q} du\, dv\, dw \qquad (1.307)$$

where

$$Q = au^2 + bv^2 + cw^2 + 2fvw + 2gwu + 2huv , \qquad (1.308)$$

where, further,

$$\left.\begin{aligned} a &= l_1^2 j_1^2 + m_1^2 j_2^2 + n_1^2 j_3^2 ; & f &= l_2 l_3 j_1^2 + m_2 m_3 j_2^2 + n_2 n_3 j_3^2 , \\ b &= l_2^2 j_1^2 + m_2^2 j_2^2 + n_2^2 j_3^2 ; & g &= l_3 l_1 j_1^2 + m_3 m_1 j_2^2 + n_3 n_1 j_3^2 , \\ c &= l_3^2 j_1^2 + m_3^2 j_2^2 + n_3^2 j_3^2 ; & h &= l_1 l_2 j_1^2 + m_1 m_2 j_2^2 + n_1 n_2 j_3^2 . \end{aligned}\right\} \qquad (1.309)$$

The quantities a, b, c, f, g, and h are referred to as the *coefficients of the velocity ellipsoid*. The number of stars $dN(u, v)$ with velocities in the range $(u, u + du)$ and $(v, v + dv)$ is obtained by integrating equation (1.307) over all w, i.e.,

$$dN(u, v) = N \frac{j_1 j_2 j_3}{\pi^{3/2}} \int_{-\infty}^{\infty} e^{-Q} dw\, du\, dv . \qquad (1.310)$$

Now our expression for Q can be re-written in the form

$$Q = \frac{1}{c} [(ca - g^2) u^2 + (bc - f^2) v^2 - 2 (fg - hc) uv] + c \left(w + \frac{fv + gu}{c} \right)^2 \tag{1.311}$$

or, more conveniently, as

$$Q = \frac{1}{c} (b_0 u^2 + a_0 v^2 - 2 h_0 u v) + c \left(w + \frac{fv + gu}{c} \right)^2 , \tag{1.312}$$

where a_0, b_0, and h_0 are the minors of a, b, and h, respectively, in the fundamental determinant associated with the quadratic form (1.308), namely,

$$D = \begin{vmatrix} a & h & g \\ h & b & f \\ g & f & c \end{vmatrix} . \tag{1.313}$$

Substituting (1.312) in equation (1.310), we find that the integral is readily evaluated. We have

$$dN(u, v) = N \frac{j_1 j_2 j_3}{\pi c^{1/2}} e^{-(b_0 u^2 + a_0 v^2 - 2 h_0 u v)/c} du\, dv . \tag{1.314}$$ [6]

To obtain the distribution of the velocities in the u-direction we have now to integrate the foregoing equation over all values of v. Thus

$$dN(u) = N \frac{j_1 j_2 j_3}{\pi c^{1/2}} e^{-\frac{1}{c a_0}(a_0 b_0 - h_0^2) u^2} \int_{-\infty}^{\infty} e^{-(a_0 v - h_0 u)^2 / a_0 c} dv\, du , \tag{1.315}$$

or, after performing the integration,

$$dN(u) = N \frac{j_1 j_2 j_3}{\sqrt{\pi a_0}} e^{-(a_0 b_0 - h_0^2) u^2 / a_0 c} du . \tag{1.316}$$

On the other hand, we have the relation

$$a_0 b_0 - h_0^2 = c D . \tag{1.317}$$

Equation (1.316) can thus be re-written as

$$dN(u) = N \frac{j_1 j_2 j_3}{\sqrt{\pi a_0}} e^{-D u^2 / a_0} du . \tag{1.318}$$

[6] This equation gives the distribution of the transverse velocities in the direction (l_1, m_1, n_1) and is thus fundamental to the analysis of the proper motions in this region of the sky.

On integrating equation (1.318) over all u, we find that

$$N = N \frac{j_1 j_2 j_3}{\sqrt{D}} ; \tag{1.319}$$

in other words, we have proved the relation

$$D = j_1^2 j_2^2 j_3^2 . \tag{1.320}$$

According to equation (1.320), equation (1.318) can be written in the form

$$dN(u) = N \frac{j_1 j_2 j_3}{\sqrt{\pi a_0}} e^{-j_1^2 j_2^2 j_3^2 u^2 / a_0} du , \tag{1.321}$$

which thus predicts, as required, a Gaussian distribution of the velocities in the u-direction. Further, the mean speed in this direction can be expressed as

$$\pi \bar{u}^2 = \frac{a_0}{j_1^2 j_2^2 j_3^2} . \tag{1.322}$$

On the other hand, according to equations (1.309), we have

$$\left. \begin{aligned} a_0 = (l_2^2 j_1^2 + m_2^2 j_2^2 + n_2^2 j_3^2)\ (l_3^2 j_1^2 + m_3^2 j_2^2 + n_3^2 j_3^2) \\ - (l_2 l_3 j_1^2 + m_2 m_3 j_2^2 + n_2 n_3 j_3^2)^2 , \end{aligned} \right\} \tag{1.323}$$

or, using Lagrange's identity,

$$\left. \begin{aligned} a_0 = (m_2 n_3 - n_2 m_3)^2 j_2^2 j_3^2 + (n_2 l_3 - l_2 n_3)^2 j_3^2 j_1^2 \\ + (l_2 m_3 - m_2 l_3)^2 j_1^2 j_2^2 . \end{aligned} \right\} \tag{1.324}$$

Since (l_1, m_1, n_1), (l_2, m_2, n_2), and (l_3, m_3, n_3) refer to mutually orthogonal directions, the foregoing equation reduces to

$$a_0 = l_1^2 j_2^2 j_3^2 + m_1^2 j_3^2 j_1^2 + n_1^2 j_1^2 j_2^2 . \tag{1.325}$$

Equation (1.322) can therefore be expressed in the form

$$\bar{u}^2 = l_1^2 \bar{u}_1^2 + m_1^2 \bar{v}_1^2 + n_1^2 \bar{w}_1^2 , \tag{1.326}$$

which is clearly equivalent to equation (1.305).

We thus see that in the neighborhood of the sun the distribution of the residual velocities takes the form

$$\Psi = e^{-(Q+\sigma)} . \tag{1.327}$$

where we have written

$$e^{-\sigma} = N \sqrt{\frac{D}{\pi^3}} . \tag{1.328}$$

We do not have equally detailed information concerning the distribution of the residual velocities in other parts of the Galaxy; but it does seem reasonable to suppose—and it is consistent with such indications as we do have—that the distribution is still of the Schwarzschild ellipsoidal type with, however, different values for the coefficients of the velocity ellipsoid.

1.4. *Observational consequences of a field of differential motions. The differential rotation of the Galaxy.*—Consider the relative motion of two stars S_1 and S_2 at some distance apart. Let the positions of the two stars be (x_1, y_1, z_1) and (x_2, y_2, z_2), respectively. The relative motion of the two stars arises from three different sources: first, the motion of S_1 relative to its immediate local standard of rest at (x_1, y_1, z_1); second, the relative motion of the local standards of rest at (x_1, y_1, z_1) and (x_2, y_2, z_2); and, third, the motion of S_2 relative to its immediate local standard of rest at (x_2, y_2, z_2). The velocity of S_2 relative to S_1 has, therefore, the components

$$\left.\begin{aligned} U_0(x_2, y_2, z_2) + u_2 - U_0(x_1, y_1, z_1) - u_1 , \\ V_0(x_2, y_2, z_2) + v_2 - V_0(x_1, y_1, z_1) - v_1 , \\ W_0(x_2, y_2, z_2) + w_2 - W_0(x_1, y_1, z_1) - w_1 . \end{aligned}\right\} \tag{1.401}$$

Thus, the presence of a field of differential motions in a stellar system introduces in the relative motion of two stars a term which depends on the position of the two stars only. This *differential-motion term* (as it may be called) has the components

$$\left.\begin{aligned} U_0(x_2, y_2, z_2) - U_0(x_1, y_1, z_1) , \\ V_0(x_2, y_2, z_2) - V_0(x_1, y_1, z_1) , \\ W_0(x_2, y_2, z_2) - W_0(x_1, y_1, z_1) . \end{aligned}\right\} \tag{1.402}$$

Following Ogrodnikoff and Milne, we shall now show that the differential-motion term in the relative velocity of two not widely separated stars can be expressed very simply in terms of the local gradient of the differential motion (U_0, V_0, W_0). For let the two points (x_1, y_1, z_1) and (x_2, y_2, z_2) be sufficiently near that we can express the values of U_0, V_0, and W_0 at (x_2, y_2, z_2) in terms of first-order Taylor expansions from (x_1, y_1, z_1). The quantities (1.402) now become

$$\left.\begin{aligned} \Delta U_0 &= \xi\left(\frac{\partial U_0}{\partial x}\right)_1 + \eta\left(\frac{\partial U_0}{\partial y}\right)_1 + \zeta\left(\frac{\partial U_0}{\partial z}\right)_1 , \\ \Delta V_0 &= \xi\left(\frac{\partial V_0}{\partial x}\right)_1 + \eta\left(\frac{\partial V_0}{\partial y}\right)_1 + \zeta\left(\frac{\partial V_0}{\partial z}\right)_1 , \\ \Delta W_0 &= \xi\left(\frac{\partial W_0}{\partial x}\right)_1 + \eta\left(\frac{\partial W_0}{\partial y}\right)_1 + \zeta\left(\frac{\partial W_0}{\partial z}\right)_1 , \end{aligned}\right\} \tag{1.403}$$

where, for the sake of brevity, we have written

$$\xi = x_2 - x_1 ; \qquad \eta = y_2 - y_1 ; \qquad \zeta = z_2 - z_1 . \tag{1.404}$$

Further, it is to be understood that all the partial derivatives in (1.403) are to be evaluated at (x_1, y_1, z_1).

The observational consequences of the term $(\Delta U_0, \Delta V_0, \Delta W_0)$ in the relative motion of two stars are best seen in the contribution which this term makes to the radial and the transverse velocities of a star as measured by an observer at rest with respect to S_1 and at (x_1, y_1, z_1). Let ΔR_0 be the radial component of the differential-motion term; let, further, $\Delta T_0^{(e)}$ and $\Delta T_0^{(p)}$ be the transverse components of $(\Delta U_0, \Delta V_0, \Delta W_0)$ parallel to the (x, y) plane and in the meridian plane passing through S_2, respectively. We clearly have

$$\left.\begin{aligned} \Delta R_0 &= \frac{1}{r}\left(\xi\Delta U_0 + \eta\Delta V_0 + \zeta\Delta W_0\right) , \\ \Delta T_0^{(e)} &= \frac{1}{(\xi^2+\eta^2)^{1/2}}\left(\xi\Delta V_0 - \eta\Delta U_0\right) \\ \Delta T_0^{(p)} &= \frac{1}{r\,(\xi^2+\eta^2)^{1/2}}\left([\xi^2+\eta^2]\Delta W_0 - \xi\zeta\Delta U_0 - \eta\zeta\Delta V_0\right) , \end{aligned}\right\} \tag{1.405}$$

where we have used r to denote the distance between the two stars.

Using in (1.405) the explicit expressions for ΔU_0, ΔV_0, and ΔW_0 as given by equations (1.403), we obtain

$$\left.\begin{aligned}
\Delta R_0 &= \frac{1}{r}\left[\left(\frac{\partial U_0}{\partial x}\right)_1 \xi^2 + \left(\frac{\partial V_0}{\partial y}\right)_1 \eta^2 + \left(\frac{\partial W_0}{\partial z}\right)_1 \zeta^2 \right.\\
&\quad + \left(\frac{\partial U_0}{\partial y} + \frac{\partial V_0}{\partial x}\right)_1 \xi\eta + \left(\frac{\partial V_0}{\partial z} + \frac{\partial W_0}{\partial y}\right)_1 \eta\zeta \\
&\quad \left. + \left(\frac{\partial W_0}{\partial x} + \frac{\partial U_0}{\partial z}\right)_1 \zeta\xi\right], \\
\Delta T_0^{(e)} &= \frac{1}{(\xi^2+\eta^2)^{1/2}}\left[\left(\frac{\partial V_0}{\partial x}\right)_1 \xi^2 - \left(\frac{\partial U_0}{\partial y}\right)_1 \eta^2 \right.\\
&\quad \left. + \left(\frac{\partial V_0}{\partial y} - \frac{\partial U_0}{\partial x}\right)_1 \xi\eta - \left(\frac{\partial U_0}{\partial z}\right)_1 \eta\zeta + \left(\frac{\partial V_0}{\partial z}\right)_1 \zeta\xi\right], \\
\Delta T_0^{(p)} &= \frac{1}{r(\xi^2+\eta^2)^{1/2}}\left[(\xi^2+\eta^2)\left\{\xi\left(\frac{\partial W_0}{\partial x}\right)_1 + \eta\left(\frac{\partial W_0}{\partial y}\right)_1 \right.\right.\\
&\quad \left. + \zeta\left(\frac{\partial W_0}{\partial z}\right)_1\right\} - \eta\zeta\left\{\xi\left(\frac{\partial V_0}{\partial x}\right)_1 + \eta\left(\frac{\partial V_0}{\partial y}\right)_1 \right.\\
&\quad \left. + \zeta\left(\frac{\partial V_0}{\partial z}\right)_1\right\} - \xi\zeta\left\{\xi\left(\frac{\partial U_0}{\partial x}\right)_1 \right.\\
&\quad \left.\left. + \eta\left(\frac{\partial U_0}{\partial y}\right)_1 + \zeta\left(\frac{\partial U_0}{\partial z}\right)_1\right\}\right].
\end{aligned}\right\} \quad (1.406)$$

To bring out explicitly the nature of the foregoing terms in the radial and the transverse velocities in the relative motion of two stars, we shall examine their behavior in some arbitrary plane. Since the orientation of our co-ordinate system has, so far, been left arbitrary, there is no loss of generality if we suppose that the stars we are considering all lie in the (xy) plane. We can then put $\zeta = 0$, and the equations (1.406) reduce to

$$\left.\begin{aligned}
\Delta R_0 &= \frac{1}{r}\left[\left(\frac{\partial U_0}{\partial x}\right)_1 \xi^2 + \left(\frac{\partial V_0}{\partial y}\right)_1 \eta^2 + \left(\frac{\partial U_0}{\partial y} + \frac{\partial V_0}{\partial x}\right)_1 \xi\eta\right], \\
\Delta T_0^{(e)} &= \frac{1}{r}\left[\left(\frac{\partial V_0}{\partial x}\right)_1 \xi^2 - \left(\frac{\partial U_0}{\partial y}\right)_1 \eta^2 + \left(\frac{\partial V_0}{\partial y} - \frac{\partial U_0}{\partial x}\right)_1 \xi\eta\right], \\
\Delta T_0^{(p)} &= \left[\xi\left(\frac{\partial W_0}{\partial x}\right)_1 + \eta\left(\frac{\partial W_0}{\partial y}\right)_1\right].
\end{aligned}\right\} \quad (1.407)$$

Let us now introduce polar co-ordinates (r, λ) in the (x, y) plane with the origin at (x_1, y_1). We then have

$$\xi = r \cos \lambda ; \qquad \eta = r \sin \lambda . \tag{1.408}$$

After some elementary reductions, equations (1.407) become

$$\left.\begin{aligned} \Delta R_0 &= r\,(K + A \sin 2\lambda + C \cos 2\lambda) \,, \\ \Delta T_0^{(e)} &= r\,(B + A \cos 2\lambda - C \sin 2\lambda) \,, \\ \Delta T_0^{(p)} &= r \left(\frac{\partial W_0}{\partial x}\right)_1 \cos \lambda + r \left(\frac{\partial W_0}{\partial y}\right)_1 \sin \lambda \,, \end{aligned}\right\} \tag{1.409}$$

where

$$\left.\begin{aligned} A &= \frac{1}{2}\left(\frac{\partial U_0}{\partial y} + \frac{\partial V_0}{\partial x}\right)_1 ; \qquad B = \frac{1}{2}\left(\frac{\partial V_0}{\partial x} - \frac{\partial U_0}{\partial y}\right)_1 \\ K &= \frac{1}{2}\left(\frac{\partial U_0}{\partial x} + \frac{\partial V_0}{\partial y}\right)_1 ; \qquad C = \frac{1}{2}\left(\frac{\partial U_0}{\partial x} - \frac{\partial V_0}{\partial y}\right)_1 . \end{aligned}\right\} \tag{1.410}$$

The expressions for the differential-motion term in the radial velocity and in the proper motion in the (x, y) plane can be rewritten alternatively in the forms

$$\Delta R_0 = r\left[\, K + \sqrt{A^2 + C^2} \sin 2\,(\lambda + \epsilon) \,\right] \tag{1.411}$$

and

$$\Delta T_0^{(e)} = r\left[\, B + \sqrt{A^2 + C^2} \cos 2\,(\lambda + \epsilon) \,\right] , \tag{1.412}$$

where

$$\tan 2\epsilon = C A^{-1} . \tag{1.413}$$

Consider, first, the differential-motion term ΔR_0 in the radial velocity. According to equation (1.411), for stars in the (x, y) plane and at a constant distance from S_1 the relative radial motions contain a constant term rK and, superposed on this, a *double wave* $r(A^2 + C^2)^{1/2} \sin 2(\lambda + \epsilon)$. Further, the term ΔR_0 is proportional to the distance r; this proportionality with the distance will, however, break down when we go to such distant stars that the first-order Taylor expansions we have used in deriving equation (1.411) cease to be valid. In order to make comparisons with observations, we shall identify the star S_1 with the sun and the (x, y) plane with the galactic plane. Also, we shall assume that the origin of our fundamental frame of reference is at the galactic center and, since it entails no loss of generality, further assume that the x-axis of the fundamental frame of reference passes through the sun. Accordingly, λ is the position angle of a star in the galactic plane relative to S_1 and measured from the direction of the anti-center. Hence, if l_0 denotes the galactic longitude of the center,

$$\lambda = l + \pi - l_0 . \tag{1.414}$$

Now, according to equation (1.402), the radial velocity of a star in the galactic plane can be written in the form

$$R + (\text{local solar motion})_l = \Delta R_0 + (u_2, v_2, w_2)_l , \tag{1.415}$$

where the subscript l denotes that the resolved component in the radial direction of the velocity in parenthesis is meant. In the foregoing equation the quantity on the left-hand side, which we shall denote by R^*, is simply the motion of the star we are considering, relative to the local standard of rest at the sun. We can therefore refer to R^* as the radial velocity of the star "corrected" for the local solar motion. Combining equations (1.411), (1.414), and (1.415), we finally have

$$R^* = r [K + \sqrt{A^2 + C^2} \sin 2 (l - l_0 + \epsilon)] + (u_2, v_2, w_2)_l . \tag{1.416}$$

According to our discussion in § 1.3, the term $(u_2, v_2, w_2)_l$ is of the nature of an accidental error and can formally be treated together with the errors of measurement of the radial velocities (which are generally quite large).

A direct comparison of equation (1.416) with the results of observations is now possible. For this purpose the most suitable material is that of Joy on the radial velocities of Cepheid variables. The particular advantage of the Cepheids for our present discussion arises from the following circumstances: First, they show a very marked concentration to the plane of the Milky Way, so that we can apply equation (1.416). Second, the Cepheids are among the most distant stars that can be observed for radial-velocity measurements. Third, their distances can be estimated from their apparent magnitudes and absolute magnitudes, the latter inferred from the period-luminosity relation. This last, however, is subject to considerable uncertainty on account of space absorption, which affects the apparent magnitudes quite seriously. Consequently, the "photometric" distances determined by a straightforward application of the period-luminosity relation cannot be taken as giving the true distances. But, using the photometric distances as a general guide, Joy has divided the Cepheids for which he had radial velocities into four main distance groups. The radial-velocity, galactic-longitude curves for these four groups are shown in Figure 5. These curves exhibit in a very striking manner the double-wave form predicted by equation (1.416). The increasing amplitude of the curve with increasing distance, which is theoretically predicted, is also confirmed very satisfactorily (Table 2).

TABLE 2

ANALYSIS OF THE GALACTIC-ROTATION TERM IN THE RADIAL VELOCITIES OF CEPHEIDS (JOY)

Group	r (Kpc)	rA (Km/Sec)	A (Km/Sec · Kpc)	$l_0-\epsilon$
1	0.42	10.6	25.1±4.8	332°2±5°4
2	1.06	24.3	22.8±1.6	323.5±2.0
3	1.66	40.6	24.5±1.6	326.5±2.3
4	2.31	39.4	17.1±1.3	325.2±2.6
Mean	....	....	20.9±0.8	325.3±1.3

On examining the observational curves a little more closely, we notice that, within the limits of the uncertainties of the observational material, there does not appear to be any definite evidence for the existence of a K-term in the expression for the radial velocity. In other words, there is no distinct preponderance of stars with radial velocities of one sign, which would be required if there was an appreciable K-term.[7] An adequate representation of the observational material does not, therefore, require the K-term in equation (1.416). We can therefore write

$$\left.\begin{aligned} R^* &= \bar{r}\sqrt{A^2+C^2}\,\sin\,2\,(l-l_0+\epsilon)+(u_2,\,v_2,\,w_2)\,_l\,,\\ K &= 0\,,\end{aligned}\right\}\quad(1.417)$$

[7] However, Trumpler's analysis of the radial velocities of galactic clusters (*Ap. J.*, **91**, 186, 1940) seems to indicate evidence for a K-term proportional to the distance of amount, −4.3 km/sec · 1000 parsecs.

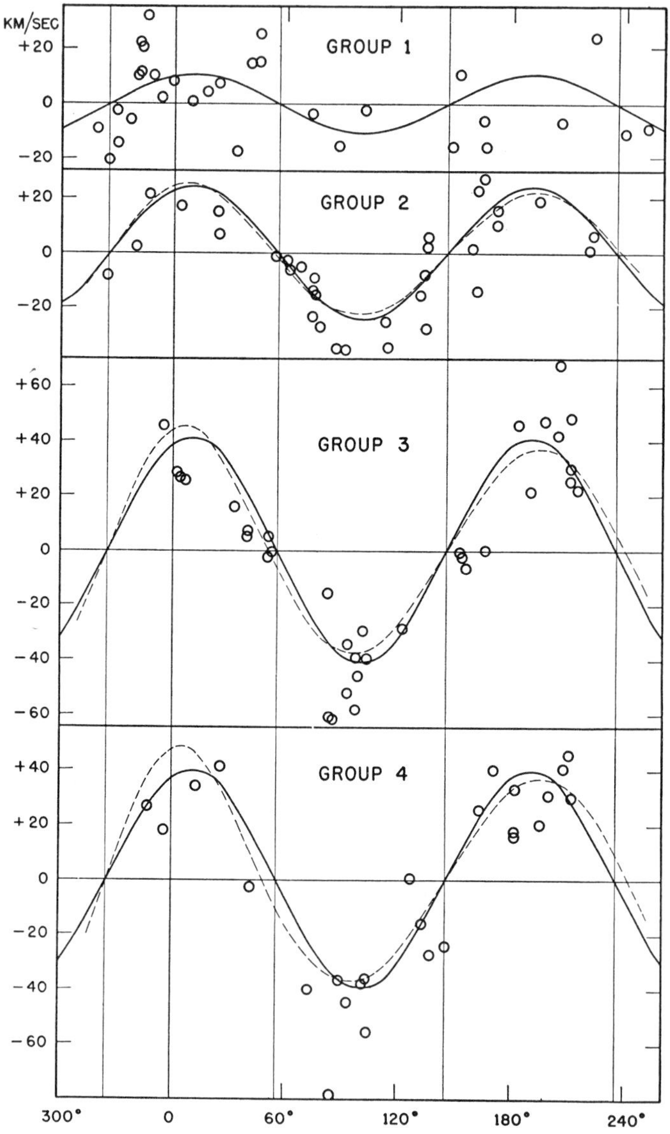

FIG. 5.—Rotational curves for groups 1–4 of Table 2. The observed radial velocities ("corrected" for the local solar motion) are plotted against galactic longitude. The continuous curves represent theoretical solutions according to equation (1.420) (Joy, *Ap. J.*, **89**, 373, 1939).

where $\bar{r}$ is used to denote a certain average distance for the stars in any given group.

Again, an inspection of the curves in Figure 5 shows that the radial-velocity, galactic-longitude curves have nodes at approximately $l = 325°$ and $l = 145°$. A more careful analysis of the material, while confirming this, shows that

$$l_0 - \epsilon = 325° \pm 1° . \tag{1.418}$$

On the other hand, the longitude of the galactic center is $325° \pm 2°$. Hence, the present indications are that $\epsilon \sim 0$. This result is also confirmed by an examination of other radial-velocity material (e.g., Plaskett and Pearce). We shall therefore assume that $\epsilon = 0$; according to equation (1.413) this implies that

$$C = 0 , \qquad (\epsilon = 0) . \tag{1.419}$$

Equation (1.417) now becomes

$$R^* = \bar{r} A \sin 2 (l - l_0) + (u_2, v_2, w_2)_l . \tag{1.420}$$

If the photometric distances for $\bar{r}$ are used, the different groups do not give a consistent determination of the constant A in equation (1.420). But, if (following Joy) we assume that space absorption is present and that it amounts to 0.85 mag. per kiloparsec and reduce the photometric distances accordingly, the general agreement is then found to be quite satisfactory (see Table 2).

Under the circumstances which led to equation (1.420) the expression (1.412) for the transverse velocity in the galactic plane takes the form

$$T^* = r [B + A \cos 2 (l - l_0)] + (u_2, v_2, w_2)_{90° + l} , \tag{1.421}$$

where T^* is the transverse velocity corrected for the local solar motion. An analysis of the existing proper-motion data for the distant stars shows that equation (1.421) is entirely consistent with our present knowledge.

The quantities A and B occurring in equations (1.420) and (1.421) are generally referred to as the *Oort constants.*

After a careful discussion of the existing observational material, Oort suggests the following values for his two constants:

$$\left.\begin{aligned} A &= + 0.018 \text{ km/sec} \cdot \text{parsec} , \\ B &= - 0.013 \text{ km/sec} \cdot \text{parsec} . \end{aligned}\right\} \tag{1.422}$$

We shall now examine a little more closely the meaning of the results $K = C = 0$ (cf. eqs. [1.417] and [1.419]). In order to do this, it is first convenient to introduce cylindrical co-ordinates (ϖ, θ, z) and denote by Π, Θ, and Z the velocities in the radial, transverse,

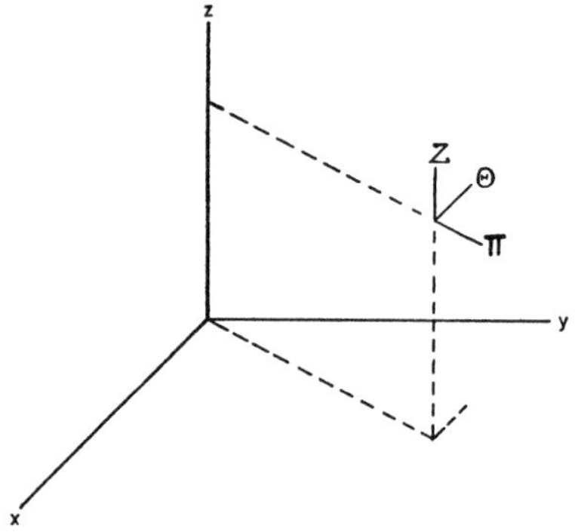

FIG. 6.—Cylindrical co-ordinates

and z-directions, respectively (see Fig. 6). Further, let the differential motion be now represented by (Π_0, Θ_0, Z_0). As may be readily verified, we have the elementary transformation formulae

$$\left.\begin{aligned} \left(\frac{\partial U_0}{\partial x}\right)_{\theta=0} &= \frac{\partial \Pi_0}{\partial \varpi}\,; \qquad \left(\frac{\partial U_0}{\partial y}\right)_{\theta=0} = \frac{1}{\varpi}\frac{\partial \Pi_0}{\partial \theta} - \frac{\Theta_0}{\varpi}\,, \\ \left(\frac{\partial V_0}{\partial x}\right)_{\theta=0} &= \frac{\partial \Theta_0}{\partial \varpi}\,; \qquad \left(\frac{\partial V_0}{\partial y}\right)_{\theta=0} = \frac{1}{\varpi}\frac{\partial \Theta_0}{\partial \theta} + \frac{\Pi_0}{\varpi}\,. \end{aligned}\right\} \tag{1.423}$$

The expressions for A, B, C, and K given by equations (1.410) now become

$$\left.\begin{aligned} A &= \frac{1}{2}\left(\frac{\partial \Theta_0}{\partial \varpi} - \frac{\Theta_0}{\varpi} + \frac{1}{\varpi}\frac{\partial \Pi_0}{\partial \theta}\right)_1; \\ B &= \frac{1}{2}\left(\frac{\partial \Theta_0}{\partial \varpi} + \frac{\Theta_0}{\varpi} - \frac{1}{\varpi}\frac{\partial \Pi_0}{\partial \theta}\right)_1; \\ C &= \frac{1}{2}\left(\frac{\partial \Pi_0}{\partial \varpi} - \frac{\Pi_0}{\varpi} - \frac{1}{\varpi}\frac{\partial \Theta_0}{\partial \theta}\right)_1; \\ K &= \frac{1}{2}\left(\frac{\partial \Pi_0}{\partial \varpi} + \frac{\Pi_0}{\varpi} + \frac{1}{\varpi}\frac{\partial \Theta_0}{\partial \theta}\right)_1. \end{aligned}\right\} \tag{1.424}$$

Hence, $K = C = 0$ implies that

$$\left(\frac{\partial \Pi_0}{\partial \varpi}\right)_1 = 0 \; ; \qquad \left(\Pi_0 + \frac{\partial \Theta_0}{\partial \theta}\right)_1 = 0 \; . \tag{1.425}$$

The simplest representation of the state of differential motions in the Galaxy is therefore obtained by setting

$$\Pi_0 \equiv 0 \; ; \qquad \Theta_0 \equiv \Theta_0 (\varpi) \; . \tag{1.426}$$

It is, however, important to note that the nonexistence of a K-term in the radial velocity and the agreement of one of the nodes in the radial-velocity, galactic-longitude curves with the longitude of the center do not necessarily imply a pure differential rotation of the Galaxy according to equations (1.426). Finally, we may add that within the limits of the observational uncertainties it appears that

$$W = Z \equiv 0 \; . \tag{1.427}$$

For the case of a simple differential rotation the expressions for the Oort constants A and B become

$$A = \frac{1}{2}\left(\frac{d\Theta_0}{d\varpi} - \frac{\Theta_0}{\varpi}\right)_1 ; \qquad B = \frac{1}{2}\left(\frac{d\Theta_0}{d\varpi} + \frac{\Theta_0}{\varpi}\right)_1 . \tag{1.428}$$

From the foregoing formulae we derive the purely kinematical relations

$$B - A = \left(\frac{\Theta_0}{\varpi}\right)_1 ; \qquad B + A = \left(\frac{d\Theta_0}{d\varpi}\right)_1 . \tag{1.429}$$

Using the values of A and B according to equation (1.422), we find that

$$\left.\begin{aligned} \left(\frac{\Theta_0}{\varpi}\right)_1 &= -\,1.0 \times 10^{-15} \text{ radian/sec} \; ; \\ \left(\frac{d\Theta_0}{d\varpi}\right)_1 &= 0.005 \text{ km/sec} \cdot \text{parsec} \; . \end{aligned}\right\} \tag{1.430}$$

Now, from the space distribution of the globular clusters and other similar evidence, it appears that the distance to the center of the galaxy is about 8000 parsecs. Combined with the first of the equations (1.430) we find

$$[\Theta_0]_1 \simeq -\,250 \text{ km/sec} \; . \tag{1.431}$$

The foregoing result is in general agreement with the determination of the solar motion with respect to the system of the globular clusters. For, according to equations (1.14) and (1.24), in the fundamental frame of reference the local standard of rest in the neighborhood of the sun has a motion which has the components

$$\left.\begin{aligned} U_0 &= 112 \pm 19 \text{ km/sec}, \\ V_0 &= 146 \pm 30 \text{ km/sec}, \\ W_0 &= 27 \pm 30 \text{ km/sec}, \end{aligned}\right\} \tag{1.432}$$

or, in cylindrical co-ordinates,

$$\left.\begin{aligned} \Theta_0 &= -184 \pm 30 \text{ km/sec}, \\ \Pi_0 &= -8 \pm 24 \text{ km/sec}, \\ Z_0 &= +27 \pm 30 \text{ km/sec}. \end{aligned}\right\} \tag{1.433}$$

Thus, combining the evidence from the radial-velocity and proper-motion data with the evidence from the motions of the globular clusters, we conclude that the Galaxy is a stellar system with differential motions. More particularly, the simplest representation of the field of differential motions is obtained on the assumption that the Galaxy is in a state of differential rotation.

1.5. *The asymmetry of stellar motions and the phenomenon of the high-velocity stars.*—In the two previous sections we have described the essential features of the stellar motions in the neighborhood of the sun both as regards the distribution of the residual velocities and as regards the character of the differential motions. There remains, however, one further aspect of the kinematics which has to be considered, and that is the extent to which the residual velocities are truly random in character. The observational evidence concerning this matter can be summarized in the following terms:

For residual velocities $|v| < 63$ km/sec the randomness appears to exist to a high degree, while for $|v| > 63$ km/sec there emerges, quite abruptly, an asymmetry in the sense that all such stars have their velocity vectors pointing almost exclusively in one hemisphere. More particularly, it is found that, but for a few uncertain exceptions, the velocity vectors for $|v| > 63$ km/sec occur only in the hemisphere centered about the direction $l = 235°$ and $b = 0°$ and avoid the opposite hemisphere.

To illustrate the nature of the phenomenon encountered and its extreme generality we shall consider the distribution in galactic longitude of all stars with radial velocities greater than 75 km/sec in certain recently published catalogues of radial velocities.[8] Figure 7 shows the observed distribution.[9] We notice at once that there are practically no velocities in the directions included between galactic longitudes $l = 340°$ and $l = 130°$. This, in essence, is *the phenomenon of the high-velocity stars* and *the asymmetry in motions* they exhibit. To discuss this asymmetry more quantitatively we should consider the space velocities, referred to the local standard of rest corresponding to the 19.6-km/sec solar motion. The problem has been treated in this manner by Oort and more recently by Miczaika. Figure 8, taken from Miczaika's paper, illustrates the distribution in galactic

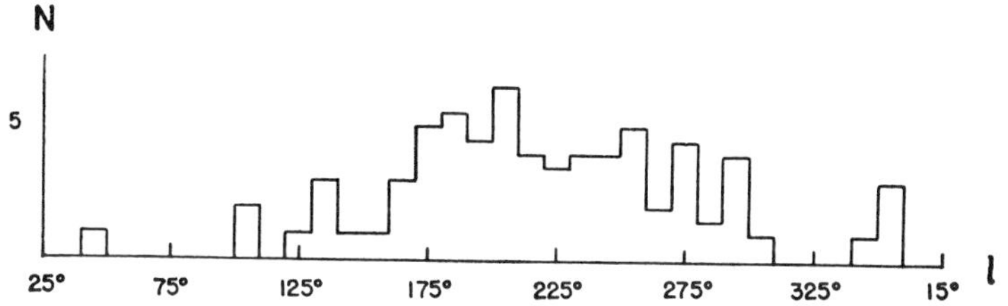

FIG. 7.—Illustrating the phenomenon of the high-velocity stars. The distribution of the directions of the velocity vectors ($|v| > 75$ km/sec) with galactic longitude.

longitude of the high-velocity stars. It is seen that but for a few exceptions the velocity vectors all occur in the interval of galactic longitude $130° \leqslant l \leqslant 350°$. There are some which scatter outside this limit, but they are very few compared to the total number. Further, the scattering outside the limits stated becomes appreci-

[8] W. H. Christie and O. C. Wilson, "Radial Velocities of 600 Stars," *Ap. J.*, **88**, 34, 1938; R. F. Sanford, "The Radial Velocities of Stars of Spectral Classes R and N," *Ap. J.*, **82**, 202, 1935; W. S. Adams and A. H. Joy, "A List of Stars with Unpublished Radial Velocities Greater than 75 Km/Sec," *Pub. A. S. P.*, **50**, 214, 1938; A. H. Joy, "Radial Velocities of 67 Variable Stars of the R R Lyrae Type," *Pub. A. S. P.*, **50**, 302, 1938.

[9] From a theoretical point of view it would have been preferable to have referred the velocities to the local standard of rest as defined by the bulk of the normal stars. However, since the velocities considered are large (>75 km/sec) the removal of the 19.6-km/sec solar motion is hardly necessary when (as in the present connection) our primary interest is merely to illustrate the general character of the phenomenon we are dealing with.

able only for stars with velocities $63 \leqslant |v| \leqslant 75$ km/sec, and this can largely be attributed to the uncertainties in the parallaxes and/or the proper motions. In any event it is found that among the stars of high velocity ($63 \leqslant |v| \leqslant 100$ km/sec) only 7 per cent of them occur outside the interval $130° \leqslant l \leqslant 350°$. Consequently, it appears that the asymmetry exhibited by the high velocities ($|v| > 63$ km/sec) is probably of considerable kinematical significance. This conclusion is further strengthened when it is noted

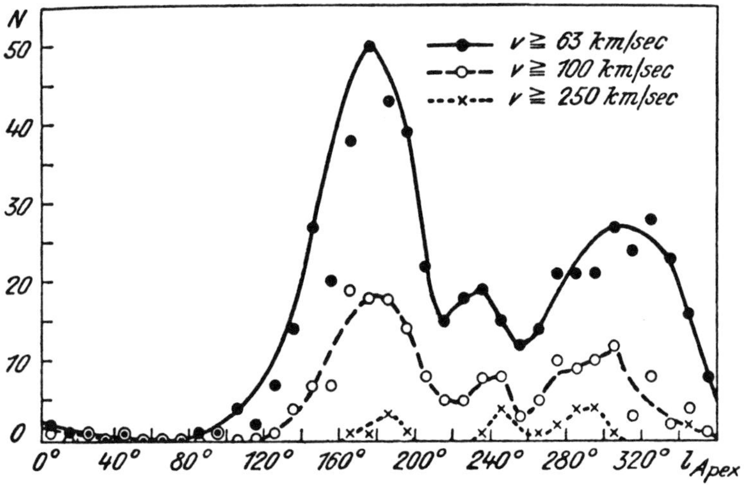

FIG. 8.—The distribution with galactic longitude of the directions of motion of the high-velocity stars (Miczaika, *A.N.*, **270**, 254, 1940).

that the hemisphere of avoidance is centered about the direction $l = 55°$ and $b = 0$, which is exactly the direction of galactic rotation.

Finally, we should refer to the important fact that the asymmetry we have described sets in quite abruptly at $|v| \geqslant 63$ km/sec. This was first made clear by Oort, who showed that if we consider the distribution in galactic longitude of stars with radial velocities between 50 and 62 km/sec, the asymmetry is practically nonexistent. Figure 9, which is taken from a paper by Oort, illustrates the point under discussion. It is particularly interesting to note that for stars with proper motions less than $0\overset{''}{.}300$ the asymmetry for the radial velocities greater than 63 km/sec and the symmetry for the velocities between 50 and 62 km/sec are clearly established. On the other hand, among the stars with the larger proper motions (>0″.300) the asymmetry for the larger velocities is not quite so absolute, while the lower-velocity group also shows indications of a slight asymmetry. This is, however, as it should be, since for the groups with the smaller proper motions the true space velocities will not be

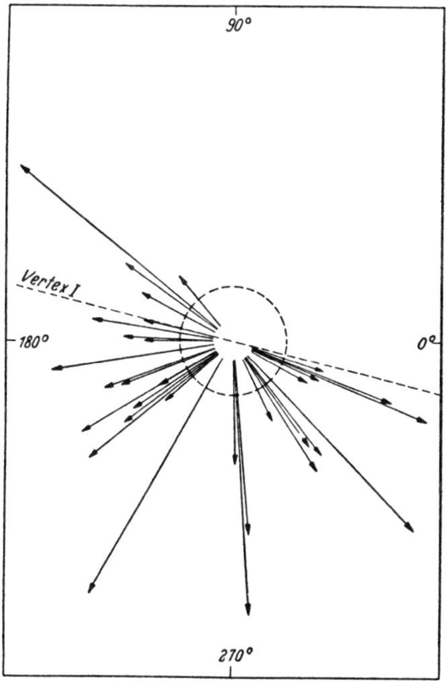

FIG. 9.—In figures 9*a*, 9*b*, and 9*c* we have illustrated (following Oort, *Groningen Pub.*, No. 40, 1926) the distribution in galactic longitude of the peculiar radial velocities larger than 50 km/sec. The radial velocities have been projected on the galactic plane, but the length of each arrow is proportional to the *total* radial velocity. The dotted circles have radii corresponding to 63 km/sec.

FIG. 9*a*.—Illustrates the distribution in galactic longitude of peculiar radial velocities greater than 100 km/sec.

greatly influenced by the transverse motions and will roughly be in directions of the radial velocities; this will not be true of the larger proper-motion groups.

So far, we have considered only the asymmetry in the motions of the high-velocity stars. The *symmetry* in the motions of stars with residual velocities less than 63 km/sec is in some respects of much greater importance and has been very well confirmed by the existing

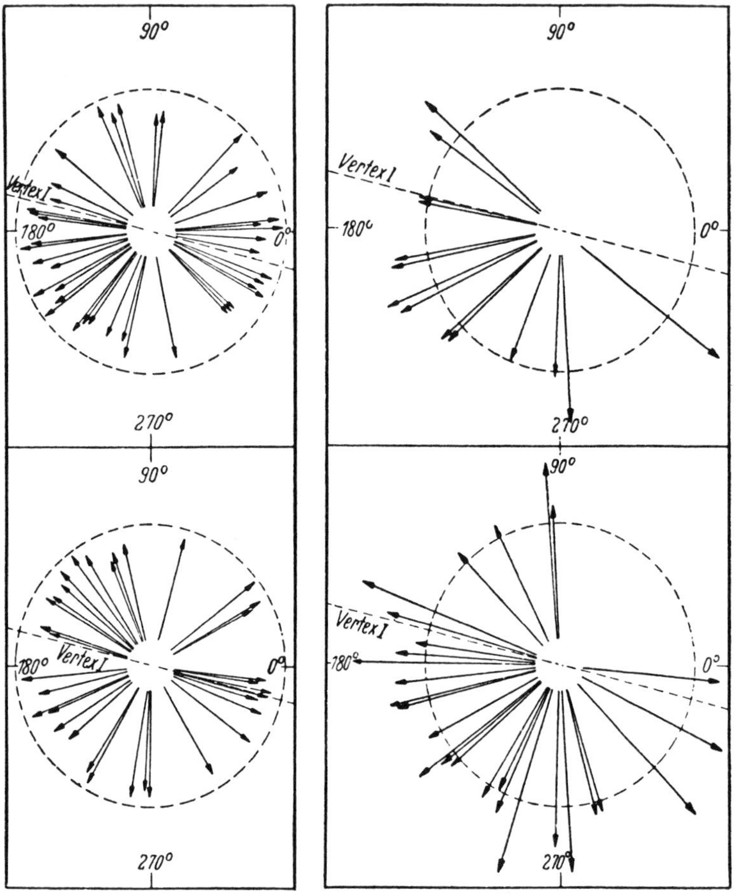

Fig. 9*b* Fig. 9*c*

Fig. 9*b*.—The distribution with galactic longitude of the peculiar radial velocities greater than 50 km/sec and less than 62 km/sec. *Above:* stars with proper motions $<0''.300$. *Below:* stars with proper motions $\geqslant 0''.300$.

Fig. 9*c*.—The distribution with galactic longitude of the peculiar radial velocities greater than 63 km/sec and less than 99 km/sec. *Above:* stars with proper motions $<0''.300$. *Below:* stars with proper motions $\geqslant 0''.300$.

observational material (cf., e.g., Figs. 3 and 4). On the other hand, it is found that there exists a considerable excess of velocities greater than 60 km/sec over what would be predicted on a Schwarzschild distribution, with the constants of the velocity ellipsoid determined to give the best fit with the observational data for the overwhelming majority of the stars. This feature in the residual motions is well brought out in an analysis by Oort of the radial velocities in the Yale catalogue of the bright stars. In Table 3 (taken from Oort's

TABLE 3

DISTRIBUTION OF RADIAL VELOCITIES (OORT)

Limits of Velocity (Km/Sec)	Observed Number	Gaussian Distribution	Limits of Velocity (Km/Sec)	Observed Number	Gaussian Distribution
0–±5	474	498	± 70– 80	18	4
± 5–10	507	473	80– 90	19	0
10–15	417	428	90–100	16	0
15–20	355	367	100–120	12	....
20–25	303	297	120–140	5	....
25–30	229	231	140–160	8	....
30–35	130	172	160–180	6	....
35–40	128	120	180–200	6	....
40–45	91	78	200–240	1	....
45–50	57	50	240–280	3	....
50–55 }	27 } 60	48	280–320	2	....
55–60 }	33 }		320–360	2	....
60–65 }	17 } 35	14	360–400	0	....
65–70 }	18 }				

paper) a comparison is made between the observed distribution of the radial velocities and a Gaussian distribution.[10] The computed

[10] It might have been preferable to have referred the velocities to the local standard of rest, but it is readily seen that this will not provide any special advantages in our present connection. For, if the stars under consideration are distributed uniformly over the sky, the frequency function for the uncorrected radial velocities ρ^* is given by (cf. eq. [1. 301])

$$F(\rho^*) = \frac{1}{4\pi}\int_0^{2\pi}\int_0^{\pi}\frac{j_{\lambda,\varphi}}{\pi^{1/2}}\, e^{-j^2_{\lambda,\varphi}(\rho^* - v_\odot \cos\lambda)^2}\sin\lambda d\lambda d\varphi\,, \tag{1.51}$$

where $v_\odot$ denotes the magnitude of the solar motion, λ the angular distance from the solar apex, and $j_{\lambda,\varphi}$ a function of direction depending on the orientation of the velocity ellipsoid (eq. [1.305]). We can re-write equation (1.51) in the form

$$F(\rho^*) = \frac{1}{4\pi}\int_0^{2\pi}\int_0^{\pi}\frac{\bar{j}}{\pi^{1/2}}\, e^{-\bar{j}^2(\rho^* - v_\odot \cos\lambda)^2}\sin\lambda d\lambda d\varphi\,, \tag{1.52}$$

where $\bar{j}$ is a certain mean value of $j_{\lambda,\varphi}$. The integration of equation (1.52) over φ is immediate. After some further reductions, equation (1.52) becomes

$$F(\rho^*) = \frac{1}{2\pi^{1/2}v_\odot}\int_{\bar{j}(\rho^* - v_\odot)}^{\bar{j}(\rho^* + v_\odot)} e^{-z^2}dz \simeq \frac{\bar{j}}{\sqrt{\pi}}\, e^{-\bar{j}^2\rho^{*2}}\,. \tag{1.53}$$

In other words, the frequency function $F(\rho^*)$ is approximately a Gaussian function.

Gaussian distribution is for a modulus $\bar{j} = 0.032$ and corresponds to a mean speed of 17.6 km/sec. It is seen that the observed distribution agrees with the computed distribution very closely for velocities less than 60 km/sec. But we also notice that there is observed a considerable excess of velocities greater than 60 km/sec over the predicted numbers. A more detailed examination of the stars which contribute to this excess shows that the velocity vectors of all these stars are, in fact, confined to the hemisphere centered about the direction $l = 235°$ and $b = 0$ and thus exhibit the asymmetry as well. We can, therefore, finally summarize the situation in the following terms: "There is absolute asymmetry for all velocities greater than 62 km/sec while those below 63 km/sec do not show any trace of it" (Oort).

From our discussion in the preceding paragraphs it would now seem that we should consider the system of the high-velocity stars as forming a subsystem distinct from the majority of the stars to which our considerations in §§ 1.3 and 1.4 strictly apply. If this conclusion be accepted, it would appear that a procedure satisfactory from a theoretical standpoint for considering the kinematics of this system of the high-velocity stars should consist of the following steps.

First, the solar motion $(u_\odot, v_\odot, w_\odot)_H$ with respect to the high-velocity stars should be determined. Second, the velocities determined with respect to the sun should be freed from the solar motion $(u_\odot, v_\odot, w_\odot)_H$. Finally, the distribution of the velocities of the high-velocity stars in the frame of reference defined by these stars themselves should be considered in a manner quite analogous to that adopted in discussing the distribution of the residual velocities of the normal stars with respect to local standard defined by themselves. A discussion of this kind seems to indicate that the system of the high-velocity stars determines a standard of rest, which has a rotational velocity about the galactic center which is different from that of the normal stars. This conclusion appears to be confirmed by the following consideration.

According to Miczaika the solar motion with respect to the system of the high-velocity stars is 56.2 km/sec in the direction $l = 45°$,

$b = 8°$. The components of this motion in the galactic system of co-ordinates are

$$\left.\begin{array}{ll} (u_{\odot})_H = 39.3 \text{ km/sec}; & (v_{\odot})_H = 39.3 \text{ km/sec}; \\ & (w_{\odot})_H = 7.8 \text{ km/sec}. \end{array}\right\} \quad (1.54)$$

According to equations (1.24) and (1.54), it now follows that the standard of rest defined by the high-velocity stars has a motion relative to the centroid of the motions of the normal stars; the components of this motion are

$$\left.\begin{array}{l} u_{\odot} - (u_{\odot})_H = -22.7 \text{ km/sec}, \\ v_{\odot} - (v_{\odot})_H = -32.1 \text{ km/sec}, \\ w_{\odot} - (w_{\odot})_H = -\ \ 0.6 \text{ km/sec}. \end{array}\right\} \quad (1.55)$$

It is readily seen that the components (1.55) define a velocity of 40 km/sec in the galactic plane and in a direction $l = 55° = \tan^{-1} 32.1/22.7$. In other words, we may say that the system of the high-velocity stars is characterized by a rotational velocity $(\Theta_0)_H$ which is less than the rotational velocity Θ_0 of the local standard of rest of the majority of the stars by about 40 km/sec.

1.6. *Extragalactic systems. Structural features.*—In §§ 1.3 and 1.4 we have described the state of motions in our galaxy in terms of certain fundamental notions (§§ 1.1 and 1.3) which appear most convenient for this purpose. It is evident that an equally explicit statement of the kinematical situation encountered in extragalactic nebulae[11] cannot be made. However, we now know sufficiently about the nebulae to analyze in a general way the nature of the problems presented by these objects. In this and in the following sections we shall briefly summarize the information which appears most relevant to the formulation of certain dynamical problems.

In some ways the most interesting aspect of the study of nebulae is their classification and their structure.[12]

Most nebulae are "regular" in the sense that they are character-

[11] In future we shall drop the adjective "extragalactic" and use the term "nebulae" to denote the extragalactic nebulae, unless otherwise stated.

[12] Our discussion will follow closely Hubble's discussion in "*The Realm of the Nebulae*," chap. ii, New Haven, 1937.

ized by definite patterns and central nuclei. But a few (about 2.5 per cent) do not show these features and are accordingly classed as "irregular" nebulae. Hubble has shown that the regular nebulae fall naturally into a continuous sequence of structural forms. This classification of Hubble appears quite fundamental inasmuch as not only the structural features but also other physical characteristics like stellar content, spectral type, color, etc., all vary systematically through the sequence.

Regular nebulae are divided broadly into two groups: the elliptical nebulae and the spirals, with a transition stage between

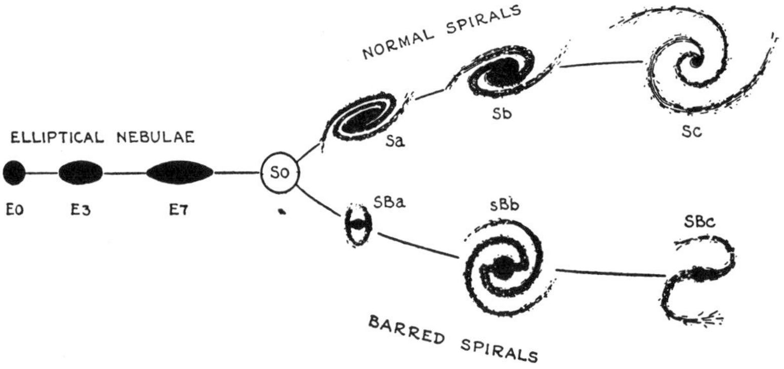

FIG. 10.—Hubble's sequence of nebular types

them. Again, the spirals fall into two classes: the "normal" spirals and the "barred" spirals. But it appears that the elliptical nebulae and the spirals can all be arranged in a single bifurcating sequence (cf. Fig. 10).

i) *Elliptical nebulae.*—Elliptical nebulae range from globular objects to lenticular bodies with a limiting ratio of the axes of about 3:1. It is generally believed that elliptical nebulae with a higher value for the ratio of the axes do not probably exist. These nebulae are apparently very highly concentrated, since indications for the resolution into stars have not been found. The shapes of these objects can, of course, be readily estimated by simple inspection. But these refer to the projected contours on the sky and not to the actual three-dimensional nebulae. However, on the assumption that the nebulae are oriented in random directions in space, it is

PLATE I

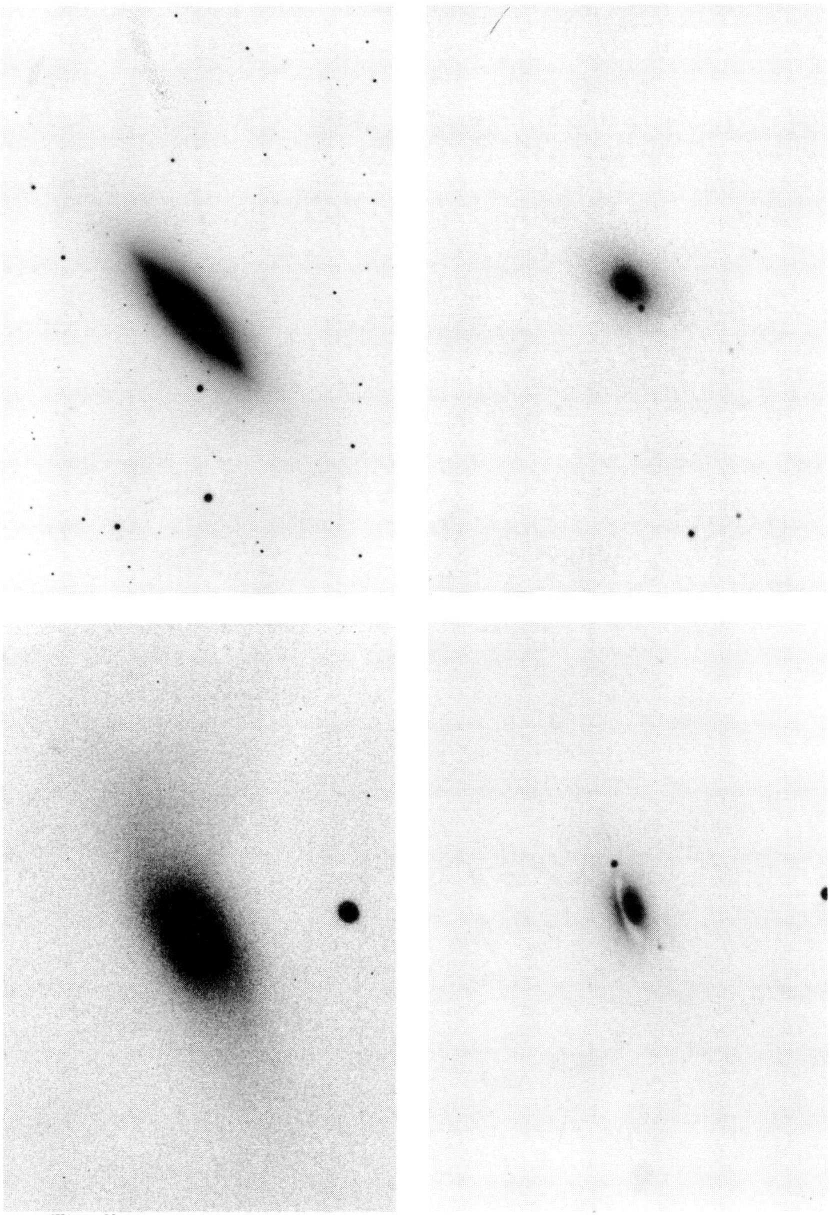

Mount Wilson Observatory

TRANSITION TYPES

Upper left: Lenticular system NGC 4530, classed as E7, the flattest of the elliptical nebulae. *Upper right:* NGC 4150, the earliest of the transition types SO. A central lens is vaguely differentiated from the main body of the nebula. *Lower:* A long and a short exposure of NGC 4526, a more advanced form of the transition type. The central lens is well differentiated, and within the lens is a ring of finely divided dark material (negative print).

possible by statistical methods to estimate the true frequency of occurrence of a given ellipticity. From an analysis of this kind, it has been concluded that objects with true forms ranging from spherical to lenticular shapes do exist. Further, it appears that truly spherical nebulae are relatively rare and that frequencies increase with increasing ellipticity.

Elliptical nebulae are designated by the symbols $E0$, $E1$, ... , $E7$, where the numerical index denotes the integer nearest to ten times the ellipticity (see Pl. I for examples of elliptical nebulae).

ii) *Transition-type nebulae.*—Nebulae belonging to this class are placed at the end of the sequence of elliptical nebulae. According to Hubble, the first evidence of internal structure is the "differentiation" of a bright central lens which has a diameter of about a third of that of the main body of the nebula. The further development seems to consist in the emergence of circular patterns of obscuration in the form of lanes of dark material silhouetted against the luminous background.

iii) *The normal spirals.*—Along this sequence the circular patterns appearing in the transition stage gradually disintegrate and are replaced by spiral structure. At the beginning of the sequence the normal spiral is characterized by a bright semistellar nucleus surrounded by a relatively large nebulosity; further, the spiral arms themselves are very closely coiled around the main body. However, as the sequence progresses, the arms become increasingly conspicuous and in the very open, well-resolved spirals like M101 the nucleus appears quite insignificant (see the Frontispiece).

About the middle of the sequence, the resolution into stars becomes apparent, the resolution increasing as the sequence progresses. Toward the end of the sequence the condensations are seen to reach the nuclear region itself. The stars that can be detected in spirals are blue supergiants. In this respect the spirals differ from the elliptical nebulae, which are known to lack supergiants.[13] The normal spirals are designated by the symbol S.

iv) *Barred spirals.*—The sequence of barred spirals branches off from the sequence of normal spirals quite early in the transition-

[13] It is thought that this may be one of the reasons why individual stars have not been detected in elliptical nebulae.

stage nebulae. At first, a bright diameter appears across the lens, which later develops into a definite bar, which stops at the rim of the lens (see Pl. II, also the Frontispiece). Meantime, the rim of the lens has condensed into a ring, and the nebula resembles the letter θ. Farther along the sequence, the ring appears to break away from the bar at its ends but on opposite sides—thus: . Beyond this point the sequence has not been followed in detail. But frequently the broken ends of the ring seem to drift apart, while the nebula begins to develop a spiral structure. Finally, in the last stages the arms are almost completely unwound and become approximate straight lines. The barred spirals are designated by the symbol *SB*.

v) *Sequence of spirals.*—The two sequences of spirals are subdivided into three main sections, denoted by the letters *a*, *b*, and *c*. Thus, *Sa*, *Sb*, and *Sc* represent *early-*, *intermediate-*, and *late*-type normal spirals. Similarly, *SBa*, *SBb*, and *SBc* denote the corresponding types in the sequence of barred spirals. Any spiral can be assigned a place in one of the two sequences, depending on the openness of the arms, the extent of the resolution into stars, and the relative luminosity of the nuclear region and the spiral arms.

vi) *The sequence of regular nebulae.*—Since the early-type spirals *Sa* and *SBa* have a certain amount of resemblance to the *E*7 elliptical nebulae, we can arrange the three classes of regular nebulae in a single bifurcated sequence (see Fig. 10). The junction of the three classes may be taken to represent the transition types, in which the differentiation of a lens from the main body is the most important characteristic.

vii) *The irregular nebulae.*—These nebulae do not fall into line with the general sequence we have described, but we may note that the irregular nebulae themselves can be divided into two roughly equal groups. Typical examples of the two groups are NGC 520 and the Magellanic Clouds, respectively. The former consist of chaotic masses of unresolved nebulosity and dark material. Very little seems to be known of these highly interesting objects, but presumably they consist of stars and "dust." The second group of irregular nebulae are highly resolved but present no nuclei or any distinct pattern. The luminosities of the Magellanic type of nebulae range from those of normal nebulae to "dwarf systems," which are hardly brighter

PLATE II

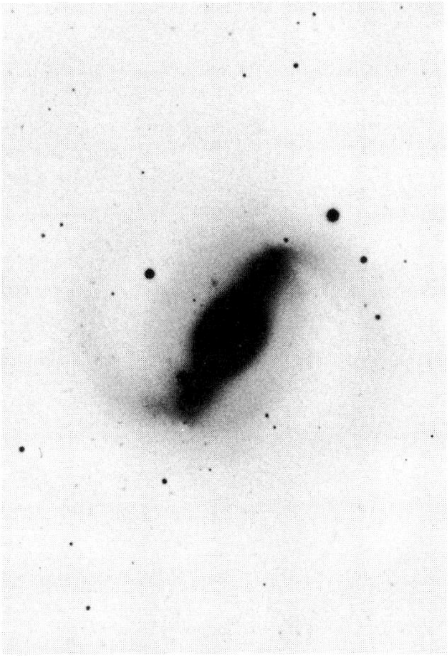

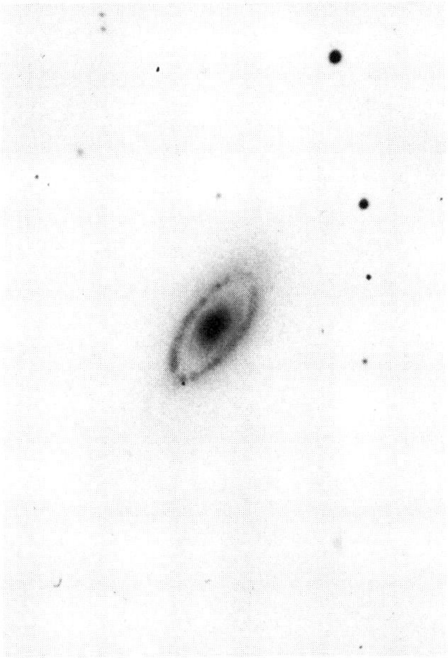

Mount Wilson Observatory

EARLY-TYPE SPIRALS

Upper left: NGC 4440, a barred spiral, SBa. *Upper right:* NGC 4324, a normal spiral, Sa, in which a ring structure has developed outside the lens and has partially disintegrated. *Lower:* NGC 3623, Sa, in which a spiral pattern has developed within the main body (negative print).

PLATE III

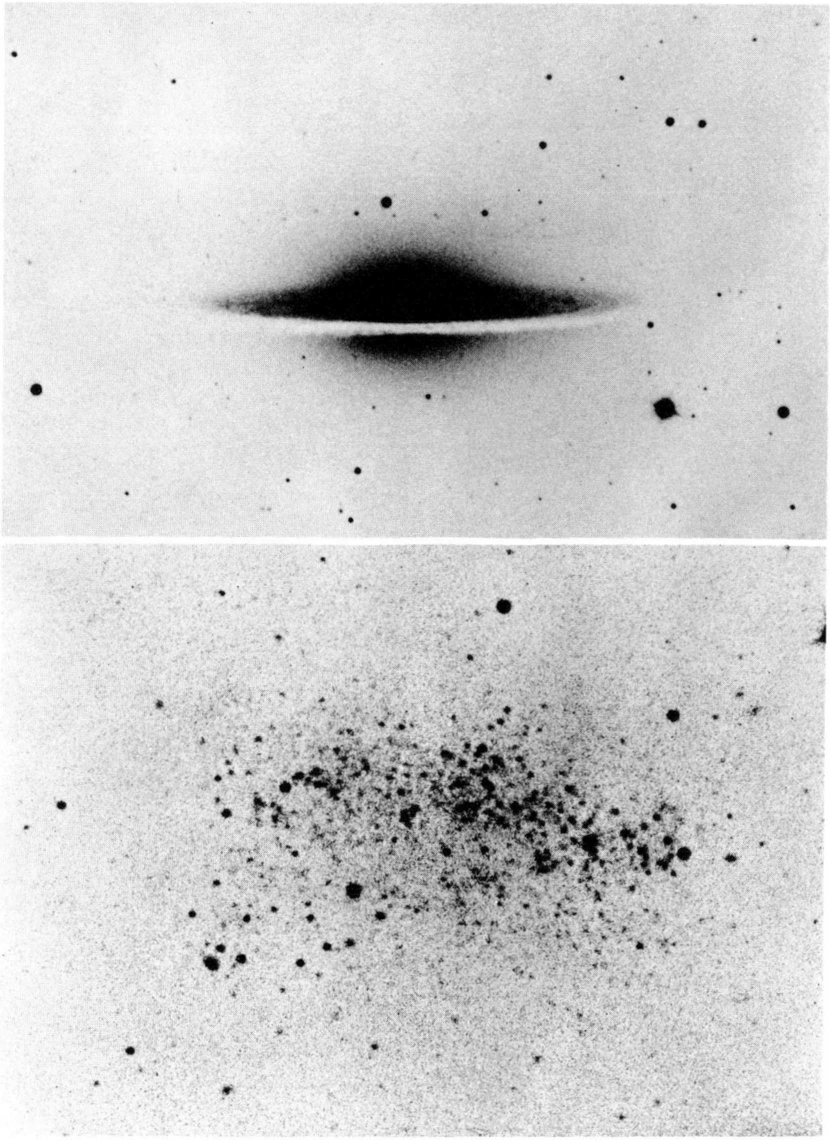

Mount Wilson Observatory

GIANT AND DWARF

Upper: NGC 4594, the brightest known giant, estimated to be 2.3×10^9 times as bright as the sun. *Lower:* Zwicky's system in Leo, the faintest known dwarf, estimated to be only 5×10^5 times as bright as the sun (negative print).

PLATE IV

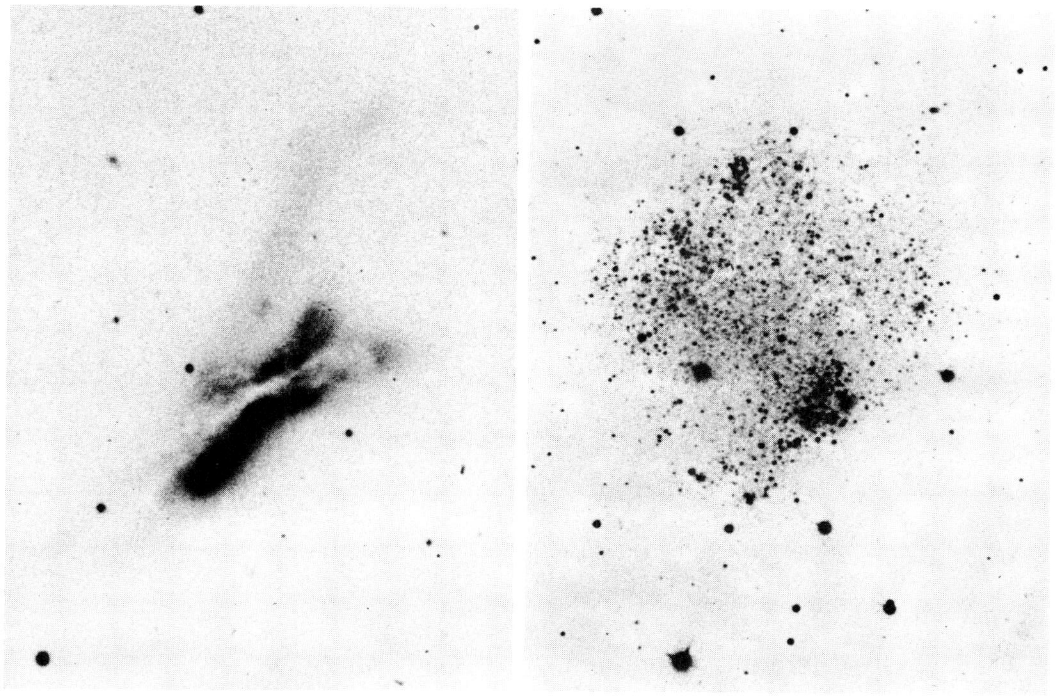

Mount Wilson Observatory

IRREGULAR NEBULAE

Left: NGC 520, a chaotic type. *Right:* Zwicky's system in Sextans, a Magellanic Cloud type (negative print)

than the globular clusters. Thus, one of these dwarf systems in Leo is known to be only about as bright as the brightest of the globular clusters, namely, ω Centauri (see Pls. III and IV for examples of irregular nebulae).

viii) *Some general features of the sequence.*—One of the most important characteristics of Hubble's classification is that nebulae of any given type are very similar. For it is found that the luminosity of a nebula of a given type varies directly as the square of the diameter. In other words, for a given luminosity and type the nebulae have (on the average) a determinate size. It is further known that for a given luminosity the sizes increase monotonically along the sequence from *E*0 to *Sc* (or *SBc*).

TABLE 4

STATISTICS ON TYPES OF NEBULAE

Type	Frequency of Occurrence (Per Cent)	Spectral Type	Color
*E*0–*E*7	17	G4	g6
Sa, *SBa*	19	G3	g5
Sb, *SBb*	25	G2	g4
Sc, *SBc*	36	F9	f7
Irregular	2.5	....	....

Table 4 gives some further data concerning the variation of other physical characteristics along the sequence.

1.7. *Extragalactic systems. Kinematical features.*—According to our discussion in § 1.2 we should expect that, as in the case of our Galaxy, the kinematics of an extragalactic system would also consist of two parts: first, the nature of the distribution of the residual velocities with respect to the immediate local standards at different points of the system and, second, the character of the differential motions present. The only means by which information concerning the former aspect of the kinematics of nebulae can be obtained would be from an analysis of the contours of spectral lines. For the residual motions in a given region of space will influence the form of the spectral lines. Consequently, from the measured line contours we should be able to infer something about the distribution of the residual velocities in various parts of the nebula. But no such analysis exists at present. On the other hand, our knowledge of the differential motions present is in a very much more advanced state. Here our information is limited to a few but well-studied nebulae: the Andromeda nebula (by Babcock), Messier 33 (by Mayall and Aller), NGC 3190 (by Hubble and Mayall).

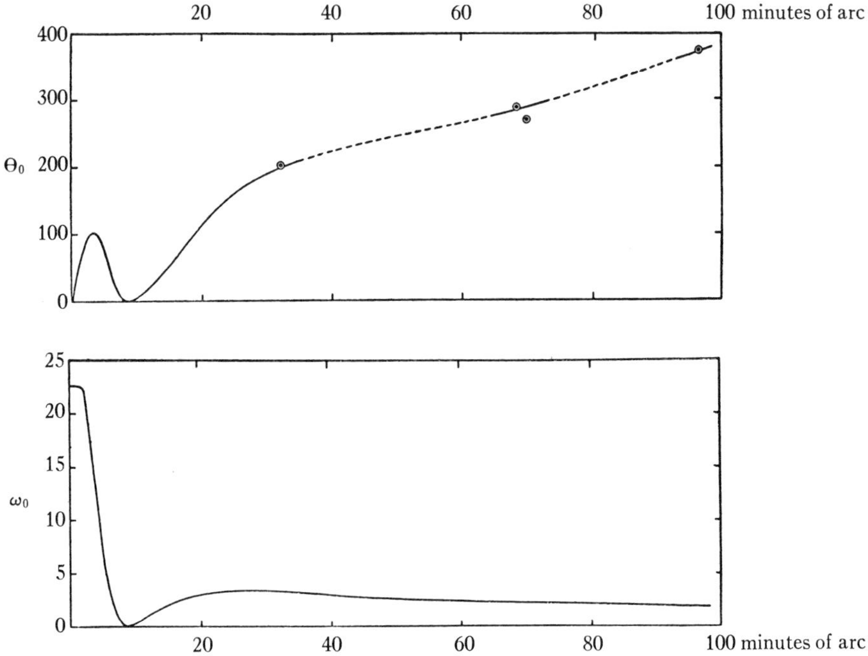

FIG. 11.—The rotation-curve for the Andromeda nebula: The rotational velocity, Θ_0, expressed in km/sec and the angular velocity, ω_0, in units of 10^{-15} radians/sec (Babcock, *Lick Obs. Bull.*, No. 498, 1939).

We shall first consider the differential motions which are present in the Andromeda nebula (see Pl. V). In Hubble's classification this nebula belongs to the class *Sb*. Further, the equatorial plane is believed to be inclined to the line of sight by about 15°. For this nebula velocities in the line of sight have been measured by Babcock along the major axis to a distance of 1°.6 from the nucleus. Allowing for the inclination of the nebula and assuming that the differential motions correspond to a pure rotation, we can convert the measured radial

PLATE V

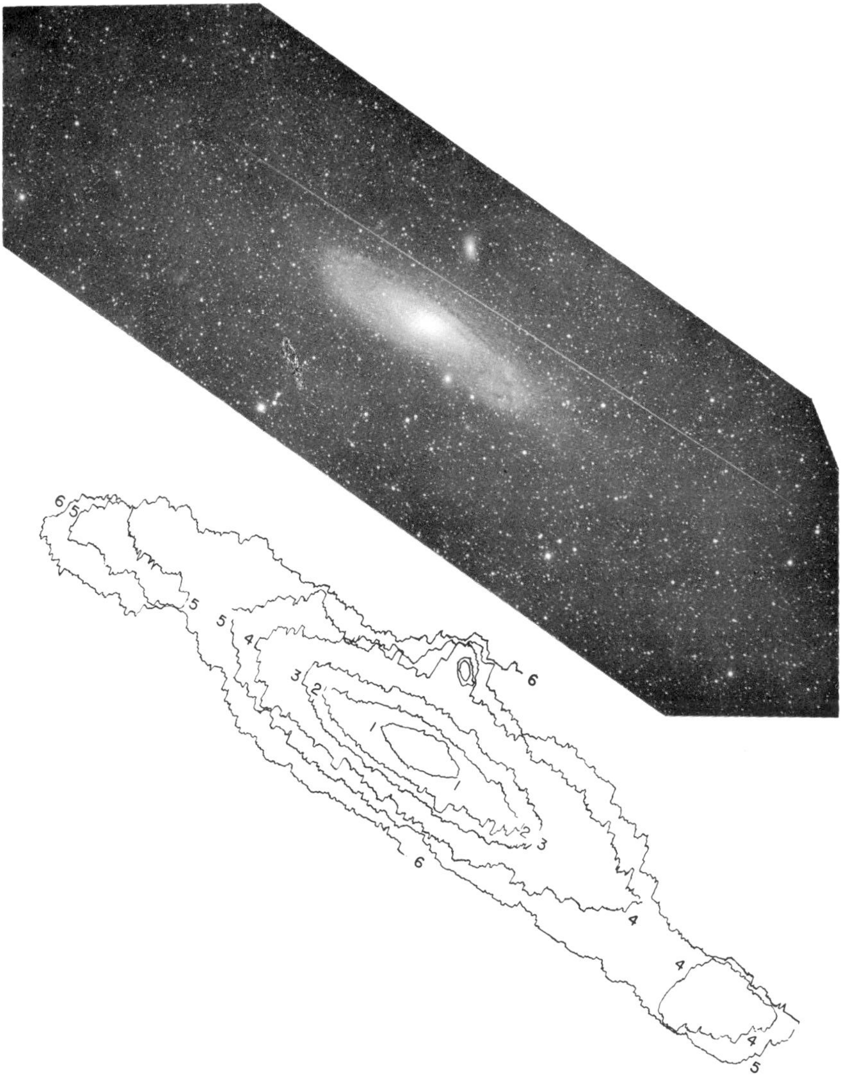

University of Michigan Observatory

ISOPHOTAL CONTOURS OF THE ANDROMEDA NEBULA

North following is at upper left. Scale: 105″ = 1 mm. (The sharp linear marking in the photograph of the nebula is a meteor trail.)

velocities to give the variation of the rotational velocities, Θ_0, with the distance from the center. Figure 11, taken from Babcock's paper, illustrates the resulting "rotation-curve." It should be pointed out that the measured radial velocities at the points farthest from the center are particularly reliable, as they have been derived from the sharp emission-line spectra of certain outlying nebulosities.

In some ways the most striking feature of the rotation-curve is that, as we recede from the nuclear regions, Θ_0 begins to increase

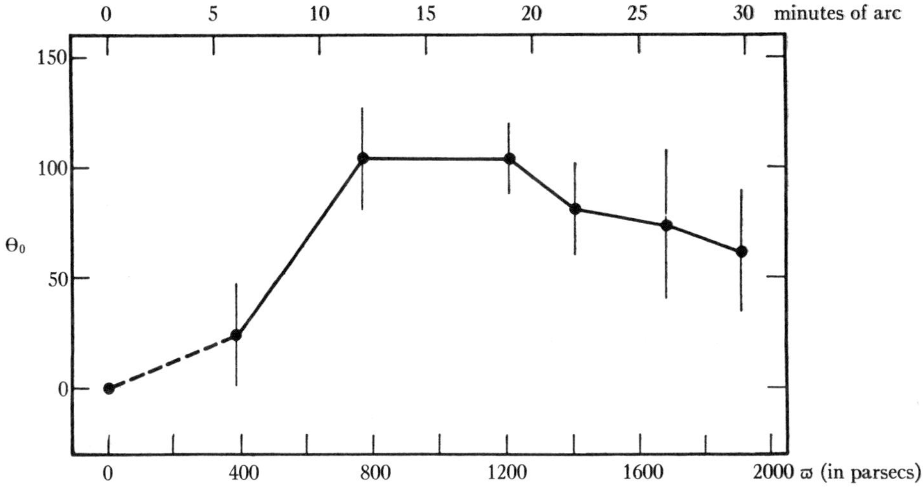

FIG. 12.—The rotation-curve for M33, the rotational velocity, Θ_0, expressed in km/sec (Mayall and Aller).

practically linearly with the distance from the center. As we shall see later in chapter iv (§ 4.2), this result is of considerable theoretical significance.

Another case which has been studied in some detail is that of M33 by Mayall and Aller (see Fig. 12). The absolute values of the rotational velocities measured in this nebula are not so large as in the Andromeda nebula. But the rotation-curve for M33 has been followed out to a distance from the center where a decrease in Θ_0 (after reaching a maximum) is perceptible.

Finally, the rotation of NGC 3190, investigated by Hubble and Mayall, is of particular interest, since, according to these authors, this case establishes the *sense* of rotation as well. Now, NGC 3190 is an early-type normal spiral, whose fundamental plane is slightly tilted to the line of sight.[14] The major axis of the image is seen to run northwest-southeast. According to Hubble, long exposures with the 100-inch reflector at Mount Wilson bring out faint extensions to the southeast, in which, apparently, an arm can be traced. It further appears that the arm recedes from the nucleus as it proceeds from the northwest toward the southeast. Finally, a heavy absorption lane (tilted about 15° to the fundamental plane) is seen silhouetted against the central region. According to Hubble and Mayall, this identifies the part of the image lying southwest as the nearer side of the nebula.

The spectrographic study of NGC 3190 at Lick and that at Mount Wilson agree in indicating that the southeast end of the image is approaching. If we accept Hubble and Mayall's identification as to the nearer side of the nebula, then the sense of rotation indicated is *inward* along the spiral (toward the center). However, it should be pointed out that there still exists considerable divergence of views regarding the true sense of rotation in spiral nebulae. In particular, Lindblad has always advocated the opposite sense for rotation—i.e., *outward* along the spiral. We shall return to these questions in chapter iv (§ 4.5).

1.8. *Globular and galactic clusters.*—Star clusters are of two kinds —globular clusters and galactic clusters. A typical example of the former class is the cluster ω Centauri, while the clusters in Pleiades and Praesepe belong to the latter class.

Star clusters present many interesting dynamical problems, but unfortunately empirical data which would be of value in such studies are badly lacking. Thus, in the case of globular clusters the only information which is entirely reliable for dynamical discussions is their spherical symmetry. The observed star counts do not give indications of the true density distribution; for, in practice, no account is taken of the absolutely faint stars, which are probably very much more numerous than the brighter stars which are counted. Again, we have no information concerning the internal motions in globular clusters, though on other grounds (cf. chap. v) we should

[14] See Hubble, *op. cit.*, Pl. III.

expect them to be fairly large (~10 km/sec). However, in spite of this lack of empirical knowledge, the mere fact of their spherical symmetry combined with the roughest estimates of their densities and motions should enable us to make some theoretical advances in our understanding of these objects.

In the case of galactic clusters our knowledge is in a somewhat better state. The internal motions in the Pleiades and in the Praesepe clusters have been measured by Titus and by Schilt and Titus, respectively. These studies present the first reliable measures of such motions and were made possible by the first-epoch plates of these clusters having been taken by Rutherfurd as early as in 1870. The results of the measures of Titus and of Schilt and Titus are

$$\left.\begin{aligned} \sqrt{\overline{u^2}} = \sqrt{\overline{v^2}} &= 0.42 \text{ km/sec} \qquad \text{(Pleiades)}\,, \\ \sqrt{\overline{u^2}} = \sqrt{\overline{v^2}} &= 0.42 \text{ km/sec} \qquad \text{(Praesepe)}\,, \end{aligned}\right\} \qquad (1.81)$$

where u and v are the transverse components of the motions relative (respectively) to the standards of rest defined by the clusters themselves. Table 5 gives some further information concerning these clusters, which we shall find useful in our dynamical considerations in chapter v.

TABLE 5

DATA ON TWO GALACTIC CLUSTERS

	Pleiades	Praesepe
Number of stars in the cluster	>175; ~200	>350, ~400
Total mass of the cluster (solar mass)	~300	~300
Radius (parsecs)	3.5	3
Parallax (seconds of arc)	0″.009	0″.008
Root mean-square velocity (km/sec)	0.42	0.42

1.9. *General remarks.*—In concluding our general kinematical considerations we may again draw attention to the importance which the notion of a *dynamical system with differential motions* plays in the whole discussion. Essentially, this implies that in dealing with stellar systems we are able to express the distribution function $\Psi(x, y, z; U, V, W; t)$ in the form

$$\Psi = \Psi(x, y, z; U - U_0, V - V_0, W - W_0; t)\ , \qquad (1.91)$$

where U_0, V_0, and W_0 are functions of position and time only. Sometimes, as when dealing with the system of the high-velocity stars in our Galaxy, it becomes necessary to generalize equation (1.91) somewhat and write

$$\Psi = \sum_i \Psi_i (x, y, z; U - U_0^{(i)}, V - V_0^{(i)}, W - W_0^{(i)}; t), \quad (1.92)$$

where the summation over the index i corresponds to the fact that under these circumstances we are to regard the stellar system as (formally) consisting of several distinct subsystems.

Again, we have seen in § 1.3, how Schwarzschild's ellipsoidal law of the distribution of the residual velocities ($u = U - U_0$; $v = V - V_0$; $w = W - W_0$) enters the discussion in a perfectly natural way. According to this law, the distribution function $\Psi(x, y, z; u, v, w; t)$ has the form

$$\Psi = \frac{N}{\pi^{3/2}} \begin{vmatrix} a & h & g \\ h & b & f \\ g & f & c \end{vmatrix}^{1/2} e^{-au^2 - bv^2 - cw^2 - 2fvw - 2gwu - 2huv}, \quad (1.93)$$

where the coefficients of the velocity ellipsoid a, b, c, f, g, and h and the number of stars per unit volume, N, are all functions of position and time. It would sometimes be useful to regard Schwarzschild's law as a special case of the general ellipsoidal distribution specified by

$$\Psi = \Psi (Q + \sigma), \quad (1.94)$$

where Ψ is an arbitrary function of the argument specified, Q, a homogeneous quadratic form in the residual velocities, and σ, a function of position and time. For the case of stellar systems consisting of several subsystems we can generalize equation (1.94) to the form

$$\Psi = \sum_i \Psi_i (Q_i + \sigma_i). \quad (1.95)$$

The function $\sum_i \Psi_i(Q_i + \sigma_i)$ *represents the most general type of distribution function which the kinematics of a stellar system requires us to consider.*

BIBLIOGRAPHICAL NOTES

The following general references may be noted.

1. W. W. CAMPBELL, *Stellar Motions*, New Haven: Yale University Press, 1913. This book has now become classical. Apart from its historical interest, the value of this book consists in its emphasis on the data of observation and on the practical methods for determining the motions of stars. A book of a different nature is—

2. A. S. EDDINGTON, *Stellar Movements and the Structure of the Universe*, London: Macmillan, 1914. Chapters v, vi, vii, viii, and xii in this book are of particular interest. These chapters deal with problems concerned with solar motion, two star streams, and general dynamical principles.

The discovery of the differential rotation of the Galaxy by Oort (1927) changed the whole complexion of the problem. More recent books which deal with these matters as well are—

3. E. VON DER PAHLEN, *Stellar Statistik*, Leipzig, 1937. Also—

4. W. M. SMART, *Stellar Dynamics*, Cambridge, England, 1938. In Pahlen see particularly Part IV (chaps. xii–xiv), which deals specifically with the kinematics and dynamics of stellar systems. In Smart's book chapters i–vi and ix deal solely with stellar kinematical problems; galactic rotation is introduced only relatively late in the development (chap. xi), and dynamical problems are considered (rather incoherently) in chapters x and xii.

Stellar dynamical problems are also considered in—

5. J. H. JEANS, *Problems of Cosmogony and Stellar Dynamics*, Cambridge, England, 1919. See particularly chapters ix–xi. Also—

6. J. H. JEANS, *Astronomy and Cosmogony*, Cambridge, England, 1928. See chapters xii–xiv.

Among the books which deal with special topics, we may note—

7. E. P. HUBBLE, *The Realm of the Nebulae*, New Haven, 1936. See chapters i–iii, vi, and vii.

8. H. SHAPLEY, *Star Clusters*, "Harvard Observatory Monographs," No. 2, 1930.

9. P. TEN BRUGGENCATE, *Sternhaufen*, Berlin, 1927.

See also the articles by SHAPLEY, CURTISS, and LINDBLAD in—

10. *Handb. d. Astrophys.* (Berlin), Vol. **5**, No. 2, and Vol. **7**.

A summary of the present state of the observations will be found in—

11. J. H. OORT, "Stellar Motions," *M.N.*, **99**, 369–384, 1939.

§ 1.1.—The general point of view adopted is that taken in—

12. S. CHANDRASEKHAR, *Astronomical Papers Dedicated to Elis Strömgren*, pp. 1–24, Copenhagen, 1940. The whole of this present monograph may, indeed, be regarded as the execution of the program outlined in the foregoing essay.

For a complete discussion of the space distribution of the globular clusters see SHAPLEY (ref. 8), particularly chapters xi and xii. Also, for a general account see—

13. J. S. PLASKETT, *The Dimensions and Structure of the Galaxy* (Halley Lecture), Oxford, 1935.

The first determinations of the solar motion with respect to the globular clusters are contained in—

14. K. LUNDMARK, *Pub. A.S.P.*, **35**, 318, 1923, and—

15. G. STRÖMBERG, *Ap. J.*, **61**, 353, 1925.

More recent determinations are found in—

16. S. W. SHIVESHWARKAR, *M.N.*, **95**, 555, 1935.

17. F. K. EDMONDSON, *A.J.*, **45**, 1, 1935.

Dr. N. U. Mayall has recently made extensive observations on the radial velocities of the globular clusters. The results of his study will be awaited with keen interest.

§ 1.2.—The practical methods for determining the local solar motion are described in CAMPBELL (ref. 1, chap. iv), EDDINGTON (ref. 2, chap. v), PAHLEN (ref. 3, chap. xiii, § I), and SMART (ref. 4, chap. iii). For a more specifically observational discussion see—

18. H. NORDSTRÖM, *Lund Medd.*, II, No. 79, 1936.

§ 1.3.—It had originally been supposed that a distribution function of the form

$$\Psi(v) = N\frac{j^3}{\pi^{3/2}}\, e^{-j^2|v|^2}$$

would prove adequate for the interpretation of the observed motions of stars with respect to the local standard of rest. But Kobold appears to have been the first to recognize its inadequacy for accounting for the observed state of stellar motions:

19. H. KOBOLD, *A.N.*, **125**, 65, 1890; **144**, 33, 1897; **150**, 271, 282, 1899. See also—

20. H. KOBOLD, *Stellar Astronomie*, Sonderausgabe aus der *Encyk. d. math. Wiss.*, Vol. **6**, 1926. See particularly pp. 335–346. However, it was Kapteyn who first clearly recognized the physical nature of the phenomenon encountered:

21. J. C. KAPTEYN, *Brit. Assoc. Rept.*, p. 257, 1905; also *M.N.*, **72**, 743, 1912. But Kapteyn interpreted the phenomenon in what now appears to be a somewhat too literal manner. For he based his interpretation on an assumed distribution function of the form

$$\Psi = N_1 \frac{j_1^3}{\pi^{3/2}} e^{-j_1^2|v-v_1|^2} + N_2 \frac{j_2^3}{\pi^{3/2}} e^{-j_2^2|v-v_2|^2}$$

where $\boldsymbol{v}_1$ and $\boldsymbol{v}_2$ are such that

$$N_1 \boldsymbol{v}_1 + N_2 \boldsymbol{v}_2 = 0 \ .$$

This assumption concerning Ψ is clearly equivalent to supposing that the stars in our neighborhood can be regarded (at any rate, formally) as belonging to one of two groups, the standard of rest defined by any one group having a motion ($\boldsymbol{v}_1$, respectively, $\boldsymbol{v}_2$) with respect to their common local standard of rest. This is the origin of the term "two star streams." On this hypothesis the direction of $\boldsymbol{v}_1$ (or $\boldsymbol{v}_2$) will define the direction of star streaming.

Soon after Kapteyn's discovery, Eddington developed methods for analyzing the data of observation on the basis of the two-star-streams hypothesis.

22. A. S. EDDINGTON, *M.N.*, **67**, 34, 1906. Also—

23. A. S. EDDINGTON, *M.N.*, **68**, 588, 1908. An account of these investigations will be found in EDDINGTON (ref. 2, chap. vi) and SMART (ref. 4, chap. iv)

As we have explained in the text, Schwarzschild's ellipsoidal hypothesis affords a more elegant and at the same time a more satisfactory basis for interpreting the data of observations. Moreover, from a theoretical standpoint, the ellipsoidal hypothesis is very much to be preferred compared to the hypothesis of the two star streams. Schwarzschild's fundamental papers are—

24. K. SCHWARZSCHILD, *Göttingen Nachrichten*, p. 614, 1907, and—

25. K. SCHWARZSCHILD, *Göttingen Nachrichten*, p. 191, 1908. Though Schwarzschild introduced the general ellipsoidal hypothesis, he, however, restricted himself to a spheroidal distribution of the velocities, while discussing the observational consequences. And, it is to Charlier and his associates (particularly, S. D. Wicksell and W. Gyllenberg) at Lund that we owe the most comprehensive analysis of the data on stellar motions on the basis of the general ellipsoidal distribution. For a general account of these studies see—

26. C. V. L. CHARLIER, *The Motion and the Distribution of the Stars*, University of California Press, 1926.

Finally, we may also refer to the relevant chapters in SMART (ref. 4, chap. v) and PAHLEN (ref. 3, chap. xii).

§ 1.4.—The theoretical standpoint adopted in the text is that of—

27. K. PILOWSKI, *Zs. f. Ap.*, **3**, 53, 279, 291, 1931; also *ibid.*, **4**, 396, 1932.

28. K. OGRODNIKOFF, *Zs. f. Ap.*, **4**, 190, 1932.

29. E. A. MILNE, *M.N.*, **95**, 560, 1935.

The first direct evidence for the existence of differential motions in the Galaxy was found by Oort:

30. J. H. OORT, *B.A.N.*, **3**, 275, 1927. Also—

31. J. H. OORT, *B.A.N.*, **4**, 79, 1927; see particularly Figs. 1 and 2 on pp. 87 and 88. In these papers, the differential galactic-*rotation* terms in the expressions for the radial velocities and the proper motions of stars are derived and compared with the observational material. Further, these papers also contain the first determinations of the "Oort Constants," *A* and *B*. Further studies by Oort are contained in—

32. J. H. OORT, *B.A.N.*, **4**, 91, 1927, and—

33. J. H. OORT, *B.A.N.*, **4**, 159, 1928.

The ideas and results of OORT found beautiful confirmation in the investigations of Plaskett and Pearce on the radial velocities of the O and B stars.

34. J. S. PLASKETT and J. A. PEARCE, *Pub. Dom. Ap. Obs., Victoria*, **5**, 277, 1936. See also PLASKETT (ref. 13). However, the most convincing evidence is that resulting from the investigations of Joy and Trumpler:

35. A. H. JOY, *Ap. J.*, **89**, 356, 1939.

36. R. J. TRUMPLER, *Ap. J.*, **91**, 186, 1940, particularly pp. 195–197.

§ 1.5.—The first indications of the asymmetry in stellar motions appear to have been noticed by—

37. B. BOSS, *Popular Astronomy*, **26**, 686, 1918, and—

38. W. ADAMS and A. H. JOY, *Ap. J.*, **49**, 179, 1919.

The most extensive investigations into the nature of this phenomenon and the related one of the high-velocity stars are those of—

39. G. STRÖMBERG, *Ap. J.*, **59**, 228, 1924; also *ibid.*, **61**, 363, 1925.

40. J. H. OORT, *Groningen Pub.*, No. 40, 1926.

41. G. MICZAIKA, *A.N.*, **270**, 249, 1940.

On the theoretical side Lindblad has always emphasized the importance of this asymmetry in stellar motions:

42. B. LINDBLAD, *Ark. f. mat., astr., och fysik*, No. 21, 1925. Further

references to Lindblad's work will be found in the bibliographical notes for chapters iii and iv.

§ 1.6.—For a complete discussion of the structural features of extragalactic nebulae see HUBBLE (ref. 7). Also, for a more recent summary see—

43. E. HUBBLE, *Sci. Monthly*, p. 391, November, 1940.

§ 1.7.—The rotation of the Andromeda nebula was first detected by—

44. V. M. SLIPHER, *Lowell Bull.*, **2**, 65, 1914; and *Popular Astronomy*, **25**, 36, 1917. Also—

45. F. G. PEASE, *Proc. Nat. Acad.*, **4**, 21, 1918.

The most extensive study of this problem is due to—

46. H. BABCOCK, *Lick Obs. Bull.*, No. 498, 1939.

And finally there exists the unpublished work of Mayall and Aller and Hubble and Mayall.

§ 1.8.—See SHAPLEY (ref. 8) and TEN BRUGGENCATE (ref. 9).

The internal motions in the Pleiades were first detected by Hertzsprung:

47. E. HERTZSPRUNG, *B.A.N.*, **7**, 187, 1934.

Results of higher accuracy for the brighter members are those of Titus:

48. J. TITUS, *A.J.*, **47**, 25, 1938.

Similarly, the internal motions in the Praesepe are detected and measured in—

49. J. SCHILT and J. TITUS, *A.J.*, **46**, 197, 1938.

§ 1.9.—See reference 12.

CHAPTER II

THE TIME OF RELAXATION OF A STELLAR SYSTEM

As we stated in our introduction to the last chapter, in stellar dynamics we are primarily concerned with interpreting the observed state of motions in stellar systems in terms of the forces which govern the motions of the individual stars in the system and the laws of dynamics. In this monograph it will be assumed that the laws of Newtonian dynamics are adequate for such purposes. But this is not to imply that eventually it may not be found necessary to introduce ideas in stellar dynamics which are outside the scope of the classical laws. It is clearly necessary to work out fully the logical consequences of a system of stellar dynamics based on Newtonian laws before we can feel convinced of the need to go outside the framework of such laws. And it is the object of this monograph to set out the general principles of such a classical system of stellar dynamics.

2.1. *An analysis of the nature of the forces acting on a star.*—According to our remarks in the foregoing paragraph, we shall assume that the forces governing the motions of the individual stars in a stellar system are essentially of a gravitational character. In a general way it is clear that these forces arise, first, from the smoothed-out distribution of matter in the system and, second, from the effect of chance stellar encounters. The forces of the first kind are derivable from a gravitational potential $\mathfrak{B}$ representing the smoothed-out distribution of matter in the system. This gravitational potential is a function of the space and time co-ordinates only. On the other hand, the forces of the second kind arise from the accidental encounters with other stars which happen to be in the neighborhood of the star we are considering. More explicitly, the manner in which these two types of forces influence the motion of any particular star can be described as follows: Consider a star which is at the point (x, y, z) at some specified instant of time $t = 0$ (say). Without loss of generality we can suppose that at $t = 0$ the star is not experiencing appreciably the effects of a chance stellar encounter. The instantaneous force acting on the star at $t = 0$ will then be given in terms of the gravitational potential $\mathfrak{B}$ of the smoothed-out distribution only. We can therefore write

$$\frac{d^2 \mathbf{r}}{dt^2} = - \text{grad } \mathfrak{B} . \tag{2.11}$$

The integration of the foregoing vector equation will uniquely determine a *theoretical orbit* for the star in terms of its position and velocity at time $t = 0$. Clearly, the star will follow this theoretical orbit only as long as stellar encounters have no appreciable influence. However, with the passage of time, stellar encounters will begin to have a cumulative effect and will tend to make the *actual orbit* of the star deviate more and more from the theoretical orbit. The question now arises: *How long will it take for the cumulative effect of stellar encounters to deviate the star so much from the orbit derived from* (2.11) *that it can no longer be described even approximately by this theoretical orbit?* It is the estimation of this time that specifies the *time of relaxation* of the stellar system.

The general ideas underlying the estimation of the time of relaxation of a stellar system outlined in the preceding paragraph can be expressed somewhat differently as follows: According to equation (2.11) we have the integral

$$\tfrac{1}{2}(\dot{x}^2 + \dot{y}^2 + \dot{z}^2) + \mathfrak{B}(x, y, z, t) = \int \frac{\partial \mathfrak{B}}{\partial t} dt + \text{constant} . \tag{2.12}$$

If $\mathfrak{B}$ is explicitly independent of the time, equation (2.12) reduces to the energy integral in its standard form. We can regard the existence of the (formal) integral (2.12) as equivalent to our being able to consider each star in the system as an independent, conservative, dynamical system. But this is true only as long as the effects of stellar encounters can be neglected. We can therefore ask: *How long will it take before the cumulative effect of stellar encounters prevents us from considering the stars as independent, conservative, dynamical systems?* Again, we can refer to this time as the time of relaxation of the stellar system.

It is now clear that for lengths of time which are short compared to the time of relaxation we can ignore the effect of stellar encounters on the motions of stars in the system. Similarly, after a length of time which is long compared with the time of relaxation we can be sure that the state of motions present must have arisen as the result of the occurrence of numerous encounters. The great importance of the notion of the time of relaxation for stellar dynamics now becomes apparent: in terms of it we are able to judge the relative importance of stellar encounters in influencing the motions of the stars.

2.2. *The formulation of the problem.*—We shall now consider in somewhat greater detail the problem of quantitatively evaluating the time of relaxation. Let us suppose that the different encounters can each be treated independently of the others and that they can be regarded individually as two-body encounters.[1] Each encounter will therefore result in (i) a deflection, $\pi - 2\Psi$, of the star from its original direction of motion and (ii) an exchange of energy, ΔE, between the two stars taking part in the encounter. The actual amounts of the deflection, $\pi - 2\Psi$, and the energy transferred, ΔE, will depend upon the initial conditions defining the particular encounter. We shall evaluate $\pi - 2\Psi$ and ΔE explicitly in §§ 2.3 and 2.4, but meantime we shall outline the general method. We evaluate the sums

$$\Sigma \sin^2 2\Psi \qquad \text{and} \qquad \Sigma \Delta E^2 \tag{2.21}$$

for all possible encounters and determine their rates of increase with time. It now appears that, when $\Sigma \sin^2 2\Psi$ becomes of the order of 1, the star would most probably have deviated quite considerably from its original direction of motion. More particularly, if T_D is the time required for $\Sigma \sin^2 2\Psi$ to become equal to 1, we may say that by then the star will, on the average, have deviated by an angle $\pi/2$ from its original direction. Similarly, when the root mean square of the energy exchanged in stellar encounters, $\sqrt{\Sigma \Delta E^2}$, becomes of the same order as the initial kinetic energy of the star, it will no longer be possible to assume even the approximate validity of the energy equation (2.12). More particularly, if T_E is the time required for $\sqrt{\Sigma \Delta E^2}$ to become equal to the initial kinetic energy of the star, we may say that by then the star will, on the average, have altered its

[1] The limitations introduced by this assumption are considered in § 2.3 (subsec. [iii]).

original energy by about an equal amount. We may accordingly define T_D and T_E as the times of relaxation from the two different points of view. It is, however, clear that, in general, T_D and T_E must be of the same order of magnitude.

2.3. *The time of relaxation*, T_E.—As we have already stated in § 2.2, we shall idealize each stellar encounter as an independent two-body problem. In describing such an encounter it is important to remember that we should always refer the physically relevant quantities to some appropriately chosen fixed frame of reference. Consider, then, the effect of encounters on a star of mass m_2 with an initial velocity $\boldsymbol{v}_2$ during its motion through other stars. Let m_1 and $\boldsymbol{v}_1$ denote the mass and the velocity of a typical *field star*. The parameters defining such an encounter are five in number. They are (i) the magnitude v_1 of the vector $\boldsymbol{v}_1$, (ii) the angle θ between the vectors $\boldsymbol{v}_1$ and $\boldsymbol{v}_2$, (iii) the azimuthal angle φ referred to a system of co-ordinates the z-axis of which coincides with the direction of $\boldsymbol{v}_2$, (iv) the impact parameter D and, finally, the angle Θ between the *orbital plane* and the *fundamental plane* containing the vectors $\boldsymbol{v}_1$ and $\boldsymbol{v}_2$ (see Figs. 13 and 14 for the relations between the various angles). For the sake of brevity we shall denote such an encounter by the symbol $(v_1, \theta, \varphi, D, \Theta)$.

Now, according to the elementary theory of the two-body problem (see Appen. I), the velocity of the center of gravity V_g remains constant during the encounter. Further, in the orbital plane each star describes a hyperbola about the other, and at the end of the encounter the direction of the relative velocity V is deflected by an amount $\pi - 2\psi$ (in the orbital plane), where

$$\cos\psi = \frac{1}{\sqrt{1+\dfrac{D^2V^4}{G^2(m_1+m_2)^2}}} \, . \qquad (2.301)^{2}$$

i) *The energy exchanged* ΔE.—We shall now consider the energy exchanged between the two stars as a result of the encounter:

By definition of V_g and V we have

$$V_g = \frac{1}{m_1+m_2}(m_1\boldsymbol{v}_1 + m_2\boldsymbol{v}_2)\,; \qquad V = \boldsymbol{v}_2 - \boldsymbol{v}_1 \, . \qquad (2.302)$$

[2] This must be distinguished from $\pi - 2\Psi$, which gives the true deflection in a fixed frame of reference.

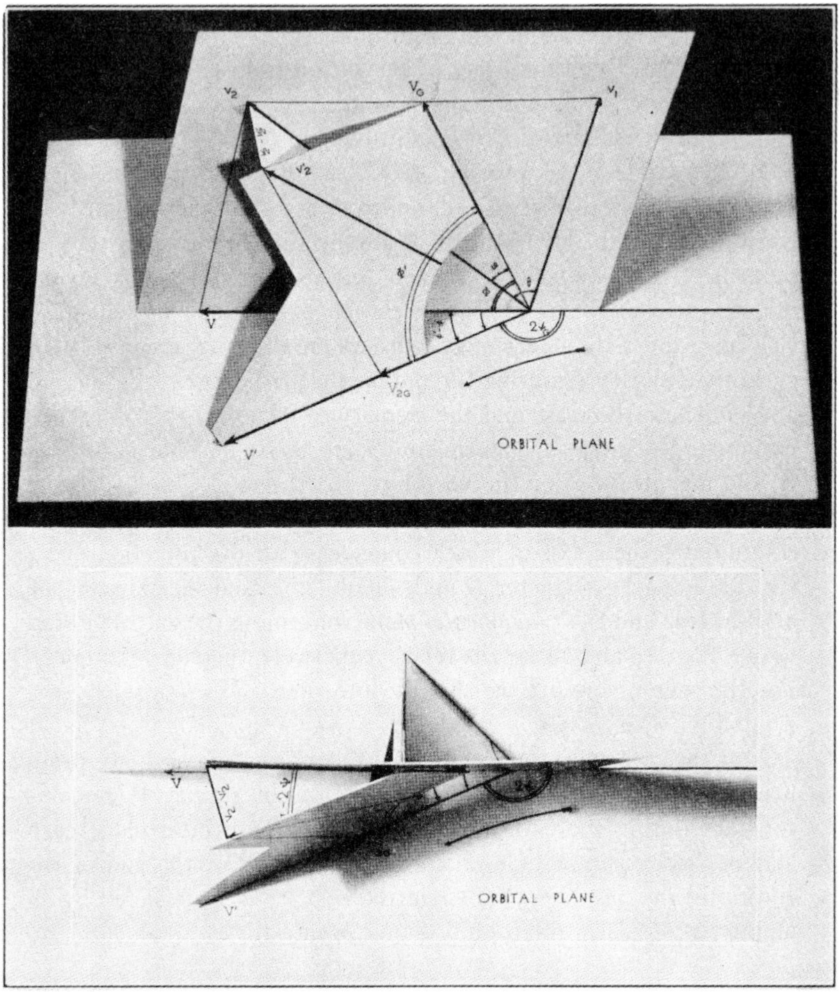

FIG. 13.—Vector model for stellar encounters. The fundamental plane is defined by the vectors v_1 and v_2 representing the velocities of the two stars before the encounter. The velocity of the center of gravity, denoted by V_g, remains constant during the encounter. In a frame of reference in which the center of gravity is at rest, the two stars describe hyperbolae in the orbital plane, which is, in general, inclined at some definite angle to the fundamental plane. The vectors V and v_{2g}, representing respectively the initial relative velocity and the initial velocity of one of the stars with respect to the center of gravity, lie in the orbital plane and are in the same direction. As a result of the encounter, these vectors are deflected by the same angle $\pi - 2\psi_g$ and become respectively V' and v'_{2g}. Finally, $v'_2 = v'_{2g} + V_g$ defines the velocity of the star at the end of the encounter. The angle $\pi - 2\Psi$ between the vectors v_2 and v'_2 measures the true deflection suffered by the star as a result of the encounter (Williamson and Chandrasekhar, *Ap. J.*, **93**, 309, 1941).

From the relations (2.302) we readily find that

$$v_2 = V_g + \frac{m_1}{m_1 + m_2} V . \tag{2.303}$$

According to equation (2.303), we have

$$v_2^2 = V_g^2 + 2 \frac{m_1}{m_1 + m_2} V_g V \cos \Phi + \left(\frac{m_1}{m_1 + m_2} \right)^2 V^2 , \tag{2.304}$$

where Φ is the angle between V_g and V. Similarly, at the end of the encounter

$$v_2'^2 = V_g^2 + 2 \frac{m_1}{m_1 + m_2} V_g V \cos \Phi' + \left(\frac{m_1}{m_1 + m_2} \right)^2 V^2 , \tag{2.305}$$

where Φ' is the angle between V_g and the relative velocity V' at the end of the encounter. Hence the change in energy, ΔE, suffered by the star as a result of the encounter is given by

$$\left. \begin{aligned} \Delta E &= \tfrac{1}{2} m_2 \left(v_2'^2 - v_2^2 \right) \\ &= \frac{m_1 m_2}{m_1 + m_2} V_g V \left(\cos \Phi' - \cos \Phi \right) . \end{aligned} \right\} \tag{2.306}$$

Now, let i be the angle which the projection of V_g on the orbital plane makes with V_g. Further, let ϕ and ϕ' be the angles which V and V' make with the projection of V_g on the orbital plane. We then have (see Fig. 14)

$$\cos \Phi = \cos \phi \cos i \, ; \qquad \cos \Phi' = \cos \phi' \cos i . \tag{2.307}$$

We can, therefore re-write equation (2.306) in the form

$$\Delta E = \frac{m_1 m_2}{m_1 + m_2} V_g V \left(\cos \phi' - \cos \phi \right) \cos i , \tag{2.308}$$

or, alternatively,

$$\Delta E = \frac{2 m_1 m_2}{m_1 + m_2} V_g V \sin \frac{\phi + \phi'}{2} \sin \frac{\phi - \phi'}{2} \cos i . \tag{2.309}$$

On the other hand, we have

$$\phi' - \phi = \pi - 2\psi , \tag{2.310}$$

whence

$$\tfrac{1}{2} (\phi + \phi') = 90^\circ - \psi + \phi \, ; \qquad \tfrac{1}{2} (\phi' - \phi) = 90^\circ - \psi . \tag{2.311}$$

Equation (2.309) now becomes

$$\Delta E = -\,2\,\frac{m_1 m_2}{m_1 + m_2}\,V_g V \cos(\phi - \psi)\cos\psi \cos i\,, \qquad (2.312)$$

where ψ is related to the impact parameter D and V according to equation (2.301).

ii) *The number of encounters* (v_1, θ, φ, D, Θ).—We shall now obtain the expression for the number of (v_1, θ, φ, D, Θ) encounters which take place in an interval of time dt. Let $N(v_1, \theta, \varphi)\, dv_1 d\theta d\varphi$ be the

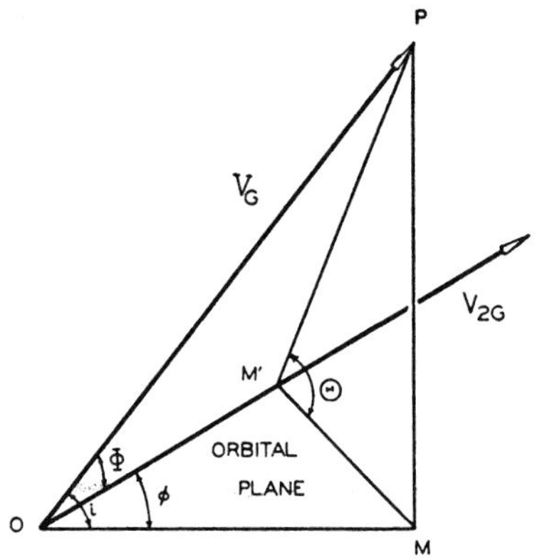

FIG. 14.—Illustrating the relationships between the various angles ϕ, Φ, i, and Θ. OM is the projection of V_g on the orbital plane. The angles $OM'P$, $OM'M$, OMP, and $M'MP$ are all right angles. We thus have the relations $\cos\Phi = \cos i \cos\phi$ and $\sin\Phi\cos\Theta = \cos i \sin\psi$.

number of field stars per unit volume with velocities in the range (v_1, $v_1 + dv_1$) and in directions confined to the element of solid angle $\sin\theta d\theta d\varphi$. The number of encounters sought (which occur in time dt) is, accordingly, given by

$$N(v_1, \theta, \varphi)\, dv_1 d\theta d\varphi \cdot \frac{d\Theta}{2\pi} \cdot 2\pi D dD \cdot V dt\,. \qquad (2.313)$$

Consequently, the contribution of these encounters to the sum $\Sigma\Delta E^2$ can be written as

$$\Sigma\Delta E^2_{(v_1, \theta, \varphi, D, \Theta)} = 2\pi N(v_1, \theta, \varphi)\,\Delta E^2\, V D dD \frac{d\Theta}{2\pi} dv_1 d\theta d\varphi dt\,; \quad (2.314)$$

or, using equation (2.312), we have

$$\left.\begin{aligned}\Sigma\Delta E^2_{(v_1,\theta,\varphi,D,\Theta)} &= 8\pi N(v_1,\theta,\varphi)\,V_g^2 V^3\left(\frac{m_1 m_2}{m_1+m_2}\right)^2\\ &\quad\times\cos^2 i\,\cos^2(\phi-\psi)\cos^2\psi\; D\,dD\,\frac{d\Theta}{2\pi}\,dv_1 d\theta d\varphi dt\,.\end{aligned}\right\}\quad(2.315)$$

Our problem now is to integrate the foregoing expression over the relevant ranges of the various parameters D, Θ, φ, θ, and v_1. We shall consider the integration over each of these variables in turn.

iii) *The integration over the impact parameter* D.—To integrate over D we shall introduce a change of variables. According to equation (2.301)

$$D\,dD = \frac{G^2(m_1+m_2)^2}{V^4}\,\frac{\sin\psi}{\cos^3\psi}\,d\psi\,. \quad (2.316)$$

Hence, we can re-write equation (2.315) as

$$\left.\begin{aligned}\Sigma\Delta E^2_{(v_1,\theta,\varphi,\psi,\Theta)} &= 8\pi N(v_1,\theta,\varphi)\,G^2 m_1^2 m_2^2\,\frac{V_g^2}{V}\\ &\quad\times\cos^2 i\,\frac{\cos^2(\phi-\psi)\sin\psi}{\cos\psi}\,d\psi\,\frac{d\Theta}{2\pi}\,dv_1 d\theta d\varphi dt\,.\end{aligned}\right\}\quad(2.317)$$

On integrating the foregoing expression over the relevant range of ψ, we shall obtain the contribution to $\Sigma\Delta E^2$ by all those encounters which we can denote by the symbol $(v_1, \theta, \varphi, \Theta)$. We thus have

$$\left.\begin{aligned}\Sigma\Delta E^2_{(v_1,\theta,\varphi,\Theta)} &= 8\pi N(v_1,\theta,\varphi)\,G^2 m_1^2 m_2^2\,\frac{V_g^2}{V}\\ &\quad\times\cos^2 i\int\frac{\cos^2(\phi-\psi)\sin\psi}{\cos\psi}\,d\psi\,\frac{d\Theta}{2\pi}\,dv_1 d\theta d\varphi dt\,.\end{aligned}\right\}\quad(2.318)$$

A consideration of the integral occurring in equation (2.318) introduces a new factor into the discussion. At first sight it would appear that the appropriate limits for ψ are 0 and $\pi/2$ corresponding to the limits 0 and ∞ for D. But we notice that the integral in (2.318) does not converge at $\psi = \pi/2$ except in the trivial case $\phi = 0$ $(v_2/v_1 = \infty)$. Further, it is readily seen that (except when $\phi = 0$) the integral in (2.318) *diverges logarithmically* as $\psi \to \pi/2$. This divergence arises essentially from the improper use of the two-body approximation to describe distant encounters in a stellar system; for the formula (2.312) for the energy exchanged between two stars involved in an encounter assumes them to be initially at an infinite distance from each other and to separate to an infinite distance at the end of the encounter. Only then could we set for the deflection $(\pi - 2\psi)$ the angle between the two asymptotes of the relative orbit given according to equation (2.301). We should therefore conclude that, in practice, a "second" encounter begins to be effective before the first can be regarded as completed in the strict sense. Hence, the use of the expression (2.301) for the angle between the two asymptotes *overestimates* the actual deflection. This difference between the actual deflection and the full (theoretical) amount (2.301) is clearly of no importance for "close" encounters, i.e., for encounters for which D is a fraction of the average distance D_0 between the stars in the system. However, for encounters for which D becomes of the same order as D_0 the errors introduced by using the expression (2.312) for ΔE become increasingly serious. Thus, the divergence of the integral occurring in (2.318) as $D \to \infty$ and $\psi \to \pi/2$ must be attributed, first, to the general overestimation of the energy exchange ΔE given by (2.312) (which is of particular importance for the distant encounters) and, second, to the increasing difficulty of describing stellar encounters on a two-body idealization when the corresponding impact parameters become of the same order as the average distance D_0 between the stars. On the other hand, if we arbitrarily disregard all encounters with impact parameters greater than a certain amount, we shall be ignoring the small but finite contributions to $\Sigma \Delta E^2$ arising from these distant encounters. Consequently, by appropriately choosing an *upper limit* $D_{\max}$ for the impact parameter D, we can compensate for the errors introduced by overestimating ΔE for encounters with $D \leqslant D_{\max}$ and, by ignoring ΔE, for the encounters with $D \geqslant D_{\max}$. In a general way it is clear that $D_{\max}$ should be equal to D_0 within a factor of 2 or 3. It would be difficult to estimate $D_{\max}$ more closely than this without going into a considerable amount of detailed calculations. However, it is seen that an error of a factor of 2 or 3 in the chosen value of $D_{\max}$ does not introduce any significant error in the final expression for the time of relaxation. This fortunate circumstance arises from the fact that the integral occurring in equation (2.318) diverges only logarithmically as $\psi \to \pi/2$. We shall therefore assume that

$$D_{\max} \simeq D_0 \,. \tag{2.319}$$

Again, for values of D_0 which come under discussion in the treatment of actual stellar systems the maximum value of ψ differs so slightly from $\pi/2$ that we can put $\psi = \pi/2$ in all terms except those which diverge at $\psi = \pi/2$. On these assumptions the evaluation of the integral in equation (2.318) gives

$$\left.\begin{aligned} \Sigma\Delta E^2_{(v_1,\,\theta,\,\varphi,\,\Theta)} &= 8\pi N\,(v_1,\,\theta,\,\varphi)\,G^2 m_1^2 m_2^2 \frac{V_0^2}{V}\cos^2 i \\ &\times \Big[\tfrac{1}{2}\cos^2\phi + \sin^2\phi\,(-\log\cos\psi_0 - \tfrac{1}{2}) \\ &+ \frac{\pi}{4}\sin 2\phi\Big]\frac{d\Theta}{2\pi}\,dv_1 d\theta d\varphi dt\,. \end{aligned}\right\} \tag{2.320}$$

Using the relations (see Fig. 14)

$$\cos\phi\cos i = \cos\Phi\,; \qquad \sin\phi\cos i = \sin\Phi\cos\Theta\,, \tag{2.321}$$

we can write equation (2.320) more conveniently as

$$\left.\begin{aligned} \Sigma\Delta E^2_{(v_1,\,\theta,\,\varphi,\,\Theta)} &= 8\pi N\,(v_1,\,\theta,\,\varphi)\,G^2 m_1^2 m_2^2 \frac{V_0^2}{V}\frac{d\Theta}{2\pi}\,dv_1 d\theta d\varphi dt \\ &\times \Big[\tfrac{1}{2}\cos^2\Phi + \frac{1}{2}\Big\{\log\Big(1+\frac{D_0^2 V^4}{G^2 (m_1+m_2)^2}\Big) - 1\Big\} \\ &\times \sin^2\Phi\cos^2\Theta + \frac{\pi}{4}\sin 2\Phi\cos\Theta\Big]\,. \end{aligned}\right\} \tag{2.322}$$

It is readily seen that in the foregoing expression the logarithmic term represents the dominant contribution to $\Sigma\Delta E^2$. For,

$$\frac{D_0}{G\,(m_1+m_2)} = 2.33\times 10^4 \frac{[\,D_0/\text{parsec}\,]}{[\,(m_1+m_2)\,/\odot\,]\,[\,10\ \text{km/sec}\,]^2}\,. \tag{2.323}$$

Consequently, $D_0^2 V^4/G^2(m_1+m_2)^2$ will generally be of the order of $10^9 - 10^{10}$. An inspection of equation (2.322) now shows that the logarithmic term in this equation will be ten to twenty times as large as the other terms.[3] We shall therefore neglect all such terms in the

[3] A more detailed calculation confirms this conclusion (see n. 4).

future and retain only the dominant term in our calculations.[4] Accordingly, in this approximation, equation (2.322) can be written as

$$\left.\begin{aligned} \Sigma\Delta E^2_{(v_1,\,\theta,\,\varphi,\,\Theta)} &= 4\pi N(v_1,\,\theta,\,\varphi)\,G^2 m_1^2 m_2^2 \frac{V_g^2}{V} \\ \times \log\left(1+\frac{D_0^2 V^4}{G^2(m_1+m_2)^2}\right) & \sin^2\Phi\cos^2\Theta\,\frac{d\Theta}{2\pi}\,dv_1 d\theta d\varphi dt\,. \end{aligned}\right\} \qquad (2.324)$$

iv) *Integration over the inclination of the orbital plane.*—The integration of equation (2.324) over the inclination of the orbital plane to the fundamental plane is simple. We find that

$$\left.\begin{aligned} \Sigma\Delta E^2_{(v_1,\,\theta,\,\varphi)} &= 2\pi N(v_1,\,\theta,\,\varphi)\,G^2 m_1^2 m_2^2 \frac{V_g^2}{V} \\ &\times \log\left(1+\frac{D_0^2 V^4}{G^2(m_1+m_2)^2}\right)\sin^2\Phi\,dv_1 d\theta d\varphi dt\,. \end{aligned}\right\} \qquad (2.325)$$

v) *Some auxiliary formulae.*—The quantities V_g, V, and Φ which occur in equation (2.325) are all determined by v_1, v_2, and θ. We shall now obtain the explicit form of these relations.

From our definitions of the vectors $\boldsymbol{V_g}$ and $\boldsymbol{V}$ we directly obtain the formulae

$$V_g^2 = \frac{1}{(m_1+m_2)^2}(m_1^2 v_1^2 + m_2^2 v_2^2 + 2m_1 m_2 v_1 v_2 \cos\theta) \qquad (2.326)$$

and

$$V^2 = v_1^2 + v_2^2 - 2v_1 v_2\cos\theta\,. \qquad (2.327)$$

On the other hand, since (cf. eq. [2.303])

$$\boldsymbol{v_1} = \boldsymbol{V_g} - \frac{m_2}{m_1+m_2}\boldsymbol{V}\,, \qquad (2.328)$$

we have

$$v_1^2 = V_g^2 - 2\frac{m_2}{m_1+m_2}V_g V\cos\Phi + \left(\frac{m_2}{m_1+m_2}\right)^2 V^2\,; \qquad (2.329)$$

or, using equations (2.326) and (2.327), we readily obtain

$$\left.\begin{aligned} 2\frac{m_2}{m_1+m_2}V_g V\cos\Phi = 2\frac{m_2}{(m_1+m_2)^2}&[m_2 v_2^2 - m_1 v_1^2 \\ &+ v_1 v_2(m_1-m_2)\cos\theta]\,. \end{aligned}\right\} \qquad (2.330)$$

[4] For a rigorous evaluation of the sum in equation (2.322), including the nondominant terms, see S. Chandrasekhar, *Ap. J.*, **93**, 285, 1941.

Hence,

$$\cos\Phi = \frac{m_2 v_2^2 - m_1 v_1^2 + v_1 v_2 (m_1 - m_2)\cos\theta}{\sqrt{(m_1^2 v_1^2 + m_2^2 v_2^2 + 2 m_1 m_2 v_1 v_2 \cos\theta)(v_1^2 + v_2^2 - 2 v_1 v_2 \cos\theta)}} . \quad (2.331)$$

From the foregoing relation we find

$$\sin\Phi = \frac{v_1 v_2 (m_1 + m_2)\sin\theta}{\sqrt{(m_1^2 v_1^2 + m_2^2 v_2^2 + 2 m_1 m_2 v_1 v_2 \cos\theta)(v_1^2 + v_2^2 - 2 v_1 v_2 \cos\theta)}} . \quad (2.332)$$

Combining equations (2.326), (2.327), and (2.332), we obtain the relation

$$\frac{V_g^2}{V}\sin^2\Phi = v_1^2 v_2^2 \frac{\sin^2\theta}{(v_1^2 + v_2^2 - 2 v_1 v_2 \cos\theta)^{3/2}} . \quad (2.333)$$

We can now write equation (2.325) in the form

$$\begin{aligned}\Sigma\Delta E^2_{(v_1,\theta,\varphi)} &= 2\pi N(v_1, \theta, \varphi) G^2 m_1^2 m_2^2 v_1^2 v_2^2 \\ &\times \frac{\sin^2\theta}{(v_1^2 + v_2^2 - 2 v_1 v_2 \cos\theta)^{3/2}} \\ &\times \log\left(1 + \frac{D_0^2 (v_1^2 + v_2^2 - 2 v_1 v_2 \cos\theta)^2}{G^2 (m_1 + m_2)^2}\right) d v_1 d\theta d\varphi dt .\end{aligned} \quad (2.334)$$

vi) *The integration over the angles θ and φ for a spherical distribution of the velocities of the field stars.*—To effect the integration of equation (2.334) over the angles θ and φ we need to know the explicit form of the function $N(v_1, \theta, \varphi)$. For a spherical distribution of the velocities we can write

$$N(v_1, \theta, \varphi)\, d v_1 d\theta d\varphi = 4\pi N f(v_1)\, v_1^2 d v_1 \frac{1}{4\pi} \sin\theta d\theta d\varphi , \quad (2.335)$$

where $f(v_1)$ denotes the frequency function defining the distribution of the velocities v_1. For a Schwarzschild ellipsoidal distribution of velocities the form of the function $N(v_1, \theta, \varphi)$ is somewhat more complicated and will depend on the orientation of the velocity ellipsoid. It would be entirely feasible to write down the form of

$N(v_1, \theta, \varphi)$ under these more general circumstances and thus take into account the phenomenon of star streaming in our analysis of stellar encounters. We shall not, however, do this but shall restrict ourselves to the simpler case of a spherical distribution of velocities. We can then write

$$N(v_1, \theta, \varphi) = \frac{1}{4\pi} N(v_1) \sin\theta \,, \tag{2.336}$$

where we have used $N(v_1)$ to denote

$$N(v_1) = 4\pi N f(v_1) v_1^2 \,. \tag{2.337}$$

With the foregoing form for $N(v_1, \theta, \varphi)$ the integration of equation (2.334) over φ is immediate. We find

$$\left.\begin{aligned} \Sigma\Delta E^2_{(v_1,\,\theta)} &= \pi N(v_1) G^2 m_1^2 m_2^2 v_1^2 v_2^2 \frac{\sin^3\theta}{(v_1^2+v_2^2-2v_1v_2\cos\theta)^{3/2}} \\ &\quad\times \log\left(1+\frac{D_0^2(v_1^2+v_2^2-2v_1v_2\cos\theta)^2}{G^2(m_1+m_2)^2}\right) dv_1 d\theta dt \,. \end{aligned}\right\} \tag{2.338}$$

The integration over θ can now be effected. We have

$$\Sigma\Delta E^2_{v_1} = 8\pi N(v_1) G^2 m_1^2 m_2^2 J \, dv_1 dt \,, \tag{2.339}$$

where J stands for the integral

$$\left.\begin{aligned} J = \tfrac{1}{8} v_1^2 v_2^2 \int_0^\pi & \frac{\sin^3\theta}{(v_1^2+v_2^2-2v_1v_2\cos\theta)^{3/2}} \\ &\times \log\left(1+\frac{D_0^2(v_1^2+v_2^2-2v_1v_2\cos\theta)^2}{G^2(m_1+m_2)^2}\right) d\theta \,. \end{aligned}\right\} \tag{2.340}$$

To evaluate J we shall use V (cf. eq. [2.327]) as the variable of integration instead of θ. We find that J reduces to

$$J = \frac{1}{32 v_1 v_2} \int_{\sqrt{b}}^{\sqrt{a}} \frac{(a-V^2)(V^2-b)}{V^2} \log(1+q^2 V^4) \, dV \,, \tag{2.341}$$

where

$$q = \frac{D_0}{G(m_1+m_2)} \,, \tag{2.342}$$

and

$$a = (v_2+v_1)^2 \,; \qquad b = (v_2-v_1)^2 \,. \tag{2.343}$$

We verify that equation (2.341) is equivalent to

$$J=\frac{1}{32\,v_1 v_2}\int_{\sqrt{b}}^{\sqrt{a}}\frac{d}{dV}\left[\frac{ab}{V}+(a+b)\,V-\tfrac{1}{3}V^3\right]\times\log\left(1+q^2V^4\right)dV\,. \tag{2.344}$$

or, after an integration by parts, to

$$\begin{aligned}J=&\frac{1}{32\,v_1 v_2}\left[\frac{ab}{V}+(a+b)\,V-\tfrac{1}{3}V^3\right]\log\left(1+q^2V^4\right)\Big|_{\sqrt{b}}^{\sqrt{a}}\\&-\frac{q^2}{8\,v_1 v_2}\int_{\sqrt{b}}^{\sqrt{a}}\left[ab\,V^2+(a+b)\,V^4-\tfrac{1}{3}V^6\right]\frac{1}{1+q^2V^4}\,dV\,.\end{aligned} \tag{2.345}$$

It is seen that in the foregoing expression for J the integrated part represents the dominant term; consequently, we can ignore the non-integrated part in our scheme of approximation (cf. eqs. [2.322] and [2.324]). We thus find

$$J=\frac{1}{16\,v_1 v_2}\left[a^{1/2}\left(b+\tfrac{1}{3}a\right)\log\left(1+q^2a^2\right)-b^{1/2}\left(a+\tfrac{1}{3}b\right)\log\left(1+q^2b^2\right)\right]. \tag{2.346}$$

Again, since qa and qb are both generally of the order of 10^4-10^5 (cf. eqs. [2.323] and [2.342]), we can write

$$\begin{aligned}\log\left(1+q^2a^2\right)&\simeq 2\log qa\,,\\ \log\left(1+q^2b^2\right)&\simeq 2\log qb\,.\end{aligned} \tag{2.347}$$

An exception arises when $v_1=v_2$, in which case $b\equiv 0$. Then $\log qb$ diverges to $-\infty$. However, we need not distinguish between $b^{1/2}\log\left(1+q^2b^2\right)$ and $b^{1/2}\log q^2b^2$, particularly as both these expressions predict the correct limiting values. We thus have

$$J=\frac{1}{8\,v_1 v_2}\left[a^{1/2}\left(b+\tfrac{1}{3}a\right)\log qa-b^{1/2}\left(a+\tfrac{1}{3}b\right)\log qb\right]. \tag{2.348}$$

Substituting for a and b according to equation (2.343), we obtain

$$\begin{aligned}J&=\frac{1}{6\,v_1 v_2}\left[\left(v_2^3+v_1^3\right)\log q\left(v_1+v_2\right)^2-\left(v_2^3-v_1^3\right)\log q\left(v_2-v_1\right)^2\right]\quad (v_2\geqslant v_1)\,,\\ J&=\frac{1}{6\,v_1 v_2}\left[\left(v_2^3+v_1^3\right)\log q\left(v_1+v_2\right)^2-\left(v_1^3-v_2^3\right)\log q\left(v_1-v_2\right)^2\right]\quad (v_2\leqslant v_1)\,;\end{aligned} \tag{2.349}$$

or, after some further rearrangements of the terms, we have

$$\left.\begin{aligned} J &= \frac{v_1^2}{3\,v_2}\log q\,v_2^2 + \frac{v_1^2}{3\,v_2}\log\left(1-\frac{v_1^2}{v_2^2}\right) \\ &\qquad + \frac{v_2^2}{3\,v_1}\log\frac{v_2+v_1}{v_2-v_1} \qquad (v_2 \geqslant v_1)\,, \\ J &= \frac{v_2^2}{3\,v_1}\log q\,v_2^2 + \frac{v_2^2}{3\,v_1}\log\left(\frac{v_1^2}{v_2^2}-1\right) \\ &\qquad + \frac{v_1^2}{3\,v_2}\log\frac{v_1+v_2}{v_1-v_2} \qquad (v_1 \geqslant v_2)\,. \end{aligned}\right\} \quad (2.350)$$

Retaining only the dominant term in equations (2.350), we have

$$\left.\begin{aligned} J &= \frac{v_1^2}{3\,v_2}\log q\,v_2^2 \qquad (v_2 \geqslant v_1)\,, \\ J &= \frac{v_2^2}{3\,v_1}\log q\,v_2^2 \qquad (v_2 \leqslant v_1)\,. \end{aligned}\right\} \quad (2.351)$$

Substituting the foregoing expressions for J in equation (2.339), we finally have

$$\left.\begin{aligned} \Sigma\Delta E^2_{v_1} &= 8\pi N(v_1)\,G^2 m_1^2 m_2^2 v_2 \log q\,v_2^2 d\,v_1 dt \\ &\qquad \times \begin{cases} \dfrac{v_1^2}{3\,v_2^2} & (v_2 \geqslant v_1)\,, \\ \dfrac{v_2}{3\,v_1} & (v_2 \leqslant v_1)\,. \end{cases} \end{aligned}\right\} \quad (2.352)$$

vii) *The integration over the velocities* $\mathbf{v}_1$.—We have now evaluated the contribution to $\Sigma\Delta E^2$ by all encounters in which the field stars have some prescribed value of v_1. However, in carrying out the integrations over θ and φ it was further assumed that the distribution of the velocities of the field stars is a spherical one. In order now to average over the velocities of the field stars we need to know the form of the function $N(v_1)$. Here we meet certain difficulties of principle. Strictly speaking, the problem of the time of relaxation is also the problem of determining the rate of approach of the system toward some kind of "thermal" equilibrium. Consequently, there exist no a priori considerations (apart from the present ones) which would suggest a particular form of $N(v_1)$. Indeed, we should rather expect that a correct statistical theory of stellar encounters would itself lead to a definite form for $N(v_1)$. However, in our present connection we are interested only in finding the effect of *a* distribution of the velocities v_1 on $\Sigma\Delta E^2_{v_1}$ and in removing the arbitrariness of using a particular value of v_1. For this purpose a Gaussian distribution of the velocities of the field stars is likely to be adequate. We shall therefore assume that (cf. eq. [2.337])

$$N(v_1)\,dv_1 = \frac{4j^3}{\sqrt{\pi}} N e^{-j^2 v_1^2} v_1^2 dv_1 , \qquad (2.353)$$

where N is the number of stars per unit volume. For this form of $N(v_1)$ the integration of equation (2.352) over v_1 can be readily effected. We have

$$\left.\begin{aligned}\Sigma\Delta E^2 &= 8\pi N G^2 m_1^2 m_2^2 v_2 \log q v_2^2 dt \\ &\times \frac{4j^3}{3\sqrt{\pi}}\left[\frac{1}{v_2^2}\int_0^{v_2} e^{-j^2 v_1^2} v_1^4 dv_1 + v_2\int_{v_2}^{\infty} e^{-j^2 v_1^2} v_1 dv_1\right]\end{aligned}\right\} \qquad (2.354)$$

The integrals occurring in equation (2.354) are expressible in terms of the error function, $\Phi(x_0)$, and its derivative, $\Phi'(x_0)$. We find that

$$\Sigma\Delta E^2 = 8\pi N G^2 m_1^2 m_2^2 v_2 G(x_0) \log q v_2^2 , \qquad (2.355)$$

where $x_0 = jv_2$, and

$$G(x_0) = \frac{1}{2x_0^2}\left[\Phi(x_0) - x_0\Phi'(x_0)\right] . \qquad (2.356)$$

The function $G(x_0)$ is tabulated in Table 6.

TABLE 6

$G(x_0)$

x_0	$G(x_0)$	x_0	$G(x_0)$	x_0	$G(x_0)$
0.0	0.0	1.0	0.2138	2.0	0.1192
.2	.0734	1.2	.2047	3.0	.0555
.4	.1368	1.4	.1862	4.0	.0313
.6	.1827	1.6	.1634	5.0	.0200
0.8	0.2079	1.8	0.1404	∞	0.0

We may again draw attention to the fact that in evaluating $\Sigma\Delta E^2$ (eq. [2.355]) we have ignored all but the dominant terms. However, a rigorous evaluation of the sum, including the nondominant terms, shows that equation (2.355) gives an accuracy of 10 per cent for $0.6 \leqslant x_0 \leqslant 1.8$. According to Table 6, the variation of $G(x_0)$ in this range is not very appreciable. We have

$$\overline{G(x_0)} \simeq 0.18 \qquad (0.6 \leqslant x_0 \leqslant 1.8) . \quad (2.357)$$

viii) *The time of relaxation* T_E *of a stellar system.*—Equation (2.355) gives us the *instantaneous* rate of increase of $\Sigma\Delta E^2$ and will therefore enable us to follow the star *statistically* during its motion. For we can re-write equation (2.355) in the form

$$\frac{\Sigma\Delta E^2}{E^2} = \frac{32\pi N G^2 m_1^2 G(x_0) \log q v_2^2}{v_2^3} dt \qquad (2.358)$$

or, more simply, as

$$\frac{\Sigma\Delta E^2}{E^2} = \frac{dt}{T_E} , \qquad (2.359)$$

where we have written

$$T_E = \frac{v_2^3}{32\pi N G^2 m_1^2 G(x_0) \log_e \left[\frac{D_0 v_2^2}{G(m_1 + m_2)}\right]} . \qquad (2.360)$$

From equation (2.359) it follows that T_E gives the *time scale* which would be required for stellar encounters to become effective in seriously invalidating the energy integral (2.12) in the orbit described in the general gravitational field of the smoothed-out distribution of matter in the system. Accordingly, we can take equation (2.360) as *defining* the time of relaxation of the system.

When we express the mass, D_0, v_2, and N in the units of solar mass, parsec, 20 km/sec, and number per cubic parsec, respectively, equation (2.360) becomes

$$\left. \begin{aligned} T_E &= 1.83 \times 10^{12} \\ &\times \frac{v_2^3}{N m_1^2 G(x_0) \log_{10} [9.31 \times 10^4 D_0 v_2^2 / (m_1 + m_2)]} \text{ years} . \end{aligned} \right\} \qquad (2.361)$$

In view of equation (2.357), we have, to a sufficient accuracy,

$$\left.\begin{aligned} T_E &= 1.0\times 10^{13} \\ &\times \frac{v_2^3}{N m_1^2 \log_{10}\left[9.3\times 10^4 D_0 v_2^2/(m_1+m_2)\right]}\ \text{years}. \end{aligned}\right\} \qquad (2.362)$$

ix) *The average rate of increase of energy of a group of stars.*—So far, we have been concerned only with the expected change in energy of a particular star through its motion in a field of other stars. While this is the most important problem related to the time of relaxation of a stellar system, it is sometimes necessary to know the average change in energy experienced by a *group of stars* in their motions through other stars. For such purposes it is necessary to average the expression for $\Sigma\Delta E^2$ over both v_1 and v_2. We shall now consider this averaging.

According to equation (2.352), we have

$$\left.\begin{aligned} \Sigma\Delta E^2_{v_1} &= 8\pi N(v_1) G^2 m_1^2 m_2^2 \log q v_2^2 d v_1 dt \\ &\times \begin{cases} \dfrac{v_1^2}{3 v_2} & (v_2 \geqslant v_1), \\[2mm] \dfrac{v_2^2}{3 v_1} & (v_2 \leqslant v_1). \end{cases} \end{aligned}\right\} \qquad (2.363)$$

In averaging this expression over v_1 and v_2, we shall adopt different distribution functions for v_1 and v_2. More particularly, we shall assume that

$$N(v_1)\, d v_1 = \frac{4}{\pi^{1/2}} N j_1^3 e^{-j_1^2 v_1^2} v_1^2 d v_1 \qquad (2.364)$$

and

$$N(v_2)\, d v_2 = \frac{4}{\pi^{1/2}} N_2 j_2^3 e^{-j_2^2 v_2^2} v_2^2 d v_2 \,. \qquad (2.365)$$

On these assumptions regarding $N(v_1)$ and $N(v_2)$, we have

$$\overline{\Sigma\Delta E^2} = \frac{16}{\pi} j_1^3 j_2^3 \int_0^\infty e^{-j_2^2 v_2^2} v_2^2 \left(\int_0^\infty e^{-j_1^2 v_1^2} v_1^2 \Sigma\Delta E^2_{v_1} d v_1\right) d v_2 \,. \qquad (2.366)$$

In effecting this double integration, we shall replace the logarithmic term $\log q v_2^2$, which occurs in our expression for $\Sigma\Delta E^2_{v_1}$, by a suitable average and take it outside the integral signs. This procedure will not introduce any appreciable inaccuracy in the calculations, since the logarithmic term is insensitive to variations in v_2. Equation (2.366) can thus be expressed in the form

$$\Sigma\overline{\Delta E^2} = 8\pi N G^2 m_1^2 m_2^2 Q \log q\overline{v^2}dt\,, \tag{2.367}$$

where we have written

$$Q = \frac{16}{3\pi} j_1^3 j_2^3 \left[\int_0^\infty e^{-j_2^2 v_2^2} v_2 \left(\int_0^{v_2} e^{-j_1^2 v_1^2} v_1^4 d\,v_1\right) d\,v_2 + \int_0^\infty e^{-j_2^2 v_2^2} v_2^4 \left(\int_{v_2}^\infty e^{-j_1^2 v_1^2} v_1 d\,v_1\right) d\,v_2\right]. \tag{2.368}$$

Inverting the order of the integration in the first of the two foregoing double integrals, we obtain

$$Q = \frac{16}{3\pi} j_1^3 j_2^3 \left[\int_0^\infty e^{-j_1^2 v_1^2} v_1^4 \left(\int_{v_1}^\infty e^{-j_2^2 v_2^2} v_2 d\,v_2\right) d\,v_1 + \int_0^\infty e^{-j_2^2 v_2^2} v_2^4 \left(\int_{v_2}^\infty e^{-j_1^2 v_1^2} v_1 d\,v_1\right) d\,v_2\right]. \tag{2.369}$$

The two inside integrals in equation (2.369) are readily evaluated, and the expression for Q becomes

$$Q = \frac{8}{3\pi} j_1^3 j_2^3 \left[\frac{1}{j_2^2}\int_0^\infty e^{-(j_1^2+j_2^2)v_1^2} v_1^4 d\,v_1 + \frac{1}{j_1^2}\int_0^\infty e^{-(j_1^2+j_2^2)v_2^2} v_2^4 d\,v_2\right] \tag{2.370}$$

or, finally,

$$Q = \frac{1}{\pi^{1/2}} \frac{j_1 j_2}{(j_1^2 + j_2^2)^{3/2}}\,. \tag{2.371}$$

Combining equations (2.367) and (2.371), we have

$$\Sigma\overline{\Delta E^2} = 8\pi^{1/2} N G^2 m_1^2 m_2^2 \frac{j_1 j_2}{(j_1^2 + j_2^2)^{3/2}} \log q\overline{v^2}dt\,. \tag{2.372}$$

For the case $j_1 = j_2 = j$, the foregoing equation becomes

$$\Sigma\overline{\Delta E^2} = (8\pi)^{1/2} N G^2 m_1^2 m_2^2 j^{-1} \log q\overline{v^2}dt\,. \tag{2.373}$$

x) *The mean time of relaxation*, $\overline{T}_E$.—We shall define the mean time of relaxation $\overline{T}_E$ as the time required for $\Sigma\overline{\Delta E^2}$ to become equal to $\overline{E}^2$ where

$$\overline{E} = \tfrac{1}{2} m_2 \overline{v_2^2}\,. \tag{2.374}$$

Since, for the distribution function (2.365),

$$\overline{v_2^2} = \frac{3}{2\,j_2^2}, \tag{2.375}$$

we have

$$\overline{E^2} = \frac{9\,m_2^2}{16\,j_2^4}. \tag{2.376}$$

According to equations (2.372) and (2.376),

$$\overline{T}_E = \frac{9\,(j_1^2 + j_2^2)^{3/2}}{128\,\pi^{1/2} N G^2 m_1^2 j_1 j_2^5 \log q\,\overline{v^2}}. \tag{2.377}$$

For the case $j_1 = j_2 = j$, we have

$$\overline{T}_E = \frac{9}{16\,(8\pi)^{1/2} N G^2 m_1^2 j^3 \log q\,\overline{v^2}} \qquad (j_1 = j_2 = j)\,. \tag{2.378}$$

Equation (2.378) can be expressed more conveniently in terms of the root mean square velocity $(\overline{v^2})^{1/2}$. We find (cf. eq. [2.375])

$$\overline{T}_E = \frac{1}{16}\left(\frac{3}{\pi}\right)^{1/2} \frac{[\,\overline{v^2}\,]^{3/2}}{N G^2 m_1^2 \log_e q\,\overline{v^2}}, \tag{2.379}$$

or, expressing the mass, $(\overline{v^2})^{1/2}$, D_0, and N in units of solar mass, 20 km/sec, parsec, and number per cubic parsec, respectively, we obtain

$$\left.\begin{aligned} \overline{T}_E &= 1.12 \times 10^{13} \\ &\times \frac{[\,\overline{v^2}\,]^{3/2}}{N m_1^2 \log_{10} [\,9.3 \times 10^4 D_0 \overline{v^2}/(m_1 + m_2)\,]}\ \text{years}, \end{aligned}\right\} \tag{2.380}$$

in which form the close similarity with equation (2.362) is evident.

2.4.—*The time of relaxation*, T$_D$.—For evaluating the time of relaxation of a stellar system from the point of view of the deflections suffered by stars as a result of stellar encounters, the first problem is clearly one of expressing the deflection, $\pi - 2\Psi$, suffered, in terms of the parameters describing an encounter. By definition the deflection $\pi - 2\Psi$ is simply the angle between the vectors representing the initial and the final directions of motion of the star. Thus, if $\boldsymbol{v}_2$

and $\boldsymbol{v}_2'$ denote the velocity of the incident star before and after the encounter, respectively, then

$$\cos(\pi - 2\Psi) = \frac{\boldsymbol{v}_2 \cdot \boldsymbol{v}_2'}{v_2 v_2'} \qquad (2.401)$$

(see Fig. 13, where the situation is made apparent).

i) *The true deflection suffered by a star as the result of a stellar encounter.*[5]—In order to determine the true deflection according to equation (2.401), we first need to specify the vector $\boldsymbol{v}_2'$. To do this we proceed as follows:

Let v_{2g} and v_{2g}' denote the velocity of the star before and after the encounter in the frame of reference in which the center of gravity is at rest. Then

$$\boldsymbol{v}_{2g} = \boldsymbol{v}_2 - \boldsymbol{V}_g\,; \qquad \boldsymbol{v}_{2g}' = \boldsymbol{v}_2' - \boldsymbol{V}_g\,, \qquad (2.402)$$

where, by definition,

$$(m_1 + m_2)\,\boldsymbol{V}_g = m_1 \boldsymbol{v}_1 + m_2 \boldsymbol{v}_2 = m_1 \boldsymbol{v}_1' + m_2 \boldsymbol{v}_2'\,. \qquad (2.403)$$

From equations (2.402) and (2.403) we obtain

$$\boldsymbol{v}_{2g} = \frac{m_1}{m_1 + m_2}\boldsymbol{V}\,; \qquad \boldsymbol{v}_{2g}' = \frac{m_1}{m_1 + m_2}\boldsymbol{V}'\,. \qquad (2.404)$$

Hence the angle between the vectors v_{2g} and v_{2g}' is the same as that between V and V', i.e., $\pi - 2\psi$, where ψ is given by equation (2.301).

Now, according to equation (2.402), we have

$$\boldsymbol{v}_2 \cdot \boldsymbol{v}_2' = \boldsymbol{v}_2 \cdot (\boldsymbol{v}_{2g}' + \boldsymbol{V}_g) \qquad (2.405)$$

or

$$v_2 v_2' \cos(\pi - 2\Psi) = \boldsymbol{v}_2 \cdot \boldsymbol{v}_{2g}' + \boldsymbol{v}_2 \cdot \boldsymbol{V}_g\,. \qquad (2.406)$$

The direction cosines of $\boldsymbol{v}_2$ with respect to $\boldsymbol{V}$, a direction in the orbital plane at right angles to $\boldsymbol{V}$ and a direction perpendicular to the orbital plane are

$$\cos(\Phi - \vartheta)\,, \qquad -\sin(\Phi - \vartheta)\cos\Theta\,, \qquad \sin(\Phi - \vartheta)\sin\Theta\,, \quad (2.407)$$

[5] The analysis which follows is taken from a paper by R. E. Williamson and S. Chandrasekhar, *Ap. J.*, **93**, 305, 1941.

where ϑ is the angle between $\boldsymbol{v}_2$ and $\boldsymbol{V}_g$. Again, since $\boldsymbol{v}'_{2g}$ is in the same direction as $\boldsymbol{V}'$, the direction cosines of $\boldsymbol{v}'_{2g}$ with respect to the same three directions are

$$\cos(\phi' - \phi) , \qquad \sin(\phi' - \phi) , \qquad 0 . \qquad (2.408)$$

Hence,

$$\left.\begin{aligned} \boldsymbol{v}_2 \cdot \boldsymbol{v}'_{2g} = v_2 v'_{2g} \{ &\cos(\phi' - \phi) \cos(\Phi - \vartheta) \\ &- \sin(\phi' - \phi) \sin(\Phi - \vartheta) \cos\Theta \} . \end{aligned}\right\} \qquad (2.409)$$

From equations (2.406) and (2.409) we obtain

$$\left.\begin{aligned} v'_2 \cos(\pi - 2\Psi) = v'_{2g} \{ &\cos(\phi' - \phi) \cos(\Phi - \vartheta) \\ &- \sin(\phi' - \phi) \sin(\Phi - \vartheta) \cos\Theta \} + V_g \cos\vartheta . \end{aligned}\right\} \qquad (2.410)$$

Since $\phi' - \phi = \pi - 2\psi$, equation (2.410) can be re-written as

$$\left.\begin{aligned} \cos 2\Psi = \frac{1}{v'_2} \{ v_{2g} [&\cos 2\psi \cos(\Phi - \vartheta) \\ &+ \sin 2\psi \sin(\Phi - \vartheta) \cos\Theta] - V_g \cos\vartheta \} . \end{aligned}\right\} \qquad (2.411)$$

On the other hand, we have the elementary relations (see Fig. 13)

$$V \cos(\Phi - \vartheta) = v_2 - v_1 \cos\theta ; \qquad V \sin(\Phi - \vartheta) = v_1 \sin\theta . \quad (2.412)$$

Again, multiplying the equation defining $\boldsymbol{V}_g$ scalarly by $\boldsymbol{v}_2$, we obtain

$$V_g \cos\vartheta = \frac{1}{m_1 + m_2} (m_1 v_1 \cos\theta + m_2 v_2) . \qquad (2.413)$$

Substituting the foregoing relations in equation (2.411) and remembering also that $v_{2g} = [m_1/(m_1 + m_2)]V$ (cf. eq. [2.404]), we have

$$\left.\begin{aligned} \cos 2\Psi = \frac{1}{(m_1 + m_2) v'_2} [&m_1 (v_2 - v_1 \cos\theta) \cos 2\psi \\ &+ m_1 v_1 \sin\theta \cos\Theta \sin 2\psi - m_1 v_1 \cos\theta - m_2 v_2] , \end{aligned}\right\} \qquad (2.414)$$

or, after some minor rearrangement of the terms,

$$\left.\begin{aligned} \cos 2\Psi = \frac{1}{(m_1 + m_2) v'_2} [&2 m_1 (v_2 - v_1 \cos\theta) \cos^2\psi \\ &+ 2 m_1 v_1 \sin\theta \cos\Theta \sin\psi \cos\psi - (m_1 + m_2) v_2] . \end{aligned}\right\} \qquad (2.415)$$

We have now to express v_2' in terms of the known quantities v_1, v_2, θ, and ψ. We find[6]

$$v_2'^2 = \frac{1}{(m_1+m_2)^2}\{(m_1+m_2)^2 v_2^2 - 4m_1[(m_2 v_2^2 - m_1 v_1^2) + (m_1-m_2)v_1 v_2 \cos\theta]\cos^2\psi - 4m_1(m_1+m_2)v_1 v_2 \sin\theta\cos\Theta\sin\psi\cos\psi\}. \quad (2.416)$$

Substituting for v_2' in equation (2.415), we have

$$\cos 2\Psi = \frac{2m_1(v_2-v_1\cos\theta)\cos^2\psi + 2m_1 v_1 \sin\theta\cos\Theta\sin\psi\cos\psi - (m_1+m_2)v_2}{\sqrt{(m_1+m_2)^2 v_2^2 - 4m_1[(m_2 v_2^2 - m_1 v_2^2) + (m_1-m_2)v_1 v_2\cos\theta]\cos^2\psi - 4m_1(m_1+m_2)v_1 v_2 \sin\theta\cos\Theta\sin\psi\cos\psi}}. \quad (2.417)$$

From the foregoing equation we finally obtain

$$\sin^2 2\Psi = 4m_1^2\cos^2\psi \times \frac{v_1^2+v_2^2-2v_1 v_2\cos\theta - [(v_2-v_1\cos\theta)\cos\psi + v_1\sin\theta\cos\Theta\sin\psi]^2}{(m_1+m_2)^2 v_2^2 - 4m_1[(m_2 v_2^2 - m_1 v_1^2) + (m_1-m_2)v_1 v_2\cos\theta]\cos^2\psi - 4m_1(m_1+m_2)v_1 v_2\sin\theta\cos\Theta\sin\psi\cos\psi}. \quad (2.418)$$

The expression for $\sin^2 2\Psi$ simplifies considerably for distant encounters. Under these circumstances $\psi \to \pi/2$ and equation (2.418) become

$$\sin^2 2\Psi \simeq \frac{4m_1^2}{(m_1+m_2)^2 v_2^2} \times [v_1^2 + v_2^2 - 2v_1 v_2 \cos\theta - v_1^2 \sin^2\theta\cos^2\Theta]\cos^2\psi, \quad (2.419)$$

or, after a slight rearrangement of the terms, we obtain

$$\sin^2 2\Psi \simeq \frac{4m_1^2}{(m_1+m_2)^2 v_2^2}[(v_2 - v_1\cos\theta)^2 + v_1^2\sin^2\theta\sin^2\Theta]\cos^2\psi. \quad (2.420)$$

ii) *The time of relaxation* T_D.—The number of $(v_1, \theta, \varphi, D, \Theta)$ encounters is given by equation (2.313), and the contribution of these encounters to the sum $\Sigma \sin^2 2\Psi$ can be written as

$$\Sigma \sin^2 2\Psi_{(v_1,\theta,\varphi,D,\Theta)} = 2\pi N(v_1, \theta, \varphi) \times \sin^2 2\Psi\, V D dD \frac{d\Theta}{2\pi} dv_1 d\theta d\varphi dt. \quad (2.421)$$

[6] For an explicit derivation see *ibid.*

Using ψ instead of D as a variable in equation (2.421), we have (cf. eq. [2.316])

$$\left.\begin{aligned}\Sigma \sin^2 2\Psi_{(v_1,\theta,\varphi,\psi,\Theta)} &= 2\pi N(v_1,\theta,\varphi) G^2 \frac{(m_1+m_2)^2}{V^3} \\ &\times \sin^2 2\Psi \frac{\sin\psi}{\cos^3\psi} d\psi \frac{d\Theta}{2\pi} dv_1 d\theta d\varphi dt\,.\end{aligned}\right\} \quad (2.422)$$

Our next problem is to integrate the foregoing equation over the relevant ranges of the variables ψ, Θ, φ, θ, and v_1. Thus, integrating over ψ, we have

$$\left.\begin{aligned}\Sigma \sin^2 2\Psi_{(v_1,\theta,\varphi,\Theta)} &= 2\pi N(v_1,\theta,\varphi) G^2 \frac{(m_1+m_2)^2}{V^3} \\ &\times \int \frac{\sin^2 2\Psi \sin\psi}{\cos^3\psi} d\psi \frac{d\Theta}{2\pi} dv_1 d\theta d\varphi dt\,.\end{aligned}\right\} \quad (2.423)$$

If, as in § 2.3, we retain only the dominant terms in evaluating the sum $\Sigma \sin^2 2\Psi$, then it is clear that it would be sufficient to use for $\sin^2 2\Psi$ the limiting form (2.420) instead of the general formula (2.418). On this approximation, equation (2.423) becomes

$$\left.\begin{aligned}\Sigma \sin^2 2\Psi_{(v_1,\theta,\varphi,\Theta)} &= 8\pi N(v_1,\theta,\varphi) G^2 m_1^2 \frac{1}{V^3 v_2^2} \\ &\times [(v_2 - v_1\cos\theta)^2 + v_1^2 \sin^2\theta \sin^2\Theta] \\ &\times \int \frac{\sin\psi}{\cos\psi} d\psi \frac{d\Theta}{2\pi} dv_1 d\theta d\varphi dt\,,\end{aligned}\right\} \quad (2.424)$$

an integral which diverges logarithmically as $\psi \to \pi/2$. This divergence arises, of course, for the same reasons that caused a similar divergence in the valuation of $\Sigma \Delta E^2$. Accordingly, in equation (2.424) we shall extend the integration over ψ from 0 to an upper limit ψ_0, corresponding to $D = D_{\max} \simeq D_0$. We thus obtain

$$\left.\begin{aligned}\Sigma \sin^2 2\Psi_{(v_1,\theta,\varphi,\Theta)} &= 4\pi N(v_1,\theta,\varphi) G^2 m_1^2 \frac{1}{V^3 v_2^2} \\ &\times [(v_2 - v_1\cos\theta)^2 + v_1^2 \sin^2\theta \sin^2\Theta] \\ &\times \log\left(1 + \frac{D_0^2 V^4}{G^2(m_1+m_2)^2}\right) \frac{d\Theta}{2\pi} dv_1 d\theta d\varphi dt\,,\end{aligned}\right\} \quad (2.425)$$

or, after integrating over Θ, we have

$$\left.\begin{aligned}\Sigma \sin^2 2\Psi_{(v_1,\theta,\varphi)} = 4\pi N(v_1, \theta, \varphi) G^2 m_1^2 \frac{1}{V^3 v_2^2} \\ \times [(v_2 - v_1 \cos\theta)^2 + \tfrac{1}{2} v_1^2 \sin^2\theta] \\ \times \log\left(1 + \frac{D_0^2 V^4}{G^2 (m_1 + m_2)^2}\right) dv_1 d\theta d\varphi dt .\end{aligned}\right\} \quad (2.426)$$

The further integrations over θ, φ, and v_1 can be effected only when the form of $N(v_1, \theta, \varphi)$ is known. As in § 2.3, we shall first introduce the assumption of a spherical distribution of the velocities v_1 (eqs. [2.336] and [2.337]). For this form of $N(v_1, \theta, \varphi)$ the integration over φ is immediate. We find

$$\left.\begin{aligned}\Sigma \sin^2 2\Psi_{(v_1,\theta)} = 2\pi N(v_1) G^2 m_1^2 \frac{1}{V^3 v_2^2} \\ \times \sin\theta [(v_2 - v_1 \cos\theta)^2 + \tfrac{1}{2} v_1^2 \sin^2\theta] \\ \times \log\left(1 + \frac{D_0^2 V^4}{G^2 (m_1 + m_2)^2}\right) dv_1 d\theta dt ,\end{aligned}\right\} \quad (2.427)$$

where

$$V^2 = v_1^2 + v_2^2 - 2 v_1 v_2 \cos\theta . \quad (2.428)$$

The integration of equation (2.427) over θ is straightforward. Retaining only the dominant term, we find

$$\left.\begin{aligned}\Sigma \sin^2 2\Psi_{v_1} = \frac{8\pi G^2 m_1^2 N(v_1)}{3 v_2^3} dv_1 dt \\ \times \begin{cases} \left(3 - \dfrac{v_1^2}{v_2^2}\right) \log \dfrac{D_0 v_2^2}{G(m_1 + m_2)} & (v_2 \geqslant v_1) , \\ 2 \dfrac{v_2}{v_1} \log \dfrac{D_0 v_2^2}{G(m_1 + m_2)} & (v_2 \leqslant v_1) . \end{cases}\end{aligned}\right\} \quad (2.429)$$

Finally, to effect the integration over v_1 we shall further specialize the spherical distribution of the velocities assumed to a Maxwellian distribution. Using the form of $N(v_1)$ appropriate to this case (eq. [2.353]), we obtain

$$\Sigma \sin^2 2\Psi = \frac{8\pi N G^2 m_1^2}{v_2^3} H(x_0) \log \frac{D_0 v_2^2}{G(m_1 + m_2)} dt , \quad (2.430)$$

where $x_0 = jv_2$ and

$$H(x_0) = \frac{1}{2x_0^2}\left[x_0\Phi'(x_0) + (2x_0^2 - 1)\Phi(x_0)\right] \qquad (2.431)$$

($\Phi[x_0]$ and $\Phi'[x_0]$ denote, respectively, the error function and its derivative). The function $H(x_0)$ is tabulated in Table 7. Equation

TABLE 7

$H(x_0)$

x_0	$H(x_0)$	T_D/T_E	x_0	$H(x_0)$	T_D/T_E
0.6	0.421	1.74	1.8	0.849	0.66
0.8	.534	1.56	2.0	.876	.55
1.0	.629	1.36	2.5	.920	0.35
1.2	.706	1.16	3.0	.944	....
1.4	.766	0.97	4.0	0.969	....
1.6	0.813	0.80			

(2.430) can be written in the form

$$\Sigma \sin^2 2\Psi = \frac{dt}{T_D}, \qquad (2.432)$$

where

$$T_D = \frac{v_2^3}{8\pi N G^2 m_1^2 H(x_0) \log\left[\frac{D_0 v_2^2}{G(m_1 + m_2)}\right]}. \qquad (2.433)$$

According to equation (2.432), T_D gives the time scale which would be required for stellar encounters to become effective in deviating the star from the orbit described by it in the general gravitational field of the smoothed-out distribution of matter in the system. We can therefore take equation (2.433) as defining the time of relaxation.

Comparing equation (2.433) with the formula for the time of relaxation T_E obtained in § 2.3 (eq. [2.360]), we notice that the two expressions are of identical forms. Further, the ratio between the times of relaxation obtained from the two different points of view is given by

$$\frac{T_D}{T_E} = 4\,\frac{G(x_0)}{H(x_0)}. \qquad (2.434)$$

This ratio is tabulated in Table 7. It is seen that T_D/T_E varies from 1.7 to 0.35 as x_0 varies from 0.6 to 2.5.

Applications of the formulae for the times of relaxation obtained in this chapter will be found in chapters iii and v.

2.5. *The mean free path.*—The formulae for the time of relaxation obtained in §§ 2.3 and 2.4 enable us to evaluate certain other quantities of interest. The first of these quantities is the *mean free path.* It may seem at first sight impossible to assign a meaning to the mean free path for a system consisting of stars idealized as mere centers of force. Nevertheless, it is possible to define a length which plays the same role for stellar dynamics as the mean free path does in the classical kinetic theory of gases, where the molecules are idealized as rigid elastic spheres.

Now, according to equation (2.359),

$$\frac{\Sigma\Delta E^2}{E^2}=\frac{dt}{T_E}. \tag{2.501}$$

As we have already indicated, $\sqrt{\Sigma\Delta E^2}$ gives the *expectation* of the change in energy that is to be anticipated in time dt. And, during this time dt, the star will have traversed a distance

$$dl=v_2 dt\,. \tag{2.502}$$

We can therefore re-write equation (2.501) in the form

$$\frac{\Sigma\Delta E^2}{E^2}=\frac{dl}{\lambda_1(v_2)}, \tag{2.503}$$

where

$$\lambda_1(v_2)=T_E v_2=\frac{v_2^4}{32\pi NG^2m_1^2G(x_0)\log_e\left[\frac{D_0v_2^2}{G(m_1+m_2)}\right]}. \tag{2.504}$$

We can take $\lambda_1(v_2)$ as defining the mean free path for a star of velocity v_2. For, according to equation (2.503), *the probability that a star will traverse a distance* l *without suffering the expected change of energy* $\sqrt{\Sigma\Delta E^2}$ *is*

$$e^{-l/\lambda_1(v_2)}\,. \tag{2.505}$$

We are therefore justified in identifying the length $\lambda_1(v_2)$ as the appropriate mean free path.

For a star moving with the average speed $\bar{v}_2$ in the system,

$$\lambda_1(\bar{v}_2) = \frac{\bar{v}_2^4}{32\pi N G^2 m_1^2 G(\bar{x}_0) \log_e \left[\frac{D_0 \bar{v}_2^2}{G(m_1+m_2)}\right]} . \qquad (2.506)$$

For a Maxwellian distribution of the velocities v_2,

$$\bar{v}_2 = \frac{2}{\pi^{1/2} j} . \qquad (2.507)$$

It would, therefore, be sufficient to use for $\bar{x}_0$ the value

$$\bar{x}_0 = j\bar{v}_2 = 2\pi^{-(1/2)} = 1.128 . \qquad (2.508)$$

From Table 6 we now find that

$$G(\bar{x}_0) = 0.212 . \qquad (2.509)$$

With this value of $G(\bar{x}_0)$, equation (2.506) becomes

$$\lambda_1(\bar{v}_2) = 0.0204 \frac{\bar{v}_2^4}{N G^2 m_1^2 \log_{10} \left[\frac{D_0 \bar{v}_2^2}{G(m_1+m_2)}\right]} . \qquad (2.510)$$

or, expressing the mass, D_0, $\bar{v}_2$, and N in units of solar mass, parsec, 20 km/sec, and number per cubic parsec, respectively, we find

$$\left.\begin{aligned} \lambda_1(\bar{v}_2) &= 1.77 \times 10^8 \\ &\times \frac{\bar{v}_2^4}{N m_1^2 \log_{10}[9.31 \times 10^4 D_0 \bar{v}_2^2/(m_1+m_2)]} \text{ parsecs} . \end{aligned}\right\} \qquad (2.511)$$

It is clear that, analogous to the length $\lambda_1(v_2)$, we can define another mean free path which will be appropriate for the discussion of the deflections experienced by stars. Thus, if the probability that a star with velocity v_2 will traverse a length l without suffering the expected deflection $\sin^{-1}(\sqrt{\Sigma \sin^2 2\Psi})$ be expressed as

$$e^{-l/\lambda_2(v_2)} , \qquad (2.512)$$

then, clearly,

$$\lambda_2(v_2) = T_D v_2 , \qquad (2.513)$$

where T_D is given by equation (2.433).

There is a simple relation between the free paths λ_1 and λ_2. For, according to equations (2.504), (2.513), and (2.434),

$$\frac{\lambda_2(v_2)}{\lambda_1(v_2)} = 4\,\frac{G(x_0)}{H(x_0)}\,. \tag{2.514}$$

For stars moving with the mean speed $\bar{v}_2$ in the system, we have (cf. eq. [2.508])

$$\frac{\lambda_2(\bar{v}_2)}{\lambda_1(\bar{v}_2)} = 4\,\frac{G(1.13)}{H(1.13)} = 1.24 \tag{2.515}$$

or, according to equation (2.511),

$$\left.\begin{aligned}\lambda_2(\bar{v}_2) &= 2.12\times 10^8\\ &\times\frac{\bar{v}_2^4}{N m_1^2 \log_{10}[9.31\times 10^4 D_0 \bar{v}_2^2/(m_1+m_2)]}\text{ parsecs}\,.\end{aligned}\right\} \tag{2.516}$$

2.6. *Viscosity*.—We have seen in § 2.5 how it is possible to give a meaning to the term "mean free path" for a stellar system. But it cannot, therefore, be concluded that the related notions of viscosity, diffusion, etc., of the kinetic theory of gases can also be extended to stellar systems. The principal difficulty in extending these concepts to stellar systems consists in the fact that the mean free paths are generally very long compared to the linear dimensions of the system. Thus, under the circumstances envisaged in stellar dynamics, viscosity and the related notions very largely lose their meanings. It is, however, of interest to compare the expression for the time of relaxation which we have obtained with the time of relaxation of a gas as ordinarily defined in terms of viscosity.

According to Maxwell,[7] the time of relaxation of a gas is given by

$$T_E = \frac{\mu}{NkT}\,, \tag{2.601}$$

where μ is the coefficient of viscosity, k is the Boltzmann constant, and T is the temperature. In order to apply this formula for stellar systems, we shall first express kT in terms of the constant j in the distribution function (eq. [2.353]). Clearly,

$$kT = \frac{m}{2j^2}\,. \tag{2.602}$$

[7] Cf., e.g., J. H. Jeans, *The Dynamical Theory of Gases*, pp. 242–244, Cambridge, England, 1921.

Equation (2.601) becomes

$$\mu = \frac{m}{2j^2} N T_E . \tag{2.603}$$

Again, since

$$\bar{v}_2 = \frac{2}{\pi^{1/2} j} \tag{2.604}$$

an alternative form for μ is

$$\mu = \frac{\pi}{8} N m T_E \, \bar{v}_2^2 . \tag{2.605}$$

This equation is to be regarded merely as another way of writing equation (2.601).

We shall now *formally* substitute for T_E occurring in equation (2.605) our expression for $T_E(\bar{v}_2)$.
We have

$$\mu = \frac{\pi}{8} N m T_E(\bar{v}_2) \, \bar{v}_2^2 \tag{2.606}$$

or, according to equations (2.504) and (2.506),

$$\mu = \frac{\pi}{8} N m \lambda_1(\bar{v}_2) \, \bar{v}_2 ; \tag{2.607}$$

in this form we recognize the standard formula for the viscosity in terms of the mean free path

$$\mu = \tfrac{1}{3} N m \sqrt{\overline{v_2^2}} \lambda \tag{2.608}$$

which does not differ appreciably from equation (2.607). Substituting for $\lambda_2(\bar{v}_2)$ according to equation (2.510) in equation (2.607), we obtain

$$\mu = 8.0 \times 10^{-3} \frac{\bar{v}_2^5}{G^2 m \log_{10} [D_0 \bar{v}_2^2 / 2m]} . \tag{2.609}$$

Now Chapman has evaluated the coefficient of viscosity for a gas with an inverse square law of force between the molecules. With slight modifications arising from the circumstance that we are now dealing with gravitational instead of electrical forces, Chapman's formula[8] becomes

$$\mu = 7.6 \times 10^{-3} \frac{\bar{v}_2^5}{G^2 m \log_{10} [D_0 \bar{v}_2^2 / 2Gm]} , \qquad (2.610)$$

which agrees very satisfactorily with equation (2.609).

Expressing $\bar{v}_2$, m, and D_0 in the units 20 km/sec, solar mass, and parsec, respectively, equation (2.609) becomes

$$\mu = 2.9 \times 10^{10} \frac{\bar{v}_2^5}{m \log_{10} [4.66 \times 10^4 D_0 \bar{v}_2^2 / m]} \text{ C.G.S. units} . \qquad (2.611)$$

To avoid misunderstanding, we should again emphasize that the applicability of the foregoing formula for μ is extremely limited by the circumstance that, in general, the mean free paths in a stellar system are several thousand times the linear dimensions of the system.

BIBLIOGRAPHICAL NOTES

The concept of the time of relaxation of a system was first introduced by Maxwell to estimate the rate at which deviations from a Maxwellian distribution of the velocities will subside.

1. J. C. Maxwell, *Proc. Roy. Soc., London*, **15,** 167, 1866. The formula (2.601) is due to Maxwell, and on the basis of this formula he states ". . . . any strain existing in air at rest would diminish according to the values of an exponential term the modulus of which is 1/5,100,000,-000 second. . . . . This *relaxation* is due to the mutual deflection of the molecules from their paths"—hence the term "the time of relaxation." For a general account of Maxwell's ideas see—

2. L. Boltzmann, *Vorlesungen über Gas Theorie* (dritte unveränderte Auflage), I, 164–166, 1923.

3. J. H. Jeans, *An Introduction to the Kinetic Theory of Gases*, pp. 233–234, Cambridge, England, 1940.

The extension of the notion of the time of relaxation to stellar systems is due to—

4. J. H. Jeans, *M. N.*, **74,** 109, 1913; also, *ibid.*, **76,** 554, 1916, and—

5. K. Schwarzschild, *Seeliger Festschrift*, p. 94, Berlin, 1924. This

[8] Cf. S. Chapman and T. G. Cowling, *The Mathematical Theory of Nonuniform Gases*, p. 179, Cambridge, England, 1939.

paper by Schwarzschild is a posthumous publication; but the investigation appears to have been carried out prior to 1917.

Though the physical ideas were correctly formulated by Jeans and Schwarzschild, a completely rigorous evaluation of the time of relaxation was not available until recently. The analysis in §§ 2.3 and 2.4 are, in the main, taken from—

6. S. CHANDRASEKHAR, *Ap. J.*, **93**, 285, 1941, and—

7. R. E. WILLIAMSON and S. CHANDRASEKHAR, *Ap. J.*, **93**, 305, 1941.

The analysis in §§ 2.3 (subsecs. [ix] and [x]) and 2.5 and 2.6 are published here for the first time. See also—

8. S. CHANDRASEKHAR, *Ap. J.*, **93**, 323, 1941.

CHAPTER III

GALACTIC DYNAMICS: THE DYNAMICS OF DIFFERENTIAL MOTIONS

The formulae for the time of relaxation of a stellar system derived in the last chapter will enable us to determine, under a given set of conditions, the extent to which we can idealize each star as an independent conservative dynamical system. By an application of the formulae of chapter ii we shall first show that in considering the dynamics of the Galaxy we can entirely disregard the effect of stellar encounters. This provides a considerable simplification and enables a straightforward application of Liouville's theorem of classical dynamics. The importance of this theorem in our present connection is that we are thus able to write down a certain linear homogeneous partial differential equation which the distribution function Ψ must satisfy. And it is to the discussion of this equation that this chapter will be mainly devoted. More particularly, our main problem will be the consideration of the circumstances under which a solution of the differential equation for Ψ will correspond to a stellar system with differential motions in the sense described in chapter i (§ 1.9).

3.1. *The time of relaxation of the Galaxy.*—To determine T_E according to equation (2.361) we need numerical values for the various quantities occurring in this formula. In the neighborhood of the sun we approximately have

$$N = 0.1 \text{ parsec}^{-3}\,; \qquad D_0 = 2.7 \text{ parsecs}\,; \qquad m_1 = 0.5\odot\,. \qquad (3.11)$$

As a typical example let us consider an "incident" star with a velocity $v_2 = 20$ km/sec. Now, if the preferential effects of star streaming are smoothed out, the motions of the near-by stars can be represented fairly well by a Maxwellian distribution with $j =$ 0.032 sec/km (cf. § 1.5, p. 32). Hence, for the case under consideration $x_0 = jv_2 \cong 0.65$. According to equation (2.361) and Table 6, we have

$$T_E = \frac{1.83 \times 10^{12}}{0.1 \times 0.25 \times 0.19 \log_{10} [9.31 \times 10^4 \times 2.7]} = 7 \times 10^{13} \text{ years}. \quad (3.12)$$

From Table 7 we now obtain

$$T_D = 1.7 \times 7 \times 10^{13} = 1.2 \times 10^{14} \text{ years}. \quad (3.13)$$

Under the conditions specified we therefore have (cf. eqs. [2.359] and [2.432])

$$\frac{\Sigma \Delta E^2}{E^2} = 3 \times 10^{-6}; \quad \Sigma \sin^2 2\Psi = 1.7 \times 10^{-6} \quad (\Delta t = 2 \times 10^8 \text{ years}). \quad (3.14)$$

In other words, during an interval of 2×10^8 years a star may be expected (on the average) to have its energy changed by a fraction 0.0017 and further suffer a deflection of 0.0013 radians (~0.07°) from its orbit, both, as the cumulative result of stellar encounters. Since the period of galactic rotation is about 2×10^8 years, it follows that a star can describe at least a hundred revolutions before any appreciable perturbations may be anticipated as the result of encounters with other stars. Again,

$$\frac{\Sigma \Delta E^2}{E^2} = 4 \times 10^{-5}; \quad \Sigma \sin^2 2\Psi = 2.5 \times 10^{-5} \quad (\Delta t = 3 \times 10^9 \text{ years}); \quad (3.15)$$

hence, in 3×10^9 years the energy may be expected to change by a fraction 0.006; meanwhile a deflection of 0.005 radians (~0.29°) from its "theoretical orbit" (cf. § 2.1) might occur. Remembering that the general time scale is itself only of the order of 3×10^9 years, it appears that a very good first approximation to galactic dynamics will be provided by disregarding the effect of stellar encounters. In stating this, we are assuming that the stellar density in other parts of the Galaxy is not of an entirely different order of magnitude from that in the general neighborhood of the sun. It should, however, be noted that even a star density of 10 per cubic parsec will permit the use of the energy integral (2.12) with an accuracy of 6 per cent for an interval of time of 3×10^9 years, while the maximum deflection suffered during this time will be of the order of 3° or 4°. But a more serious limitation would be set if the conditions in the Galaxy 3×10^9 years ago had been very different from the present conditions. This is perhaps not altogether unlikely; indeed it appears even probable that the *initial conditions* for the present state of motions was provided during those "early times" under totally different conditions. Nevertheless, *the Galaxy is at present in a state in which each star can be idealized as an independent conservative dynamical system to a very high degree of accuracy.*

According to our remarks in the preceding paragraph, the motion of any given star will be governed by the Hamiltonian

$$\left.\begin{aligned} H &= \frac{1}{2m}\left(p_x^2 + p_y^2 + p_z^2\right) + m\mathfrak{B}(x, y, z, t)\,, \\ p_x &= mU\,; \qquad p_y = mV\,; \qquad p_z = mW\,. \end{aligned}\right\} \tag{3.16}$$

The Hamiltonian (3.16) is different for stars of different masses. However, we can treat all the stars on the same footing by considering the *Hamiltonian per unit mass* $\mathfrak{H}$:

$$\mathfrak{H} = \tfrac{1}{2}\left(U^2 + V^2 + W^2\right) + \mathfrak{B}(x, y, z, t)\,. \tag{3.17}$$

The canonical equations now take the forms

$$\left.\begin{aligned} \dot{x} &= \frac{\partial \mathfrak{H}}{\partial U}\,; \qquad \dot{y} = \frac{\partial \mathfrak{H}}{\partial V}\,; \qquad \dot{z} = \frac{\partial \mathfrak{H}}{\partial W}\,, \\ \dot{U} &= -\frac{\partial \mathfrak{H}}{\partial x}\,; \qquad \dot{V} = -\frac{\partial \mathfrak{H}}{\partial y}\,; \qquad \dot{W} = -\frac{\partial \mathfrak{H}}{\partial z}\,. \end{aligned}\right\} \tag{3.18}$$

Thus, in the variables x, y, z, U, V, and W the equations of motion are the same for all stars of different masses.

Now each star can be represented by a point in the *six-dimensional phase space* (x, y, z, U, V, W). Consequently, the distribution function $\Psi\,(x, y, z; U, V, W; t)$ defines a *continuous density of points* in the phase space, the motion of each point in this space being governed by the *same* set of canonical equations (3.18). This is precisely the situation encountered in the classical treatments of *Liouville's theorem*. In view of the fundamental importance of this theorem for stellar dynamics, we shall consider it separately in the next section.

3.2. *Liouville's theorem.*—Let us consider a conservative dynamical system with n degrees of freedom. A state of the system is fully defined by specifying the n Hamiltonian co-ordinates $(q_1, q_2, \ldots, q_n)$ and their conjugate momenta $(p_1, p_2, \ldots, p_n)$. It can be conveniently represented geometrically in a space of $2n$ dimensions whose rectangular Cartesian co-ordinates are the n p's and the n q's. This space is called the *phase space* of the system and the point $(q_1, \ldots, q_n, p_1, \ldots, p_n)$ its *representative point*. The equations of motion are

$$\dot{p}_s = -\frac{\partial H}{\partial q_s}; \qquad \dot{q}_s = \frac{\partial H}{\partial p_s} \qquad (s = 1, \ldots, n), \quad (3.21)$$

where H is the Hamiltonian function. Through every point of the phase space passes a definite *trajectory* of the system which satisfies the equations of motion (3.21).

Let Ψ be the density of a "fine dust" of representative points in any element of phase space. Consider a fixed-volume element in the phase space bounded by $q_1, q_1 + dq_1, \ldots, q_n, q_n + dq_n, p_1, p_1 + dp_1, \ldots, p_n, p_n + dp_n$, of extension $d\Omega (= dq_1 \ldots dp_n)$. The representative points crossing the face p_s of area $dS (= dq_1 \ldots dp_{s-1}\, dp_{s+1} \ldots dp_n)$ have a component $\dot{p}_s$ normal to that face and the rate of increase in $\Psi d\Omega$ due to motion across this face is

$$(\Psi \dot{p}_s dS)_{p_s}.$$

There is a similar loss,

$$(\Psi \dot{p}_s dS)_{p_s + dp_s},$$

due to motion across the opposite face. Hence the net increase for this pair of faces is

$$-\frac{\partial}{\partial p_s}(\Psi \dot{p}_s)\, dp_s dS = -\frac{\partial}{\partial p_s}(\Psi \dot{p}_s)\, d\Omega. \qquad (3.22)$$

Summing over all the $2n$ pairs of faces, the net increase in $\Psi d\Omega$ due to the entire motion is

$$-\sum_{s=1}^{n}\left\{\frac{\partial}{\partial p_s}(\Psi \dot{p}_s) + \frac{\partial}{\partial q_s}(\Psi \dot{q}_s)\right\} d\Omega \qquad (3.23)$$

which gives the rate of increase of Ψ in the fixed element of phase extension $d\Omega$ and is therefore the same as $(\partial\Psi/\partial t)d\Omega$. Hence,

$$\frac{\partial\Psi}{\partial t}+\sum_{s=1}^{n}\left\{\frac{\partial}{\partial p_s}(\Psi\dot{p}_s)+\frac{\partial}{\partial q_s}(\Psi\dot{q}_s)\right\}=0\,, \tag{3.24}$$

or, somewhat differently,

$$\frac{\partial\Psi}{\partial t}+\sum_{s=1}^{n}\left(\dot{p}_s\frac{\partial\Psi}{\partial p_s}+\dot{q}_s\frac{\partial\Psi}{\partial q_s}\right)=-\Psi\sum_{s=1}^{n}\left(\frac{\partial\dot{p}_s}{\partial p_s}+\frac{\partial\dot{q}_s}{\partial q_s}\right). \tag{3.25}$$

But, according to the equations of motion (3.21), the right-hand side of the foregoing equation vanishes identically. Hence,

$$\frac{\partial\Psi}{\partial t}+\sum_{s=1}^{n}\left(\frac{\partial H}{\partial p_s}\frac{\partial\Psi}{\partial q_s}-\frac{\partial H}{\partial q_s}\frac{\partial\Psi}{\partial p_s}\right)=0\,. \tag{3.26}$$

This is Liouville's theorem. Equation (3.26) is sometimes written in the form

$$\frac{D\Psi}{Dt}=0 \tag{3.27}$$

where D/Dt stands for the "Stokes operator"

$$\frac{D}{Dt}=\frac{\partial}{\partial t}+\sum_{s=1}^{n}\left(\dot{p}_s\frac{\partial}{\partial p_s}+\dot{q}_s\frac{\partial}{\partial q_s}\right). \tag{3.28}$$

Equation (3.27) has a simple physical interpretation. The meaning becomes apparent when we write it in the form

$$\frac{\partial\Psi}{\partial t}dt+\sum_{s=1}^{n}\left(\frac{\partial\Psi}{\partial p_s}\dot{p}_s dt+\frac{\partial\Psi}{\partial q_s}\dot{q}_s dt\right)=0\,. \tag{3.29}$$

In this equation the first term on the left-hand side represents the increment in Ψ due to an increment of dt in t (with fixed values of the co-ordinates and the momenta), while the rest of the expression represents the increments in Ψ due to increments in the p's and the q's of amounts $\dot{p}_s dt$ and $\dot{q}_s dt$ ($s = 1, \ldots, n$). These latter increments in the p's and q's are precisely the increments which they respectively receive during the movement of the system in time dt. Hence the whole expression on the left-hand side of equation (3.29) represents the total increment in Ψ for varying phase of the moving system, and Liouville's theorem asserts that this vanishes. We have thus shown that Liouville's theorem is equivalent to the statement that the density of any element of phase space remains constant during its motion according to the canonical equations (3.21).

3.3. *The consequences of Liouville's theorem for stellar dynamics.*— The importance of Liouville's theorem for stellar dynamics is now apparent. For, under the circumstances in which stellar encounters can be ignored, each star can be idealized as an independent conservative dynamical system, the motion of which is governed by the Hamiltonian (3.17):

$$\mathfrak{H} = \tfrac{1}{2}(U^2 + V^2 + W^2) + \mathfrak{V}(x, y, z; t) . \qquad (3.301)$$

Further, as we have already remarked in § 3.1, the distribution function $\Psi(x, y, z; U, V, W; t)$ defines a "fine dust" of representative points of the dynamical system (3.301) in the six-dimensional phase space (x, y, z, U, V, W). Liouville's theorem is therefore directly applicable to this case. We have (cf. eq. [3.26])

$$\frac{\partial \Psi}{\partial t} + \sum_{x,\,y,\,z} \left(\frac{\partial \mathfrak{H}}{\partial U} \frac{\partial \Psi}{\partial x} - \frac{\partial \mathfrak{H}}{\partial x} \frac{\partial \Psi}{\partial U} \right) = 0 , \qquad (3.302)$$

or, more explicitly,

$$\left.\begin{aligned} &\frac{\partial \Psi}{\partial t} + U \frac{\partial \Psi}{\partial x} + V \frac{\partial \Psi}{\partial y} + W \frac{\partial \Psi}{\partial z} - \frac{\partial \mathfrak{V}}{\partial x} \frac{\partial \Psi}{\partial U} \\ &\qquad\qquad - \frac{\partial \mathfrak{V}}{\partial y} \frac{\partial \Psi}{\partial V} - \frac{\partial \mathfrak{V}}{\partial z} \frac{\partial \Psi}{\partial W} = 0 , \end{aligned}\right\} \qquad (3.303)$$

which is our fundamental differential equation for the distribution function Ψ. Equation (3.303) is often referred to as the *equation of continuity*, though this must be carefully distinguished from the ordinary macroscopic equation of continuity of hydrodynamics.

Now Liouville's equation (3.303) can be regarded *either* as a linear *homogeneous* partial differential equation for Ψ *or* as a linear *nonhomogeneous* partial differential equation for $\mathfrak{V}$. The former is the more obvious way of looking at it; but the latter appears more fundamental for stellar dynamics. This will become apparent when we consider Liouville's equation (3.303) more closely from the first of the two points of view stated.

Equation (3.303) considered as an equation for Ψ is a partial differential equation of the standard Lagrangian type in the seven variables x, y, z, U, V, W, and t. The general solution can therefore be directly written down in terms of six independent integrals of the Lagrangian subsidiary equations

$$dt=\frac{dx}{U}=\frac{dy}{V}=\frac{dz}{W}=-\frac{dU}{\frac{\partial\mathfrak{B}}{\partial x}}=-\frac{dV}{\frac{\partial\mathfrak{B}}{\partial y}}=-\frac{dW}{\frac{\partial\mathfrak{B}}{\partial z}}. \qquad (3.304)$$

But these are precisely the equations of motion. Hence, if

$$I_1=\text{constant}\ ;\ \ldots.;\qquad I_6=\text{constant}\ , \qquad (3.305)$$

represent six integrals corresponding to the most general solution of the equations of motion (3.304), the general solution of the equation of continuity (see Goursat, *Mathematical Analysis*, II, Part II, 214–225, New York: Ginn & Co., 1917) can be written as

$$\Psi(x,\ y,\ z;\ U,\ V,W;\ t)\equiv\Psi(I_1,\ I_2,\ \ldots.,\ I_6)\ , \qquad (3.306)$$

where the quantity on the right-hand side denotes an arbitrary function of the arguments specified. Stated in this manner, it might appear that we have now solved our problem. But this is far from being the case! Actually, equation (3.306) represents only a *formal* solution, for the explicit form of the general solution can be given only when *all* the six integrals $I_1, \ldots., I_6$ are known; but the equations of motion determining these integrals involve the potential function $\mathfrak{B}(x,\ y,\ z;\ t)$, and this is largely unspecified. Indeed, one of the principal problems of stellar dynamics consists precisely in the characterization of $\mathfrak{B}(x,\ y,\ z;\ t)$. However, with suitable restrictions on $\mathfrak{B}$ we may be able to write down the explicit form of one or more integrals of the equations of motion, but it is clear that it would be difficult to restrict $\mathfrak{B}$ without losing at the same time some degree of generality. And under no circumstances can we specify all the six integrals without complete loss of generality. It is, however, of some interest to examine the kind of integrals which can be written down explicitly and the restrictions on $\mathfrak{B}$ which they correspondingly require.

i) *Stationary potential* $\mathfrak{B}\equiv\mathfrak{B}(x,\ y,\ z)$.—If $\mathfrak{B}$ is explicitly independent of time, the equations of motion (3.304) always admit of the energy integral

$$I_1 = \tfrac{1}{2}(U^2 + V^2 + W^2) + \mathfrak{V}(x, y, z) = \text{constant} . \quad (3.307)$$

ii) *Axially symmetrical potential* $\mathfrak{V} \equiv \mathfrak{V}(\varpi, z)$.—We shall now consider the case when the potential has an axial symmetry about some fixed direction in space. Choose a system of cylindrical co-ordinates (ϖ, θ, z) with the z-axis along the axis of symmetry (see Fig. 6). Then

$$\mathfrak{V}(x, y, z) \equiv \mathfrak{V}(\varpi, z) . \quad (3.308)$$

The equations of motion in this system of co-ordinates are readily obtained in terms of the Lagrangian function

$$\mathfrak{L} = \tfrac{1}{2}(\dot{\varpi}^2 + \varpi^2\dot{\theta}^2 + \dot{z}^2) - \mathfrak{V}(\varpi, z) , \quad (3.309)$$

or

$$\mathfrak{L} = \tfrac{1}{2}(\Pi^2 + \Theta^2 + \mathrm{Z}^2) - \mathfrak{V}(\varpi, z) , \quad (3.310)$$

where Π, Θ, and Z denote the components of linear velocity along the radial, transverse, and z-directions, respectively:

$$\Pi = \dot{\varpi} ; \qquad \Theta = \varpi\dot{\theta} ; \qquad \mathrm{Z} = \dot{z} . \quad (3.311)$$

The Lagrangian equations of motion are

$$\frac{d^2\varpi}{dt^2} = \varpi\dot{\theta}^2 - \frac{\partial\mathfrak{V}}{\partial\varpi} , \quad (3.312)$$

$$\frac{d}{dt}(\varpi^2\dot{\theta}) = -\frac{\partial\mathfrak{V}}{\partial\theta} = 0 , \quad (3.313)$$

and

$$\frac{d^2 z}{dt^2} = -\frac{\partial\mathfrak{V}}{\partial z} . \quad (3.314)$$

The energy integral (3.307) now takes the form

$$I_1 = \tfrac{1}{2}(\Pi^2 + \Theta^2 + \mathrm{Z}^2) + \mathfrak{V}(\varpi, z) = \text{constant} . \quad (3.315)$$

But, according to equation (3.313), we now have the additional *angular-momentum integral*

$$I_2 = \varpi^2\dot{\theta} = \varpi\Theta = \text{constant} . \quad (3.316)$$

iii) *Potential separable in* ϖ *and* z, $\mathfrak{V}(\varpi, z) = \mathfrak{V}_1(\varpi) + \mathfrak{V}_2(z)$.— This restriction on the form of $\mathfrak{V}$ may appear artificial. But it may be appropriate for considering motions which are closely confined to the plane of the Galaxy (or to the plane of symmetry in extragalactic system). Under these circumstances equation (3.314) becomes

$$\frac{d^2 z}{dt^2} = -\frac{d\mathfrak{B}_2}{dz} \tag{3.317}$$

and yields the further integral

$$I_3 = \tfrac{1}{2}Z^2 + \mathfrak{B}_2(z) = \text{constant}\,. \tag{3.318}$$

In terms of the three integrals I_1, I_2, and I_3 we have the special solutions

$$\Psi(I_1)\,; \qquad \Psi(I_1, I_2)\,; \qquad \Psi(I_1, I_2, I_3) \tag{3.319}$$

for the three cases enumerated. But since these are only special solutions, the physical implications of our tacitly ignoring the other integrals (which must exist in any physical problem) are left obscure. Also, when we consider stellar systems in nonsteady states, the potential $\mathfrak{B}$ will in general be explicitly dependent on time, and under these circumstances the present method becomes still further limited in its applications. We are therefore led to consider a different line of attack on the equation of continuity (3.303) by regarding it as a differential equation for $\mathfrak{B}$ instead of for Ψ. As we shall see, this approach appears less barren for investigation.

3.4. *The dynamics of stellar systems with differential motions; the general theory.*—We have seen in § 3.3 that it will be more profitable to consider the equation of continuity (3.303) as a nonhomogeneous partial differential equation for $\mathfrak{B}(x, y, z; t)$ rather than as a homogeneous differential equation for $\Psi(x, y, z; U, V, W; t)$, though in the latter case the formal solution can be readily written down. However, from whichever of the two points of view we may choose to regard the equation of continuity, there is always an essential indeterminateness in the information which can in principle be obtained from it; for the equation involves both Ψ and $\mathfrak{B}$, and both are to a larger or smaller extent "unknown." On the other hand, if we consider the equation of continuity as an equation for $\mathfrak{B}(x, y, z; t)$, we can make use of our knowledge of stellar kinematics (chap. i). But in using this information we need not specify the details of any particular situation; we need only state the broad aspects of the kinematical descriptions. In this manner we can retain for the theory a considerable amount of flexibility and generality.

Now one of the most important characteristics of stellar kinematics consists in the introduction of a general field of differential motions and the ellipsoidal distribution of the residual velocities. The question at once suggests itself: What restrictions do the existence of a general field of differential motions and the ellipsoidal distribution of the residual velocities imply for the dynamical aspects of the problem? Or, to put the same question somewhat differently: In what way does the equation of continuity restrict $\mathfrak{V}$ in order that Ψ may correspond to a stellar system with differential motions and an ellipsoidal distribution of the residual velocities? More precisely, the mathematical problem which thus presents itself can be formulated as follows.

We shall first state our fundamental assumptions in the form of three postulates. Our first assumption is:

I. *At any given point* (x, y, z) *we can define uniquely a local standard of rest which is a continuous function of position and time.*

Let U_0, V_0, and W_0 denote the components of the motion of the local centroid at (x, y, z) along the three fixed principal directions. According to our assumption, U_0, V_0, and W_0 are continuous functions of x, y, z, and of the time t.

The components of the residual motion at (x, y, z) along the three principal directions are clearly

$$U - U_0 \, ; \qquad V - V_0 \, ; \qquad W - W_0 \, . \tag{3.401}$$

Our second assumption is:

II. *The distribution function* Ψ(x, y, z; U, V, W; t) *is of the generalized Schwarzschild type, i.e.,*

$$\Psi(x, y, z; U, V, W; t) \equiv \Psi(Q + \sigma) \, , \tag{3.402}$$

where Q *stands for*

$$\left. \begin{aligned} Q = a(U - U_0)^2 + b(V - V_0)^2 + c(W - W_0)^2 \\ + 2f(V - V_0)(W - W_0) + 2g(W - W_0)(U - U_0) \\ + 2h(U - U_0)(V - V_0) \, ; \end{aligned} \right\} \tag{3.403}$$

further, the coefficients of the velocity ellipsoid a, b, c, f, g, *and* h *and the function* σ *are all continuous functions of position and time.* These are our only two kinematical postulates. Our third assumption is of a dynamical nature.

III. *The motions of the individual stars are governed by a potential function* $\mathfrak{B}$(x, y, z; t) *per unit mass.*

This third postulate is, of course, equivalent to asserting the validity of Liouville's theorem under the circumstances envisaged in stellar dynamics and implies that the distribution function Ψ satisfies the equation of continuity,

$$\left.\begin{aligned}\frac{\partial\Psi}{\partial t}+U\frac{\partial\Psi}{\partial x}+V\frac{\partial\Psi}{\partial y}+W\frac{\partial\Psi}{\partial z}-\frac{\partial\mathfrak{B}}{\partial x}\frac{\partial\Psi}{\partial U}&\\-\frac{\partial\mathfrak{B}}{\partial y}\frac{\partial\Psi}{\partial V}-\frac{\partial\mathfrak{B}}{\partial z}\frac{\partial\Psi}{\partial W}=0\,.&\end{aligned}\right\}\quad(3.404)$$

The dynamical problem is: *Under what circumstances will the equation of continuity* (3.404), *regarded as a partial differential equation for* Ψ, *admit of a solution of the form* (3.402)?

Before we proceed to the mathematical analysis of this problem, we may draw an analogy between our present problem in stellar dynamics and a well-known problem of classical dynamics, namely, to determine the law of force which must act toward a given point in order that a given curve (e.g., a conic section) may be described. In stellar dynamics we do not specify the equation of the orbit described; instead, what we do specify is essentially an *integral* of the equations of motion (see below) and require the law of force acting on the system. More particularly, we require the character of the field of force in which the dynamical system may possess an integral which is a general quadratic form in the velocities. In the general form the problem is, indeed, not new to dynamical theory. It was, in fact, first considered by Bertrand as early as 1852. However, the special case of an integral which is quadratic in the velocities does not appear to have been considered in any detail in the classical literature. Its importance for stellar dynamics has only recently been recognized.

A. *The fundamental differential equations.*—We shall now obtain the fundamental differential equations of our problem.

Substituting the assumed form for Ψ, namely, $\Psi(Q+\sigma)$, in the equation of continuity, we have

$$\frac{d\Psi}{d(Q+\sigma)}\frac{D(Q+\sigma)}{Dt}=0\,.\qquad(3.405)$$

Hence,

$$\frac{D(Q+\sigma)}{Dt}=0\ , \qquad (3.406)^{1}$$

or, more explicitly,

$$\left.\begin{aligned}\Big(\frac{\partial}{\partial t}+U\frac{\partial}{\partial x}+V\frac{\partial}{\partial y}+W\frac{\partial}{\partial z}-\frac{\partial\mathfrak{B}}{\partial x}\frac{\partial}{\partial U}\\ -\frac{\partial\mathfrak{B}}{\partial y}\frac{\partial}{\partial V}-\frac{\partial\mathfrak{B}}{\partial z}\frac{\partial}{\partial W}\Big)(Q+\sigma)=0\ .\end{aligned}\right\}\qquad(3.407)$$

Now, according to equation (3.403), we have

$$\left.\begin{aligned}Q+\sigma=aU^2+bV^2+cW^2+2fVW+2gWU+2hUV\\ -2\Delta_1U-2\Delta_2V-2\Delta_3W-\chi\ ,\end{aligned}\right\}\qquad(3.408)$$

where

$$\left.\begin{aligned}\Delta_1&=aU_0+hV_0+gW_0\ ,\\ \Delta_2&=hU_0+bV_0+fW_0\ ,\\ \Delta_3&=gU_0+fV_0+cW_0\ ,\end{aligned}\right\}\qquad(3.409)$$

and

$$\left.\begin{aligned}-\chi=Q_0+\sigma=aU_0^2+bV_0^2+cW_0^2+2fV_0W_0\\ +2gW_0U_0+2hU_0V_0+\sigma\ .\end{aligned}\right\}\qquad(3.410)$$

[1] This is the condition that $Q+\sigma$ is an integral of the equations of motion (see, e.g., E. T. Whittaker, *Analytical Dynamics*, p. 231, Cambridge, England, 1936).

Substituting in equation (3.407) for $Q + \sigma$ according to equation (3.408), we obtain

$$\left.\begin{aligned}
& U^2 \frac{\partial a}{\partial t} + V^2 \frac{\partial b}{\partial t} + W^2 \frac{\partial c}{\partial t} + 2\,VW \frac{\partial f}{\partial t} \\
& \qquad + 2WU \frac{\partial g}{\partial t} + 2\,U\,V \frac{\partial h}{\partial t} - 2\,U \frac{\partial \Delta_1}{\partial t} \\
& \qquad - 2\,V \frac{\partial \Delta_2}{\partial t} - 2W \frac{\partial \Delta_3}{\partial t} - \frac{\partial \chi}{\partial t} \\
& + U \left[U^2 \frac{\partial a}{\partial x} + V^2 \frac{\partial b}{\partial x} + W^2 \frac{\partial c}{\partial x} + 2\,VW \frac{\partial f}{\partial x} \right. \\
& \qquad + 2WU \frac{\partial g}{\partial x} + 2\,U\,V \frac{\partial h}{\partial x} - 2\,U \frac{\partial \Delta_1}{\partial x} \\
& \qquad \left. - 2\,V \frac{\partial \Delta_2}{\partial x} - 2W \frac{\partial \Delta_3}{\partial x} - \frac{\partial \chi}{\partial x} \right] \\
& + V \left[U^2 \frac{\partial a}{\partial y} + V^2 \frac{\partial b}{\partial y} + W^2 \frac{\partial c}{\partial y} + 2\,VW \frac{\partial f}{\partial y} \right. \\
& \qquad + 2WU \frac{\partial g}{\partial y} + 2\,U\,V \frac{\partial h}{\partial y} - 2\,U \frac{\partial \Delta_1}{\partial y} \\
& \qquad \left. - 2\,V \frac{\partial \Delta_2}{\partial y} - 2W \frac{\partial \Delta_3}{\partial y} - \frac{\partial \chi}{\partial y} \right] \\
& + W \left[U^2 \frac{\partial a}{\partial z} + V^2 \frac{\partial b}{\partial z} + W^2 \frac{\partial c}{\partial z} + 2\,VW \frac{\partial f}{\partial z} \right. \\
& \qquad + 2WU \frac{\partial g}{\partial z} + 2\,U\,V \frac{\partial h}{\partial z} - 2\,U \frac{\partial \Delta_1}{\partial z} \\
& \qquad \left. - 2\,V \frac{\partial \Delta_2}{\partial z} - 2W \frac{\partial \Delta_3}{\partial z} - \frac{\partial \chi}{\partial z} \right] \\
& \qquad - 2 \frac{\partial \mathfrak{B}}{\partial x} [\, aU + hV + gW - \Delta_1] \\
& \qquad - 2 \frac{\partial \mathfrak{B}}{\partial y} [\, hU + bV + fW - \Delta_2] \\
& \qquad - 2 \frac{\partial \mathfrak{B}}{\partial z} [\, gU + fV + cW - \Delta_3] = 0 \,.
\end{aligned}\right\} \quad (3.411)$$

Equation (3.408) is seen to be a polynomial of the third degree in U, V, and W. Hence the coefficients of the different power combinations of U, V, and W must vanish separately. Thus, equating the coefficients of U^3, V^3, W^3, U^2V, U^2W, V^2U, V^2W, W^2U, W^2V, UVW, U^2, V^2, W^2, UV, VW, WU, U, V, W, and the constant terms, we obtain, respectively,

$$\left.\begin{array}{l}
\dfrac{\partial a}{\partial x}=0\,,\ \ (\mathrm{i})\,; \quad \dfrac{\partial b}{\partial y}=0\,,\ \ (\mathrm{ii})\,; \quad \dfrac{\partial c}{\partial z}=0\,,\ \ (\mathrm{iii})\,; \\[2ex]
2\dfrac{\partial h}{\partial x}+\dfrac{\partial a}{\partial y}=0\,,\ \ (\mathrm{iv})\,; \quad 2\dfrac{\partial g}{\partial x}+\dfrac{\partial a}{\partial z}=0\,,\ \ (\mathrm{v})\,; \\[2ex]
2\dfrac{\partial h}{\partial y}+\dfrac{\partial b}{\partial x}=0\,,\ \ (\mathrm{vi})\,; \quad 2\dfrac{\partial f}{\partial y}+\dfrac{\partial b}{\partial z}=0\,,\ \ (\mathrm{vii})\,; \\[2ex]
2\dfrac{\partial g}{\partial z}+\dfrac{\partial c}{\partial x}=0\,,\ \ (\mathrm{viii})\,; \quad 2\dfrac{\partial f}{\partial z}+\dfrac{\partial c}{\partial y}=0\,,\ \ (\mathrm{ix})\,; \\[2ex]
\dfrac{\partial f}{\partial x}+\dfrac{\partial g}{\partial y}+\dfrac{\partial h}{\partial z}=0\,,\ \ (\mathrm{x})\,;
\end{array}\right\} \qquad (\mathrm{I})$$

$$\left.\begin{array}{ll}
\dfrac{\partial \Delta_1}{\partial x}=\dfrac{1}{2}\dfrac{\partial a}{\partial t}\,,\ \ (\mathrm{i})\,; & \dfrac{\partial \Delta_2}{\partial x}+\dfrac{\partial \Delta_1}{\partial y}=\dfrac{\partial h}{\partial t}\,,\ \ (\mathrm{iv})\,; \\[2ex]
\dfrac{\partial \Delta_2}{\partial y}=\dfrac{1}{2}\dfrac{\partial b}{\partial t}\,,\ \ (\mathrm{ii})\,; & \dfrac{\partial \Delta_3}{\partial y}+\dfrac{\partial \Delta_2}{\partial z}=\dfrac{\partial f}{\partial t}\,,\ \ (\mathrm{v})\,; \\[2ex]
\dfrac{\partial \Delta_3}{\partial z}=\dfrac{1}{2}\dfrac{\partial c}{\partial t}\,,\ \ (\mathrm{iii})\,; & \dfrac{\partial \Delta_1}{\partial z}+\dfrac{\partial \Delta_3}{\partial x}=\dfrac{\partial g}{\partial t}\,,\ \ (\mathrm{vi})\,;
\end{array}\right\} \qquad (\mathrm{II})$$

and

$$\left.\begin{array}{l}
a\dfrac{\partial \mathfrak{V}}{\partial x}+h\dfrac{\partial \mathfrak{V}}{\partial y}+g\dfrac{\partial \mathfrak{V}}{\partial z}+\dfrac{\partial \Delta_1}{\partial t}=-\dfrac{1}{2}\dfrac{\partial \chi}{\partial x}\,,\ \ (\mathrm{i})\,; \\[2ex]
h\dfrac{\partial \mathfrak{V}}{\partial x}+b\dfrac{\partial \mathfrak{V}}{\partial y}+f\dfrac{\partial \mathfrak{V}}{\partial z}+\dfrac{\partial \Delta_2}{\partial t}=-\dfrac{1}{2}\dfrac{\partial \chi}{\partial y}\,,\ \ (\mathrm{ii})\,; \\[2ex]
g\dfrac{\partial \mathfrak{V}}{\partial x}+f\dfrac{\partial \mathfrak{V}}{\partial y}+c\dfrac{\partial \mathfrak{V}}{\partial z}+\dfrac{\partial \Delta_3}{\partial t}=-\dfrac{1}{2}\dfrac{\partial \chi}{\partial z}\,,\ \ (\mathrm{iii})\,; \\[2ex]
\Delta_1\dfrac{\partial \mathfrak{V}}{\partial x}+\Delta_2\dfrac{\partial \mathfrak{V}}{\partial y}+\Delta_3\dfrac{\partial \mathfrak{V}}{\partial z}=\dfrac{1}{2}\dfrac{\partial \chi}{\partial t}\,,\ \ (\mathrm{iv})\,.
\end{array}\right\} \qquad (\mathrm{III})$$

We now see that the twenty partial differential equations which result break up into three distinct sets of equations. The first group of ten equations involves only the coefficients of the velocity ellipsoid. Further, these equations do not involve any differentiations with respect to time. As we shall presently see, these ten equations are sufficient to determine the dependence of the coefficients of the velocity ellipsoid on the space co-ordinates; their dependence on time is, however, left unspecified.

The second group of six equations involves the Δ's and the time derivatives of the coefficients of the velocity ellipsoid. These equations, as we shall see, are sufficient to determine the dependence of the Δ's on the space co-ordinates. Further, the equations (II) are found to introduce some restrictions on the dependence of the coefficients of the velocity ellipsoid on time. Thus, if in particular we consider stellar systems *without* differential motions (i.e., $U_0 \equiv V_0 \equiv W_0 \equiv 0$), then the Δ's all vanish identically, and the equations (II) now imply that the coefficients of the velocity ellipsoid do not depend on the time.[2]

The last group of four equations (III) are of a nature different from the rest and lead to six other integrability conditions (see eqs. [3.448] and [3.450] below).

B. *The solution for the coefficients of the velocity ellipsoid.*—A simple examination of the differential equations (I) reveals that

$$\left.\begin{array}{l} a \text{ is independent of } x \text{ and quadratic in } y \text{ and } z, \\ b \text{ is independent of } y \text{ and quadratic in } z \text{ and } x, \\ c \text{ is independent of } z \text{ and quadratic in } x \text{ and } y, \\ f \text{ is linear in } y \text{ and } z \text{ and quadratic in } x, \\ g \text{ is linear in } z \text{ and } x \text{ and quadratic in } y, \\ h \text{ is linear in } x \text{ and } y \text{ and quadratic in } z. \end{array}\right\} \quad (3.412)$$

The solutions for f, g, and h must therefore be of the following forms:

$$\left.\begin{array}{l} f = f_1 + f_2 y + f_3 z + f_4 y z\,, \\ g = g_1 + g_2 z + g_3 x + g_4 z x\,, \\ h = h_1 + h_2 x + h_3 y + h_4 x y\,, \end{array}\right\} \quad (3.413)$$

where $(f_1, \ldots, f_4)$, $(g_1, \ldots, g_4)$, and $(h_1, \ldots, h_4)$ are general polynomials of the second degree in x, y, and z, respectively. We can therefore write

$$\left.\begin{array}{ll} f_n = f_{n0} + f_{n1} x + f_{n2} x^2 & (n = 1, \ldots, 4)\,, \\ g_n = g_{n0} + g_{n1} y + g_{n2} y^2 & (n = 1, \ldots, 4)\,, \\ h_n = h_{n0} + h_{n1} z + h_{n2} z^2 & (n = 1, \ldots, 4)\,, \end{array}\right\} \quad (3.414)$$

[2] It is thus apparent that the consideration of nonsteady states is nontrivial only for the case of stellar systems *with* differential motions.

where $f_{n0}, \ldots, h_{n2}$ are all functions of time, arbitrary in the first instance. Differentiating equations (iv) and (v) partially with respect to z and y, respectively, we find that

$$\frac{\partial^2 g}{\partial x \partial y} = \frac{\partial^2 h}{\partial x \partial z}. \tag{3.415}$$

Similarly from (vi) and (vii) and from (viii) and (ix) we obtain

$$\frac{\partial^2 h}{\partial y \partial z} = \frac{\partial^2 f}{\partial y \partial x}; \qquad \frac{\partial^2 f}{\partial z \partial x} = \frac{\partial^2 g}{\partial z \partial y}. \tag{3.416}$$

Substituting for f, g, and h from (3.413) in equations (3.415) and (3.416), we have

$$\left.\begin{aligned} \frac{\partial}{\partial y}(g_3 + g_4 z) &= \frac{\partial}{\partial z}(h_2 + h_4 y), \\ \frac{\partial}{\partial z}(h_3 + h_4 x) &= \frac{\partial}{\partial x}(f_2 + f_4 z), \\ \frac{\partial}{\partial x}(f_3 + f_4 y) &= \frac{\partial}{\partial y}(g_2 + g_4 x). \end{aligned}\right\} \tag{3.417}$$

From equations (3.414) and (3.417) we now find

$$\left.\begin{aligned} g_{31} + 2g_{32}y + z(g_{41} + 2g_{42}y) &= h_{21} + 2h_{22}z + y(h_{41} + 2h_{42}z), \\ h_{31} + 2h_{32}z + x(h_{41} + 2h_{42}z) &= f_{21} + 2f_{22}x + z(f_{41} + 2f_{42}x), \\ f_{31} + 2f_{32}x + y(f_{41} + 2f_{42}x) &= g_{21} + 2g_{22}y + x(g_{41} + 2g_{42}y). \end{aligned}\right\} \tag{3.418}$$

Equating the coefficients of x, y, z, etc., in the foregoing equations, we find

$$\left.\begin{aligned} g_{31} &= h_{21}; & g_{41} &= 2h_{22}; & 2g_{32} &= h_{41}; & g_{42} &= h_{42}, \\ h_{31} &= f_{21}; & h_{41} &= 2f_{22}; & 2h_{32} &= f_{41}; & h_{42} &= f_{42}, \\ f_{31} &= g_{21}; & f_{41} &= 2g_{22}; & 2f_{32} &= g_{41}; & f_{42} &= g_{42}. \end{aligned}\right\} \tag{3.419}$$

On substituting equations (3.413) and (3.414) in equation (x) of (I) we obtain

$$\left.\begin{aligned} &(f_{11} + 2f_{12}x) + (f_{21} + 2f_{22}x)y + (f_{31} + 2f_{32}x)z \\ &\qquad\qquad + (f_{41} + 2f_{42}x)yz \\ &+ (g_{11} + 2g_{12}y) + (g_{21} + 2g_{22}y)z + (g_{31} + 2g_{32}y)x \\ &\qquad\qquad + (g_{41} + 2g_{42}y)zx \\ &+ (h_{11} + 2h_{12}z) + (h_{21} + 2h_{22}z)x + (h_{31} + 2h_{32}z)y \\ &\qquad\qquad + (h_{41} + 2h_{42}z)xy = 0. \end{aligned}\right\} \tag{3.420}$$

On equating the coefficients of x, y, etc., we find

$$\left.\begin{aligned} f_{11}+g_{11}+h_{11}&=0\,; & f_{42}+\ g_{42}+h_{42}&=0\,,\\ 2f_{12}+g_{31}+h_{21}&=0\,; & 2f_{22}+2g_{32}+h_{41}&=0\,,\\ 2g_{12}+h_{31}+f_{21}&=0\,; & 2g_{22}+2h_{32}+f_{41}&=0\,,\\ 2h_{12}+f_{31}+g_{21}&=0\,; & 2h_{22}+2f_{32}+g_{41}&=0\,. \end{aligned}\right\} \tag{3.421}$$

From equations (3.419) and (3.421) we easily find that

$$\left.\begin{aligned} f_{12}&=-h_{21}=-g_{31}\,; & f_{22}&=g_{32}=h_{41}=h_{42}=0\,,\\ g_{12}&=-f_{21}=-h_{31}\,; & g_{22}&=h_{32}=f_{41}=f_{42}=0\,,\\ h_{12}&=-g_{21}=-f_{31}\,; & h_{22}&=f_{32}=g_{41}=g_{42}=0\,. \end{aligned}\right\} \tag{3.422}$$

Hence, our solutions for f, g, and h are

$$\left.\begin{aligned} f&=(f_{10}+f_{11}x-h_{21}x^2)+(f_{20}+f_{21}x)\,y\\ &\qquad\qquad+(f_{30}+g_{21}x)\,z+f_{40}yz\,,\\ g&=(g_{10}+g_{11}y-f_{21}y^2)+(g_{20}+g_{21}y)\,z\\ &\qquad\qquad+(g_{30}+h_{21}y)\,x+g_{40}zx\,,\\ h&=(h_{10}+h_{11}z-g_{21}z^2)+(h_{20}+h_{21}z)\,x\\ &\qquad\qquad+(h_{30}+f_{21}z)\,y+h_{40}xy\,. \end{aligned}\right\} \tag{3.423}$$

In the foregoing expressions for f, g, and h the coefficients f_{10}, g_{10}, h_{10}, f_{20}, g_{20}, h_{20}, f_{21}, g_{21}, h_{21}, f_{30}, g_{30}, h_{30}, f_{40}, g_{40}, and h_{40} are all, for the present, arbitrary functions of time. Of the three remaining coefficients—f_{11}, g_{11}, and h_{11}—two are again arbitrary, and the third has to be found from the relation (cf. eq. [3.421])

$$f_{11}+g_{11}+h_{11}=0\,. \tag{3.424}$$

The solutions for a, b, and c now readily follow. Thus, from equation (iv) of (I) we have

$$\frac{\partial a}{\partial y}=-2\frac{\partial h}{\partial x}=-2(h_{20}+h_{21}z)-2h_{40}y\,. \tag{3.425}$$

On the other hand, according to equation (3.412), a is independent of x and quadratic in z. Hence, on integrating equation (3.425), we have

$$a=-2(h_{20}+h_{21}z)\,y-h_{40}y^2-(a_0+a_1z+a_2z^2)\,. \tag{3.426}$$

where a_0, a_1, and a_2 are functions of time. From equation (v) of (I) and equations (3.423) and (3.426) we now have

$$2h_{21}y+a_1+2a_2z=2g_{30}+2h_{21}y+2g_{40}z\,. \tag{3.427}$$

Hence,

$$a_1 = 2g_{30}\,; \qquad a_2 = g_{40}\,. \tag{3.428}$$

Our solution for a is therefore given by

$$a = -2(h_{20} + h_{21}z)y - h_{40}y^2 - (a_0 + 2g_{30}z + g_{40}z^2)\,. \tag{3.429}$$

Similarly,

$$\left.\begin{aligned} b &= -2(f_{20} + f_{21}x)z - f_{40}z^2 - (b_0 + 2h_{30}x + h_{40}x^2)\,, \\ c &= -2(g_{20} + g_{21}y)x - g_{40}x^2 - (c_0 + 2f_{30}y + f_{40}y^2)\,. \end{aligned}\right\} \tag{3.430}$$

Equations (3.423), (3.429), and (3.430) represent, then, the general solution of the ten partial differential equations of (I).

C. *The solution for the motions of the local centroids.*—We shall now consider the six equations (II). From these equations and the nature of the dependence of the coefficients of the velocity ellipsoid on x, y, and z (see eq. [3.412]) we readily conclude that

$$\left.\begin{aligned} &\Delta_1 \text{ is linear in } x \text{ and quadratic in } y \text{ and } z, \\ &\Delta_2 \text{ is linear in } y \text{ and quadratic in } z \text{ and } x, \\ &\Delta_3 \text{ is linear in } z \text{ and quadratic in } x \text{ and } y. \end{aligned}\right\} \tag{3.431}$$

On the other hand, since a, b, and c are independent of x, y, and z, respectively, we readily infer from equations (i), (ii), and (iii) that

$$\left.\begin{aligned} \Delta_1 &= \frac{1}{2}\frac{\partial a}{\partial t}x + \alpha_{22}y^2z^2 + \alpha_{21}y^2z + \alpha_{12}yz^2 + \alpha_{20}y^2 + \alpha_{02}z^2 \\ &\qquad + \alpha_{11}yz + \beta_3 y + \gamma_2 z + \delta_1\,, \\ \Delta_2 &= \frac{1}{2}\frac{\partial b}{\partial t}y + \beta_{22}z^2x^2 + \beta_{21}z^2x + \beta_{12}zx^2 + \beta_{20}z^2 + \beta_{02}x^2 \\ &\qquad + \beta_{11}zx + \beta_1 z + \gamma_3 x + \delta_2\,, \\ \Delta_3 &= \frac{1}{2}\frac{\partial c}{\partial t}z + \gamma_{22}x^2y^2 + \gamma_{21}x^2y + \gamma_{12}xy^2 + \gamma_{20}x^2 + \gamma_{02}y^2 \\ &\qquad + \gamma_{11}xy + \beta_2 x + \gamma_1 y + \delta_3\,, \end{aligned}\right\} \tag{3.432}$$

where $\alpha_{22}, \ldots, \delta_3$ are all functions of time and arbitrary in the first instance. Substituting for Δ_1 and Δ_2 according to equation (3.432) in equation (iv), we obtain

$$\left.\begin{aligned} &\frac{\partial}{\partial t}(h_{10}+h_{11}z+h_{20}x+h_{30}y-g_{21}z^2+h_{21}zx+f_{21}zy+h_{40}xy) \\ &\quad = 2\beta_{22}z^2x + 2\alpha_{22}yz^2 + (\beta_{21}+\alpha_{12})z^2 + 2\beta_{12}zx + 2\alpha_{21}yz \\ &\quad + (\alpha_{11}+\beta_{11})z + 2\beta_{02}x + 2\alpha_{20}y + \beta_3 + \gamma_3 \\ &\quad - y\frac{\partial}{\partial t}(h_{30} + h_{40}x + f_{21}z) - x\frac{\partial}{\partial t}(h_{20} + h_{40}y + h_{21}z)\,. \end{aligned}\right\} \tag{3.433}$$

Equating the coefficients of the different combinations of the powers of x, y, and z in the foregoing equation, we obtain

$$\left.\begin{aligned} &\frac{dh_{40}}{dt} = \alpha_{22} = \beta_{22} = 0 , \\ \alpha_{20} = \frac{dh_{30}}{dt} ; \quad &\beta_{02} = \frac{dh_{20}}{dt} ; \quad \beta_{21} + \alpha_{12} = -\frac{dg_{21}}{dt} ; \\ \beta_{12} = &\frac{dh_{21}}{dt} ; \quad \alpha_{21} = \frac{df_{21}}{dt} , \end{aligned}\right\} \tag{3.434}$$

and

$$\alpha_{11} + \beta_{11} = \frac{dh_{11}}{dt} ; \qquad \beta_3 + \gamma_3 = \frac{dh_{10}}{dt} . \tag{3.435}$$

By cyclically permuting the quantities ($\alpha_{..}$, $\beta_{..}$, $\gamma_{..}$) and ($f_{..}$, $g_{..}$, $h_{..}$) in the foregoing equations, we shall obtain the similar relations which would result from equations (v) and (vi) of (II). Combining all these relations, we readily find that

$$\alpha_{22} = \beta_{22} = \gamma_{22} = \alpha_{21} = \beta_{21} = \gamma_{21} = \alpha_{12} = \beta_{12} = \gamma_{12} = 0 ; \tag{3.436}$$

$$f_{40},\ g_{40},\ h_{40},\ f_{21},\ g_{21},\ h_{21} \text{ are all constants} ; \tag{3.437}$$

$$\left.\begin{aligned} \alpha_{20} = \frac{dh_{30}}{dt} ; \quad \beta_{20} = \frac{df_{30}}{dt} ; \quad \gamma_{20} = \frac{dg_{30}}{dt} , \\ \alpha_{02} = \frac{dg_{20}}{dt} ; \quad \beta_{02} = \frac{dh_{20}}{dt} ; \quad \gamma_{02} = \frac{df_{20}}{dt} ; \end{aligned}\right\} \tag{3.438}$$

$$\beta_1 + \gamma_1 = \frac{df_{10}}{dt} ; \qquad \beta_2 + \gamma_2 = \frac{dg_{10}}{dt} ; \qquad \beta_3 + \gamma_3 = \frac{dh_{10}}{dt} ; \tag{3.439}$$

and

$$\beta_{11} + \gamma_{11} = \frac{df_{11}}{dt} ; \qquad \gamma_{11} + \alpha_{11} = \frac{dg_{11}}{dt} ; \qquad \alpha_{11} + \beta_{11} = \frac{dh_{11}}{dt} . \tag{3.440}$$

Adding the three equations (3.440) and using equation (3.424), we find

$$\alpha_{11} + \beta_{11} + \gamma_{11} = 0 . \tag{3.441}$$

We can therefore re-write equations (3.440) in the forms

$$\alpha_{11} = -\frac{df_{11}}{dt} ; \qquad \beta_{11} = -\frac{dg_{11}}{dt} ; \qquad \gamma_{11} = -\frac{dh_{11}}{dt} . \tag{3.442}$$

Finally, substituting for α_{20}, β_{20}, γ_{20}, α_{02}, β_{02}, γ_{02}, α_{11}, β_{11}, and γ_{11} according to equations (3.438) and (3.442) in our expressions (3.432) for the Δ's and after some minor rearranging of the terms, we obtain

112993

$$\left.\begin{aligned}
\Delta_1 &= y\left(y\,\frac{dh_{30}}{dt} - x\,\frac{dh_{20}}{dt}\right) - z\left(x\,\frac{dg_{30}}{dt} - z\,\frac{dg_{20}}{dt}\right) - \frac{df_{11}}{dt}\,yz \\
&\qquad - \frac{1}{2}\frac{da_0}{dt}\,x + \beta_3 y + \gamma_2 z + \delta_1\,, \\
\Delta_2 &= z\left(z\,\frac{df_{30}}{dt} - y\,\frac{df_{20}}{dt}\right) - x\left(y\,\frac{dh_{30}}{dt} - x\,\frac{dh_{20}}{dt}\right) - \frac{dg_{11}}{dt}\,zx \\
&\qquad - \frac{1}{2}\frac{db_0}{dt}\,y + \beta_1 z + \gamma_3 x + \delta_2\,, \\
\Delta_3 &= x\left(x\,\frac{dg_{30}}{dt} - z\,\frac{dg_{20}}{dt}\right) - y\left(z\,\frac{df_{30}}{dt} - y\,\frac{df_{20}}{dt}\right) - \frac{dh_{11}}{dt}\,xy \\
&\qquad - \frac{1}{2}\frac{dc_0}{dt}\,z + \beta_2 x + \gamma_1 y + \delta_3\,.
\end{aligned}\right\} \quad (3.443)$$

We now see that the solution for the coefficients of the velocity ellipsoid involves fourteen arbitrary functions of time and six constants of integration. The arbitrary functions are a_0, b_0, c_0, f_{10}, g_{10}, h_{10}, f_{20}, g_{20}, h_{20}, f_{30}, g_{30}, h_{30}, and any two of the three quantities f_{11}, g_{11}, and h_{11}. Again, the solution for the Δ's introduces six further arbitrary functions of time. These can be taken to be β_1, β_2, β_3, δ_1, δ_2, and δ_3. (The functions γ_1, γ_2, and γ_3 are related to β_1, β_2, β_3, f_{10}, g_{10}, and h_{10} according to the relations [3.439]).

D. *The integrability conditions.*—We have now solved the sixteen differential equations (I) and (II) for the coefficients of the velocity ellipsoid and the motions of the local centroids. These solutions are seen to involve twenty arbitrary functions of time and six constants of integration. But it should not be concluded that the solution for the physical problem involves this degree of arbitrariness. Indeed, the further discussion of the relations (III) will impose restrictions of a very far-reaching character on the possible solutions. The mathematical problem which is presented can be formulated as follows:

It is convenient to introduce a symbol for the matrix associated with our fundamental quadratic form. Let

$$\boldsymbol{A} = \begin{pmatrix} a & h & g \\ h & b & f \\ g & f & c \end{pmatrix} . \qquad (3.444)$$

Further, let

$$\boldsymbol{\Delta} = (\Delta_1, \Delta_2, \Delta_3) . \qquad (3.445)$$

Equations (III) can be written in the forms

$$\boldsymbol{A} \text{ grad } \mathfrak{V} + \frac{\partial \boldsymbol{\Delta}}{\partial t} = -\tfrac{1}{2} \text{ grad } \chi \qquad (3.446)$$

and

$$\boldsymbol{\Delta} \cdot \text{grad } \mathfrak{V} = +\frac{1}{2} \frac{\partial \chi}{\partial t} . \qquad (3.447)$$

Taking the curl of both sides of equation (3.446), we obtain

$$\text{curl } (\mathbf{4} \text{ grad } \mathfrak{V}) + \frac{\partial}{\partial t} (\text{curl } \boldsymbol{\Delta}) = 0 . \qquad (3.448)$$

The vector equation (3.448) represents three simultaneous partial differential equations of the second order for $\mathfrak{V}$.

Again, taking the gradient of both the sides of equation (3.447) we have

$$\text{grad } (\boldsymbol{\Delta} \cdot \text{grad } \mathfrak{V}) = \frac{1}{2} \frac{\partial}{\partial t} \text{grad } \chi ; \qquad (3.449)$$

or, using equation (3.446), we obtain

$$\text{grad } (\boldsymbol{\Delta} \cdot \text{grad } \mathfrak{V}) + \frac{\partial}{\partial t} (\boldsymbol{A} \text{ grad } \mathfrak{V}) + \frac{\partial^2 \boldsymbol{\Delta}}{\partial t^2} = 0 . \qquad (3.450)$$

The vector equation (3.450) again represents three simultaneous partial differential equations of the second order for $\mathfrak{V}$.

Now, we know the elements of the matrix $\boldsymbol{A}$ and the components of the vector $\boldsymbol{\Delta}$, apart from some arbitrary functions of time and some constants of integration. Consequently, in the six simultaneous partial differential equations of the second order for $\mathfrak{V}$ which the vector equations (3.448) and (3.450) represent, the coefficients of the various derivatives of $\mathfrak{V}$ are of known forms. It is therefore clear that there should be restrictions on these coefficients of the various derivatives of $\mathfrak{B}$ in the six equations, in order that all these partial differential equations may admit of a common solution $\mathfrak{B}$. If we could enumerate all the different circumstances under which the six differential equations (3.448) and (3.450) will admit of a common solution, we would then have solved our dynamical problem completely. Actually, it has not so far been possible to solve this problem in its most general form. However, several special solutions are known, and we shall give an account of some of them in §§ 3.5, 3.6, 3.7, and 4.1.

E. *The solutions for the coefficients of the velocity ellipse and the motions of the local centroids for the two-dimensional problem.*—It is often possible to obtain an insight into the essential features of a situation by considering the two-dimensional problem. In this manner we can, in the first instance, avoid the additional complexities involved in dealing with the general three-dimensional problem. We shall therefore conclude our discussion of the general theory by writing down the solution for a, b, h, Δ_1, and Δ_2 appropriate for the discussion of the two-dimensional problem. These can be obtained quite readily from equations (3.423), (3.429), (3.430), and (3.443) by setting all the coefficients which occur in the expressions for c, f, g, and Δ_3 equal to zero. We find

$$\left.\begin{aligned} a &= -a_0 - 2h_2 y - h_4 y^2 , \\ b &= -b_0 - 2h_3 x - h_4 x^2 , \\ h &= h_1 + h_2 x + h_3 y + h_4 x y , \end{aligned}\right\} \tag{3.451}$$

where

$$h_4 = \text{constant} , \tag{3.452}$$

and a_0, b_0, h_1, h_2, and h_3 are arbitrary functions of time. Further,

$$\left.\begin{aligned} \Delta_1 &= y\left(y\frac{dh_3}{dt} - x\frac{dh_2}{dt}\right) - \frac{1}{2}\frac{da_0}{dt}x + \beta_3 y + \delta_1 , \\ \Delta_2 &= -x\left(y\frac{dh_3}{dt} - x\frac{dh_2}{dt}\right) - \frac{1}{2}\frac{db_0}{dt}y + \gamma_3 x + \delta_2 , \end{aligned}\right\} \tag{3.453}$$

where δ_1 and δ_2 are arbitrary frunctions of time and

$$\beta_3 + \gamma_3 = \frac{dh_1}{dt} ; \tag{3.454}$$

thus, only one of the two quantities β_3 and γ_3 can be an arbitrary function of time.

Finally, we may note that the equations (III) reduce in our present case to

$$a\frac{\partial\mathfrak{B}}{\partial x}+h\frac{\partial\mathfrak{B}}{\partial y}+\frac{\partial\Delta_1}{\partial t}=-\frac{1}{2}\frac{\partial\chi}{\partial x},$$

$$h\frac{\partial\mathfrak{B}}{\partial x}+b\frac{\partial\mathfrak{B}}{\partial y}+\frac{\partial\Delta_2}{\partial t}=-\frac{1}{2}\frac{\partial\chi}{\partial y}, \qquad (3.455)$$

$$\Delta_1\frac{\partial\mathfrak{B}}{\partial x}+\Delta_2\frac{\partial\mathfrak{B}}{\partial y}=+\frac{1}{2}\frac{\partial\chi}{\partial t}.$$

3.5. *The helical symmetry of stellar systems with differential motions and in steady states.*—For stellar systems in steady states it is possible to prove a very general theorem in the dynamics of differential motions; for, under the circumstances of a steady state, equation (3.447) reduces to a simple linear homogeneous partial differential equation for $\mathfrak{B}$:

$$\mathbf{\Delta}\cdot\text{grad}\,\mathfrak{B}=0\,. \qquad (3.501)$$

Hence,

$$\mathfrak{B}(x,\,y,\,z)\equiv\mathfrak{B}(I_1,\,I_2)\,, \qquad (3.502)$$

where I_1 and I_2 are any two integrals of the corresponding subsidiary equations

$$\frac{dx}{\Delta_1}=\frac{dy}{\Delta_2}=\frac{dz}{\Delta_3}. \qquad (3.503)$$

On the other hand, under steady-state conditions our solution for the Δ's reduces to (eqs. [3.439]) and [3.443])

$$\left.\begin{aligned}\Delta_1&=\beta_3 y-\beta_2 z+\delta_1\,,\\ \Delta_2&=\beta_1 z-\beta_3 x+\delta_2\,,\\ \Delta_3&=\beta_2 x-\beta_1 y+\delta_3\,,\end{aligned}\right\} \qquad (3.504)$$

where β_1, β_2, β_3, δ_1, δ_2, and δ_3 are now all constants. The foregoing solution for the Δ's can be written as a single vector equation, as

$$\mathbf{\Delta}=\boldsymbol{r}\times\boldsymbol{\beta}+\boldsymbol{\delta}\,, \qquad (3.505)$$

where $\boldsymbol{r}$, $\boldsymbol{\beta}$, and $\boldsymbol{\delta}$ represent the vectors (x, y, z), $(\beta_1, \beta_2, \beta_3)$, and $(\delta_1, \delta_2, \delta_3)$, respectively.

So far, the choice of the origin and the orientation of our coordinate system has been left arbitrary. Since $\boldsymbol{\beta}$ is some constant vector, we can clearly choose the z-axis of our co-ordinate system to coincide with the direction of $\boldsymbol{\beta}$. We can then write

$$\boldsymbol{\beta} = (0,\ 0,\ \beta)\ , \tag{3.506}$$

and the solution (3.505) for $\boldsymbol{\Delta}$ becomes

$$\Delta_1 = \beta y + \delta_1\ ; \qquad \Delta_2 = -\beta x + \delta_2\ ; \qquad \Delta_3 = \delta_3\ . \tag{3.507}$$

Again, (if $|\boldsymbol{\beta}| \neq 0$), by a translation of the origin to $(-\delta_2/\beta, + \delta_1/\beta, 0)$, we can further simplify the form of the solutions for the Δ's to

$$\Delta_1 = \beta y\ ; \qquad \Delta_2 = -\beta x\ ; \qquad \Delta_3 = \delta_3\ . \tag{3.508}$$

We shall assume that the co-ordinate system has been chosen in this manner.

The equations (3.503) now take the simple forms

$$\frac{dx}{\beta y} = \frac{dy}{-\beta x} = \frac{dz}{\delta_3}\ . \tag{3.509}$$

Two independent integrals of the foregoing equations are readily obtained. Thus, according to equation (3.509), we have

$$x dx + y dy = 0 \qquad (|\boldsymbol{\beta}| \neq 0) \tag{3.510}$$

or

$$x^2 + y^2 = k^2 = \text{constant}\ , \tag{3.511}$$

which is one of our integrals. Using this integral in equation (3.509) we obtain

$$\frac{dx}{\beta\sqrt{k^2 - x^2}} = \frac{dz}{\delta_3}\ . \tag{3.512}$$

The foregoing equation admits of immediate integration. We have

$$z + \frac{\delta_3}{\beta}\cos^{-1}\frac{x}{k} = \text{constant} \tag{3.513}$$

or, according to (3.511),

$$z + \frac{\delta_3}{\beta}\cos^{-1}\frac{x}{\sqrt{x^2 + y^2}} = \text{constant}\ , \tag{3.514}$$

which is our second independent integral of equations (3.509).

In cylindrical co-ordinates (ϖ, θ, z) the two integrals (3.511) and (3.514) take the simpler forms

$$\varpi = \text{constant} = I_1 \tag{3.515}$$

and

$$z + \frac{\delta_3}{\beta}\,\theta = \text{constant} = I_2\,. \qquad (3.516)$$

The foregoing integrals have simple geometrical interpretations. The first integral, I_1, represents right circular cylinders about the z-axis, and the second integral, I_2, represents right circular *helicoids*, also about the z-axis.

Finally, according to (3.502),

$$\mathfrak{B} \equiv \mathfrak{B}\left(\varpi,\ z + \frac{\delta_3}{\beta}\,\theta\right), \qquad (3.517)$$

where the quantity on the right-hand side stands for an arbitrary function of the arguments specified. The case of axial symmetry is included in equation (3.517) as a special case, namely, when $\delta_3 = 0$:

$$\mathfrak{B} \equiv \mathfrak{B}(\varpi,\ z) \qquad (\delta_3 = 0)\,. \qquad (3.518)$$

Remembering that, according to our present choice of the orientation of the co-ordinate system, the z-axis is in the direction of $\boldsymbol{\beta}$, the condition $\delta_3 = 0$ is clearly equivalent to the orthogonality of the vectors $\boldsymbol{\beta}$ and $\boldsymbol{\delta}$ in a general co-ordinate system. We have thus proved the following theorem:

For stellar systems in steady states and with differential motions the potential $\mathfrak{B}$ must necessarily be characterized by helical symmetry. The case of axial symmetry is included as a special case when $\boldsymbol{\beta}$ and $\boldsymbol{\delta}$ are orthogonal.

Some further consequences of this fundamental theorem may be noted. Now we should, in general, require that the potential $\mathfrak{B}$ be a single-valued function of position. Hence,

$$\mathfrak{B}(\varpi,\ \theta,\ z) \equiv \mathfrak{B}(\varpi,\ \theta + 2n\pi,\ z) \qquad (3.519)$$

for *all* integral values of n (positive or negative). According to equation (3.517), the foregoing condition for single-valuedness requires that

$$\left.\begin{aligned} \mathfrak{B}\left(\varpi,\ z + \frac{\delta_3}{\beta}\,\theta\right) &\equiv \mathfrak{B}\left(\varpi,\ z + \frac{\delta_3}{\beta}\,[\,\theta + 2n\pi\,]\right), \\ &\equiv \mathfrak{B}\left(\varpi,\ z + \frac{2n\,\delta_3\pi}{\beta} + \frac{\delta_3}{\beta}\,\theta\right). \end{aligned}\right\} \qquad (3.520)$$

In other words, $\mathfrak{V}$ *is periodic with period* $2\pi\delta_3/\beta$ *in* z. If we now suppose that the stellar system is of finite extent, we should conclude that $\delta_3 = 0$. We have thus proved:

For stellar systems with differential motions, which are in steady states and are of finite spatial extent, the potential $\mathfrak{V}$ *must necessarily be characterized by axial symmetry.*

The importance of the foregoing theorems for stellar dynamics consists in the fact that we are thus able to regard the existence of differential motions, on the one hand, and an axis of symmetry, on the other, as entirely equivalent in their dynamical implications for stellar systems in steady states. And it should be remembered in this connnection that the existence of differential motions and an axis of symmetry are the two most characteristic features of stellar systems.

3.6. *The two-dimensional problem: stellar systems with circular symmetry and in nonsteady states.*—In this section our principal problem will be the isolation of the most general form of a circularly symmetrical potential, $\mathfrak{V}(\varpi, t)$, which will be compatible with equations (3.455). Apart from its obvious importance, the interest in this case arises chiefly from the circumstance that under steady-state conditions the circular symmetry can be *proved* (§ 3.5). It is therefore natural that we should begin our analysis of the general problem by inquiring into the freedom which is gained by making $\mathfrak{V}$ a function of time as well but retaining its circularly symmetrical character.

The mathematical problem hinges on the discussion of the integrability conditions of the equations (3.455). For the case of circular symmetry these equations take the forms

$$\left.\begin{aligned} (ax+hy)\frac{\partial\mathfrak{V}}{\partial\tau}+\frac{\partial\Delta_1}{\partial t} &= -\frac{1}{2}\frac{\partial\chi}{\partial x}\,, \\ (hx+by)\frac{\partial\mathfrak{V}}{\partial\tau}+\frac{\partial\Delta_2}{\partial t} &= -\frac{1}{2}\frac{\partial\chi}{\partial y}\,, \\ (\Delta_1 x+\Delta_2 y)\frac{\partial\mathfrak{V}}{\partial\tau} &= +\frac{1}{2}\frac{\partial\chi}{\partial t}\,, \end{aligned}\right\} \qquad (3.601)$$

where we have introduced a new variable τ defined by

$$\tau = \tfrac{1}{2}(x^2+y^2) = \tfrac{1}{2}\varpi^2 . \qquad (3.602)$$

The conditions for the integrability of the equations (3.601) are

$$\left.\begin{aligned} &\frac{\partial}{\partial y}\left\{(ax+hy)\frac{\partial\mathfrak{B}}{\partial\tau}\right\}+\frac{\partial^2\Delta_1}{\partial y\,\partial t} \\ &\qquad\qquad = \frac{\partial}{\partial x}\left\{(hx+by)\frac{\partial\mathfrak{B}}{\partial\tau}\right\}+\frac{\partial^2\Delta_2}{\partial x\,\partial t}, \\ &\frac{\partial}{\partial t}\left\{(ax+hy)\frac{\partial\mathfrak{B}}{\partial\tau}\right\}+\frac{\partial^2\Delta_1}{\partial t^2}+\frac{\partial}{\partial x}\left\{(\Delta_1 x+\Delta_2 y)\frac{\partial\mathfrak{B}}{\partial\tau}\right\}=0, \\ &\frac{\partial}{\partial t}\left\{(hx+by)\frac{\partial\mathfrak{B}}{\partial\tau}\right\}+\frac{\partial^2\Delta_2}{\partial t^2}+\frac{\partial}{\partial y}\left\{(\Delta_1 x+\Delta_2 y)\frac{\partial\mathfrak{B}}{\partial\tau}\right\}=0. \end{aligned}\right\} \tag{3.603}$$

Substituting for a, b, h, Δ_1, and Δ_2 according to (3.451) and (3.453) in the foregoing equations and after some further reductions, we obtain

$$\left.\begin{aligned} &\{h_1(y^2-x^2)+(b_0-a_0)xy+2(h_3 y-h_2 x)\tau\}\frac{\partial^2\mathfrak{B}}{\partial\tau^2} \\ &\qquad +3(h_3 y-h_2 x)\frac{\partial\mathfrak{B}}{\partial\tau}+\frac{\partial}{\partial t}\left\{3\left(y\frac{dh_3}{dt}-x\frac{dh_2}{dt}\right)\right. \\ &\qquad\qquad\qquad\qquad \left.+\beta_3-\gamma_3\right\}=0, \end{aligned}\right\} \tag{3.604}$$

$$\left.\begin{aligned} &x\left\{-\tfrac{1}{2}x^2\frac{da_0}{dt}-\tfrac{1}{2}y^2\frac{db_0}{dt}+xy\frac{dh_1}{dt}+\delta_1 x+\delta_2 y\right\}\frac{\partial^2\mathfrak{B}}{\partial\tau^2} \\ &\quad +\{-a_0 x+h_1 y+y(h_3 y-h_2 x)\}\frac{\partial^2\mathfrak{B}}{\partial t\,\partial\tau} \\ &\quad +\left\{y\left(y\frac{dh_3}{dt}-x\frac{dh_2}{dt}\right)-2x\frac{da_0}{dt}+2y\frac{dh_1}{dt}+\delta_1\right\}\frac{\partial\mathfrak{B}}{\partial\tau} \\ &\quad +\frac{\partial^2}{\partial t^2}\left\{y\left(y\frac{dh_3}{dt}-x\frac{dh_2}{dt}\right)-\tfrac{1}{2}x\frac{da_0}{dt}+\beta_3 y+\delta_1\right\}=0, \end{aligned}\right\} \tag{3.605}$$

and

$$\left.\begin{aligned} &y\left\{-\tfrac{1}{2}x^2\frac{da_0}{dt}-\tfrac{1}{2}y^2\frac{db_0}{dt}+xy\frac{dh_1}{dt}+\delta_1 x+\delta_2 y\right\}\frac{\partial^2\mathfrak{B}}{\partial\tau^2} \\ &\quad +\{-b_0 y+h_1 x-x(h_3 y-h_2 x)\}\frac{\partial^2\mathfrak{B}}{\partial t\,\partial\tau} \\ &\quad +\left\{-x\left(y\frac{dh_3}{dt}-x\frac{dh_2}{dt}\right)-2y\frac{db_0}{dt}+2x\frac{dh_1}{dt}+\delta_2\right\}\frac{\partial\mathfrak{B}}{\partial\tau} \\ &\quad +\frac{\partial^2}{\partial t^2}\left\{-x\left(y\frac{dh_3}{dt}-x\frac{dh_2}{dt}\right)-\tfrac{1}{2}y\frac{db_0}{dt}+\gamma_3 y+\delta_2\right\}=0. \end{aligned}\right\} \tag{3.606}$$

A simple inspection of the foregoing equations shows that, unless $\partial^2\mathfrak{B}/\partial\tau^2 \equiv 0$, the circular symmetry of $\mathfrak{B}$ necessarily requires that

$$\left.\begin{aligned} a_0 = b_0 = -\kappa(t)\,; \qquad & h_1 = 0\,, \\ \beta_3 = -\gamma_3 = \beta = \text{constant}\,; \qquad & \delta_1 = \delta_2 = 0\,, \end{aligned}\right\} \tag{3.607}$$

and that, further, the ratio of h_2 and h_3 is a constant. We can therefore write

$$h_2 = h_{20}\phi\,; \qquad h_3 = h_{30}\phi\,, \tag{3.608}$$

where ϕ is a function of time and h_{20} and h_{30} are two constants.[3] On the other hand, if $\partial^2\mathfrak{B}/\partial\tau^2 \equiv 0$, then

$$\mathfrak{B} = C(x^2 + y^2)\,, \tag{3.609}$$

where C is a function of time only. For this case it is possible to satisfy all the integrability conditions with none of the coefficients vanishing. We shall, however, exclude this case from our present considerations.[4]

Introducing the conditions (3.607) and (3.608) in equations (3.604)–(3.606), we obtain

$$\left.\begin{aligned} &\phi(h_{30}y - h_{20}x)\left(2\tau\frac{\partial^2\mathfrak{B}}{\partial\tau^2} + 3\frac{\partial\mathfrak{B}}{\partial\tau} + 3\frac{\ddot{\phi}}{\phi}\right) = 0\,, \\ &y(h_{30}y - h_{20}x)\left(\phi\frac{\partial^2\mathfrak{B}}{\partial t\,\partial\tau} + \dot{\phi}\frac{\partial\mathfrak{B}}{\partial\tau} + \dddot{\phi}\right) \\ &\quad + x\left(\tau\frac{d\kappa}{dt}\frac{\partial^2\mathfrak{B}}{\partial\tau^2} + \kappa\frac{\partial^2\mathfrak{B}}{\partial t\,\partial\tau} + 2\frac{d\kappa}{dt}\frac{\partial\mathfrak{B}}{\partial\tau} + \frac{1}{2}\frac{d^3\kappa}{dt^3}\right) = 0\,, \\ &-x(h_{30}y - h_{20}x)\left(\phi\frac{\partial^2\mathfrak{B}}{\partial t\,\partial\tau} + \dot{\phi}\frac{\partial\mathfrak{B}}{\partial\tau} + \dddot{\phi}\right) \\ &\quad + y\left(\tau\frac{d\kappa}{dt}\frac{\partial^2\mathfrak{B}}{\partial\tau^2} + \kappa\frac{\partial^2\mathfrak{B}}{\partial t\,\partial\tau} + 2\frac{d\kappa}{dt}\frac{\partial\mathfrak{B}}{\partial\tau} + \frac{1}{2}\frac{d^3\kappa}{dt^3}\right) = 0\,. \end{aligned}\right\} \tag{3.610}$$

i) *Special case,* h_{20} *and/or* $h_{30} \neq 0$.—In this case the integrability conditions (3.610) reduce to the following three equations:

$$2\tau\frac{\partial^2\mathfrak{B}}{\partial\tau^2} + 3\frac{\partial\mathfrak{B}}{\partial\tau} + 3\frac{\ddot{\phi}}{\phi} = 0\,, \tag{3.611}$$

$$\phi\frac{\partial^2\mathfrak{B}}{\partial t\,\partial\tau} + \dot{\phi}\frac{\partial\mathfrak{B}}{\partial\tau} + \dddot{\phi} = 0\,, \tag{3.612}$$

[3] These conditions appear fairly obvious, but an explicit proof is somewhat too lengthy to give, and the interested reader might refer to the appropriate sections in S. Chandrasekhar, *Ap. J.*, **90**, 1–154, 1939, and **92**, 441–642, 1940.

[4] For a consideration of this special case see *ibid*.

and

$$\tau\frac{d\kappa}{dt}\frac{\partial^2\mathfrak{B}}{\partial\tau^2}+\kappa\frac{\partial^2\mathfrak{B}}{\partial t\partial\tau}+2\frac{d\kappa}{dt}\frac{\partial\mathfrak{B}}{\partial\tau}+\frac{1}{2}\frac{d^3\kappa}{dt^3}=0\,. \tag{3.613}$$

Equations (3.611) and (3.612) are readily integrated. Consider, first, equation (3.611). Since we can re-write this equation in the form

$$\frac{2}{\tau^{1/2}}\frac{\partial}{\partial\tau}\left(\tau^{3/2}\frac{\partial\mathfrak{B}}{\partial\tau}\right)=-3\frac{\ddot{\phi}}{\phi}, \tag{3.614}$$

we have

$$\tau^{3/2}\frac{\partial\mathfrak{B}}{\partial\tau}=-\frac{\ddot{\phi}}{\phi}\tau^{3/2}+F(t)\,, \tag{3.615}$$

where $F(t)$ is a function of time only. Again, since equation (3.612) is clearly equivalent to

$$\frac{\partial}{\partial t}\left(\phi\frac{\partial\mathfrak{B}}{\partial\tau}+\ddot{\phi}\right)=0 \tag{3.616}$$

we have

$$\phi\frac{\partial\mathfrak{B}}{\partial\tau}+\ddot{\phi}=G(\tau)\,, \tag{3.617}$$

where $G(\tau)$ is a function of τ only. Combining equations (3.615) and (3.617), we conclude that the compatibility of equations (3.611) and (3.612) necessarily require that $\mathfrak{B}(\tau, t)$ be such that

$$\frac{\partial\mathfrak{B}}{\partial\tau}=-\frac{\ddot{\phi}}{\phi}+\frac{q_0}{\phi}\frac{1}{\tau^{3/2}}, \tag{3.618}$$

where q_0 is a constant.

We have, finally, to consider equation (3.613). In our present connection we are not interested in the most general solution of this equation.[5] According to (3.618), we need consider only a solution of (3.613) which is of the form

$$\frac{\partial\mathfrak{B}}{\partial\tau}=C(t)+\frac{D(t)}{\tau^{3/2}}, \tag{3.619}$$

where, as we have indicated, C and D are functions of time only. Substituting, then, equation (3.619) in equation (3.613), we have

$$\left.\begin{aligned}-\frac{3}{2}\frac{D}{\tau^{3/2}}\frac{d\kappa}{dt}+\kappa\left(\frac{dC}{dt}+\frac{1}{\tau^{3/2}}\frac{dD}{dt}\right)+2\frac{d\kappa}{dt}\left(C+\frac{D}{\tau^{3/2}}\right)&\\+\frac{1}{2}\frac{d^3\kappa}{dt^3}=0\,.&\end{aligned}\right\} \tag{3.620}$$

[5] This is, however, needed for the discussion of the general case and is obtained later in the present section.

Since κ, C, and D are functions of time only, the foregoing equation is equivalent to the two equations

$$\tfrac{1}{2} D \frac{d\kappa}{dt} + \kappa \frac{dD}{dt} = 0 \tag{3.621}$$

and

$$2C \frac{d\kappa}{dt} + \kappa \frac{dC}{dt} + \frac{1}{2} \frac{d^3\kappa}{dt^3} = 0 \,. \tag{3.622}$$

Equation (3.621) admits of immediate integration. We have

$$\kappa D^2 = \text{constant} = q_0^2 \text{ (say)} \,. \tag{3.623}$$

Consider, next, equation (3.622). Multiplying this equation throughout by κ, we have

$$\frac{d}{dt}(\kappa^2 C) + \tfrac{1}{2} \kappa \frac{d^3\kappa}{dt^3} = 0 \,. \tag{3.624}$$

It is, however, readily verified that

$$\kappa \frac{d^3\kappa}{dt^3} = \frac{d}{dt} \left\{ \kappa \frac{d^2\kappa}{dt^2} - \frac{1}{2} \left(\frac{d\kappa}{dt} \right)^2 \right\} . \tag{3.625}$$

Hence, combining equations (3.624) and (3.625), we have

$$\frac{d}{dt} \left\{ \kappa^2 C + \frac{\kappa}{2} \frac{d^2\kappa}{dt^2} - \frac{1}{4} \left(\frac{d\kappa}{dt} \right)^2 \right\} = 0 \tag{3.626}$$

or

$$\kappa^2 C + \frac{1}{2} \left\{ \kappa \frac{d^2\kappa}{dt^2} - \frac{1}{2} \left(\frac{d\kappa}{dt} \right)^2 \right\} = q \,, \tag{3.627}$$

where q is a constant of integration. We can express our solution (3.627) for C more conveniently as follows:

It is easily seen that

$$\frac{d^2}{dt^2} \sqrt{\kappa} = \frac{1}{2} \frac{d}{dt} \left(\frac{1}{\sqrt{\kappa}} \frac{d\kappa}{dt} \right) = \tfrac{1}{2} \kappa^{-3/2} \left\{ \kappa \frac{d^2\kappa}{dt^2} - \frac{1}{2} \left(\frac{d\kappa}{dt} \right)^2 \right\} . \tag{3.628}$$

Equations (3.627) and (3.628) can be combined to give

$$C = \frac{q}{\kappa^2} - \frac{1}{\sqrt{\kappa}} \frac{d^2}{dt^2} \sqrt{\kappa} \,. \tag{3.629}$$

Finally, substituting for C and D according to equations (3.623) and (3.629) in equation (3.619), we obtain

$$\frac{\partial \mathfrak{V}}{\partial \tau} = \frac{q}{\kappa^2} - \frac{1}{\sqrt{\kappa}} \frac{d^2}{dt^2} \sqrt{\kappa} + \frac{q_0}{\sqrt{\kappa}} \frac{1}{\tau^{3/2}} \tag{3.630}$$

as a solution of equation (3.613), which is of the required form.

Comparing equations (3.618) and (3.630), we now conclude that in the latter equation we should set

$$q = 0 \qquad \text{and} \qquad \kappa = \phi^2 \tag{3.631}$$

for the compatibility of all the three equations (3.611)–(3.613).

We have thus proved that with the solutions for a, b, h, Δ_1, and Δ_2 of the forms

$$\left.\begin{aligned} a &= \phi^2 - 2h_{20}\phi y - h_4 y^2 \,, \\ b &= \phi^2 - 2h_{30}\phi x - h_4 x^2 \,, \\ h &= h_{20}\phi x + h_{30}\phi y + h_4 xy \,, \\ \Delta_1 &= +\dot{\phi}\,(h_{30}y - h_{20}x)\,y + \phi\dot{\phi}x + \beta y \,, \\ \Delta_2 &= -\dot{\phi}\,(h_{30}y - h_{20}x)\,x + \phi\dot{\phi}y - \beta x \,, \end{aligned}\right\} \tag{3.632}$$

the conditions of integrability of equations (3.601) are satisfied for a potential function

$$\mathfrak{V} = -\frac{\ddot{\phi}}{\phi}\,\tau - \frac{2q_0}{\phi}\,\frac{1}{\tau^{1/2}} + \mathfrak{V}_0(t) \,, \tag{3.633}$$

where q_0 is a constant and $\mathfrak{V}_0$ is an arbitrary function of time only.

Substituting our present solutions for a, b, h, Δ_1, Δ_2, and $\mathfrak{V}$ (eqs. [3.632] and [3.633]) in the original equations (3.601), we obtain, after some minor reductions,

$$\left.\begin{aligned} +\frac{1}{2}\frac{\partial\chi}{\partial t} &= -2\dot{\phi}\ddot{\phi}\tau + \frac{2q_0\dot{\phi}}{\tau^{1/2}} \,, \\ -\frac{1}{2}\frac{\partial\chi}{\partial x} &= \dot{\phi}^2 x + \frac{q_0\phi x}{\tau^{3/2}} + q_0 y\,(h_{30}y - h_{20}x)\,\frac{1}{\tau^{3/2}} \,, \\ -\frac{1}{2}\frac{\partial\chi}{\partial y} &= \dot{\phi}^2 y + \frac{q_0\phi y}{\tau^{3/2}} - q_0 x\,(h_{30}y - h_{20}x)\,\frac{1}{\tau^{3/2}} \,. \end{aligned}\right\} \tag{3.634}$$

It is readily verified that the solution for χ satisfying the foregoing equations is given by

$$-\tfrac{1}{2}\chi = \dot{\phi}^2\tau + \frac{2q_0}{\tau^{1/2}}\,(h_{30}x + h_{20}y - \phi) + \text{constant} \,. \tag{3.635}$$

This completes our discussion of the special case. The interest in this case (h_{20} and/or $h_{30} \neq 0$) arises chiefly from the circumstance that the potential function (3.633) can be interpreted as due to a central mass and a "flat" uniform spheroidal distribution of mass coextensive with the system.[6]

ii) *The general case.*—The discussion of the equations (3.604)–(3.606) has shown that in our solution for a, b, h, Δ_1, and Δ_2

$$\left.\begin{aligned} a_0 = b_0 = -\kappa\ ; \qquad \beta_3 = -\gamma_3 = \beta = \text{constant}\ , \\ h_1 = \delta_1 = \delta_2 = 0\ . \end{aligned}\right\} \qquad (3.636)^7$$

Further, if h_2 and h_3 are not both identically zero, then we are led to a perfectly definite form for the force function (cf. preceding subsection). Consequently, more general forms of the force function become possible only if h_2 and h_3 are also zero. In that case our solutions for a, b, h, Δ_1, and Δ_2 reduce to

$$a = \kappa - h_4 y^2\ ; \qquad b = \kappa - h_4 x^2\ ; \qquad h = h_4 xy\ , \qquad (3.637)$$

and

$$\Delta_1 = \frac{1}{2}\frac{d\kappa}{dt}x + \beta y\ ; \qquad \Delta_2 = \frac{1}{2}\frac{d\kappa}{dt}y - \beta x\ , \qquad (3.638)$$

where h_4 and β are constants. The integrability conditions (3.604)–(3.606) now reduce to the single equation (3.613). In view of the great importance of this equation for our present discussion, it will be of interest to derive it directly from the equations (3.601) with a, b, h, Δ_1, and Δ_2 given according to equations (3.637) and (3.638). Substituting, then, for a, b, h, Δ_1, and Δ_2 from (3.637) and (3.638) in equation (3.601), we obtain

$$\left.\begin{aligned} x\left(\kappa\frac{\partial\mathfrak{B}}{\partial\tau} + \frac{1}{2}\frac{d^2\kappa}{dt^2}\right) = -\frac{1}{2}\frac{\partial\chi}{\partial x}\ , \\ y\left(\kappa\frac{\partial\mathfrak{B}}{\partial\tau} + \frac{1}{2}\frac{d^2\kappa}{dt^2}\right) = -\frac{1}{2}\frac{\partial\chi}{\partial y}\ , \end{aligned}\right\} \qquad (3.639)$$

and

$$\tau\frac{d\kappa}{dt}\frac{\partial\mathfrak{B}}{\partial\tau} = +\frac{1}{2}\frac{\partial\chi}{\partial t}\ . \qquad (3.640)$$

[6] It is of interest to recall in this connection that a model of the Galaxy based on a potential function arising from precisely such a superposition was first introduced by Oort from other empirical considerations. For a further discussion of this case see Chandrasekhar, *Ap. J.*, **92**, 476–480, 1940, and J. Titus, *Ap. J.*, **93**, 57, 1941.

[7] It should be remembered that in proving this we explicitly excluded the case of the quasi-elastic field of force.

From equations (3.639) we readily infer that χ is also characterized by circular symmetry:

$$\chi \equiv \chi(\tau, t) . \tag{3.641}$$

The two equations (3.639) are therefore equivalent to the single equation

$$\kappa \frac{\partial \mathfrak{V}}{\partial \tau} + \frac{1}{2} \frac{d^2 \kappa}{dt^2} = -\frac{1}{2} \frac{\partial \chi}{\partial \tau} . \tag{3.642}$$

The condition for the integrability of the equations (3.640) and (3.642) is therefore given by

$$\frac{\partial}{\partial t}\left(\kappa \frac{\partial \mathfrak{V}}{\partial \tau} + \frac{1}{2} \frac{d^2 \kappa}{dt^2} \right) + \frac{\partial}{\partial \tau}\left(\tau \frac{d\kappa}{dt} \frac{\partial \mathfrak{V}}{\partial \tau} \right) = 0 ; \tag{3.643}$$

or, after some reductions, we have

$$\tau \frac{d\kappa}{dt} \frac{\partial^2 \mathfrak{V}}{\partial \tau^2} + \kappa \frac{\partial^2 \mathfrak{V}}{\partial t \partial \tau} + 2 \frac{d\kappa}{dt} \frac{\partial \mathfrak{V}}{\partial \tau} + \frac{1}{2} \frac{d^3 \kappa}{dt^3} = 0 \tag{3.644}$$

which is our fundamental differential equation for $\mathfrak{V}(\tau, t)$.

To obtain the most general solution of equation (3.644) we proceed as follows:

First, we notice that we can re-write equation (3.644) in the form

$$\frac{\partial}{\partial \tau}\left(\tau \frac{d\kappa}{dt} \frac{\partial \mathfrak{V}}{\partial \tau} + \kappa \frac{\partial \mathfrak{V}}{\partial t} + \frac{d\kappa}{dt} \mathfrak{V} + \frac{1}{2} \frac{d^3 \kappa}{dt^3} \tau \right) = 0 . \tag{3.645}$$

Hence,

$$\tau \frac{d\kappa}{dt} \frac{\partial \mathfrak{V}}{\partial \tau} + \frac{\partial}{\partial t}(\kappa \mathfrak{V}) + \frac{1}{2} \frac{d^3 \kappa}{dt^3} \tau = G(t) , \tag{3.646}$$

where $G(t)$ is an arbitrary function of time. It is now seen that there is no loss of generality involved in setting $G(t) = 0$. For, if we write

$$\mathfrak{V} = \mathfrak{V}_1(\tau, t) + \frac{1}{\kappa} \int^t G(t)\, dt , \tag{3.647}$$

it readily follows from equation (3.646) that $\mathfrak{V}_1$ satisfies the differential equation

$$\tau \frac{d\kappa}{dt} \frac{\partial \mathfrak{V}}{\partial \tau} + \frac{\partial}{\partial t}(\kappa \mathfrak{V}) + \frac{1}{2} \frac{d^3 \kappa}{dt^3} \tau = 0 . \tag{3.648}$$

Since the addition of an arbitrary function of time to the gravitational potential has no physical significance, we can simply ignore the additive term in equation (3.647). We have thus reduced our problem to solving a simple linear nonhomogeneous partial differential equation for $\kappa\mathfrak{V}$:

$$\tau\,\frac{d\,\kappa}{dt}\,\frac{\partial F}{\partial\tau} + \kappa\,\frac{\partial F}{\partial t} + \tfrac{1}{2}\,\kappa\,\frac{d^3\kappa}{dt^3}\,\tau = 0\ , \qquad (3.649)$$

where we have written

$$\kappa\,\mathfrak{V} = F\ . \qquad (3.650)$$

Instead of seeking a solution of equation (3.649) directly, we shall define it by means of an equation not solved for F:

$$\Omega(F,\,\tau,\,t) = 0\ , \qquad (3.651)$$

where the function Ω of the three variables F, τ, and t is now the unknown function. Equation (3.649) now becomes

$$\tau\,\frac{d\,\kappa}{dt}\,\frac{\partial\Omega}{\partial\tau} + \kappa\,\frac{\partial\Omega}{\partial t} - \tfrac{1}{2}\,\kappa\,\frac{d^3\kappa}{dt^3}\,\tau\,\frac{\partial\Omega}{\partial F} = 0\ , \qquad (3.652)$$

since, according to equation (3.651),

$$\frac{\partial\Omega}{\partial\tau} + \frac{\partial\Omega}{\partial F}\,\frac{\partial F}{\partial\tau} = 0\ ; \qquad \frac{\partial\Omega}{\partial t} + \frac{\partial\Omega}{\partial F}\,\frac{\partial F}{\partial t} = 0\ . \qquad (3.652')$$

Equation (3.652) is seen to be a *homogeneous* linear partial differential equation for Ω in the three variables F, τ, and t.

To solve equation (3.652), we first write down the appropriate subsidiary equations, which are

$$\frac{d\tau}{\tau\,\dfrac{d\,\kappa}{dt}} = \frac{dt}{\kappa} = -\frac{dF}{\tfrac{1}{2}\,\kappa\,\dfrac{d^3\kappa}{dt^3}\,\tau}\ . \qquad (3.653)$$

These equations can be expressed alternatively in the forms

$$\frac{d\tau}{\tau} = \frac{d\,\kappa}{\kappa} \qquad (3.654)$$

and

$$\frac{dF}{dt} = -\frac{\tau}{2}\,\frac{d^3\kappa}{dt^3}\ . \qquad (3.655)$$

Equation (3.654) admits of immediate integration. We have

$$\frac{\tau}{\kappa} = A = \text{constant}\ . \qquad (3.656)$$

From equations (3.655) and (3.656) we now find that

$$\frac{dF}{dt} = -\frac{A}{2}\kappa\frac{d^3\kappa}{dt^3} = -\frac{A}{2}\frac{d}{dt}\left\{\kappa\frac{d^2\kappa}{dt^2} - \frac{1}{2}\left(\frac{d\kappa}{dt}\right)^2\right\}. \quad (3.657)$$

Hence,

$$F + \frac{A}{2}\left\{\kappa\frac{d^2\kappa}{dt^2} - \frac{1}{2}\left(\frac{d\kappa}{dt}\right)^2\right\} = \text{constant}\ , \quad (3.658)$$

or, using equation (3.656) to eliminate A, we have

$$F + \frac{\tau}{2\kappa}\left\{\kappa\frac{d^2\kappa}{dt^2} - \frac{1}{2}\left(\frac{d\kappa}{dt}\right)^2\right\} = \text{constant}\ . \quad (3.659)$$

The foregoing equation can be expressed more conveniently by using the elementary relation (3.628). We find

$$F + \tau\sqrt{\kappa}\,\frac{d^2}{dt^2}\sqrt{\kappa} = \text{constant}\ . \quad (3.660)$$

Equations (3.656) and (3.660) represent two independent integrals of the subsidiary equations (3.653). Hence,

$$\Omega \equiv \Omega\left(F + \tau\phi\ddot{\phi},\ \frac{\tau}{\phi^2}\right), \quad (3.661)$$

where the quantity on the right-hand side stands for an arbitrary function of the arguments specified; further, in equation (3.661) we have written

$$\kappa = \phi^2\ . \quad (3.662)$$

It is now clear that, according to equation (3.651), we can express the solution (3.661) alternatively in the form

$$F + \tau\phi\ddot{\phi} = \mathfrak{V}_1\left(\frac{\tau}{\phi^2}\right), \quad (3.663)$$

where $\mathfrak{V}_1$ is an arbitrary function of the argument specified. Finally, reverting to our original variable $\mathfrak{V}$, we have

$$\mathfrak{V} = \frac{1}{\phi^2}F = -\frac{\ddot{\phi}}{\phi}\tau + \frac{1}{\phi^2}\mathfrak{V}_1\left(\frac{\tau}{\phi^2}\right). \quad (3.664)$$

We have thus proved that *the most general form of the potential function which is compatible with the relations (3.601) is given by equation (3.664)*. Further, the solutions for a, b, h, Δ_1, and Δ_2 appropriate to this case are given (cf. eqs. [3.637] and [3.638]) by

$$a = \phi^2 + \kappa_2 y^2\ ; \qquad b = \phi^2 + \kappa_2 x^2\ ; \qquad h = -\kappa_2 xy\ , \quad (3.665)[8]$$

[8] In this equation we have written κ_2 instead of $-h_4$ as in equation (3.637).

and

$$\left.\begin{aligned}\Delta_1 &= a\,U_0 + h\,V_0 = \phi\dot{\phi}x + \beta y\,,\\ \Delta_2 &= h\,U_0 + b\,V_0 = \phi\dot{\phi}y - \beta x\,,\end{aligned}\right\} \qquad (3.666)$$

where κ_2 and β are two constants. From equations (3.665) and (3.666) we readily obtain[9]

$$\left.\begin{aligned}U_0 &= \frac{\dot{\phi}}{\phi}\,x + \frac{\beta y}{\phi^2 + \kappa_2(x^2+y^2)}\,;\\ V_0 &= \frac{\dot{\phi}}{\phi}\,y - \frac{\beta x}{\phi^2 + \kappa_2(x^2+y^2)}\,.\end{aligned}\right\} \qquad (3.667)$$

Substituting our present solution for $\mathfrak{V}$ (eq. [3.664]) in equations (3.640) and (3.642) and remembering that $\kappa = \phi^2$, we obtain

$$\left.\begin{aligned}\phi^2\left(-\frac{\ddot{\phi}}{\phi} + \frac{1}{\phi^4}\,\mathfrak{V}_1'\right) + \dot{\phi}^2 + \phi\ddot{\phi} &= -\frac{1}{2}\frac{\partial\chi}{\partial\tau}\,,\\ 2\tau\phi\dot{\phi}\left(-\frac{\ddot{\phi}}{\phi} + \frac{1}{\phi^4}\,\mathfrak{V}_1'\right) &= +\frac{1}{2}\frac{\partial\chi}{\partial t}\,,\end{aligned}\right\} \qquad (3.668)$$

where we have used $\mathfrak{V}_1'$ to denote the derivative of $\mathfrak{V}_1$ with respect to its argument τ/ϕ^2. After some further reductions, equations (3.668) become

$$\left.\begin{aligned}\dot{\phi}^2 + \frac{1}{\phi^2}\,\mathfrak{V}_1' &= -\frac{1}{2}\frac{\partial\chi}{\partial\tau}\,,\\ 2\tau\dot{\phi}\ddot{\phi} - \frac{2\tau\dot{\phi}}{\phi^3}\,\mathfrak{V}_1' &= -\frac{1}{2}\frac{\partial\chi}{\partial t}\,.\end{aligned}\right\} \qquad (3.669)$$

It is readily verified that the solution for χ which satisfies the foregoing equations is given by

$$-\tfrac{1}{2}\chi = \dot{\phi}^2\tau + \mathfrak{V}_1\left(\frac{\tau}{\phi^2}\right) + \text{constant}\,. \qquad (3.670)$$

The corresponding solution for σ may also be noted. Since (eq. [3.410])

$$\left.\begin{aligned}-\chi = Q_0 + \sigma &= a\,U_0^2 + b\,V_0^2 + 2h\,U_0\,V_0 + \sigma\,,\\ &= U_0\Delta_1 + V_0\Delta_2 + \sigma\,,\end{aligned}\right\} \qquad (3.671)$$

[9] For, according to equations (3.666),

$$U_0 = \frac{b\Delta_1 - h\Delta_2}{ab - h^2}\,; \qquad V_0 = \frac{a\Delta_2 - h\Delta_1}{ab - h^2}\,. \qquad (3.667')$$

Further, $ab - h^2 = \phi^2(\phi^2 + \kappa_2\varpi^2)$.

we have, according to equations (3.666) and (3.667),

$$-\chi=\left(\dot{\phi}^2+\frac{\beta^2}{\phi^2+\kappa_2\varpi^2}\right)\varpi^2+\sigma\,. \qquad (3.672)$$

Combining equations (3.670) and (3.672), we finally obtain

$$\sigma=-\frac{\beta^2\varpi^2}{\phi^2+\kappa_2\varpi^2}+2\mathfrak{V}_1\left(\frac{\varpi}{\phi}\right)+\text{constant}\,. \qquad (3.673)$$

This completes our discussion of the two-dimensional problem.

3.7. *Examples of stellar systems having axial symmetries and in nonsteady states.*—In this section we shall generalize the results of § 3.6 to three-dimensional stellar systems with axial symmetries. For this purpose we shall assume for the coefficients of the velocity ellipsoid and the Δ's solutions which are simple generalizations of the forms proved necessary in the rigorous analysis of the two-dimensional problem with circular symmetry. Corresponding to the solution (3.637), we shall assume that

$$\left.\begin{aligned} a=\kappa_1+\kappa_2 y^2\,;\qquad b=\kappa_1+\kappa_2 x^2\,;\qquad c=\kappa_3\,;\\ h=-\kappa_2 xy\,;\qquad f=g=0\,,\end{aligned}\right\} \qquad (3.701)$$

where κ_1 and κ_3 are functions of time and κ_2 is a constant. Again, in analogy with equation (3.638) we shall assume that

$$\Delta_1=\frac{1}{2}\frac{d\kappa_1}{dt}x+\beta y\,;\quad \Delta_2=\frac{1}{2}\frac{d\kappa_1}{dt}y-\beta x\,;\quad \Delta_3=\frac{1}{2}\frac{d\kappa_3}{dt}z\,, \qquad (3.702)$$

where β is a constant.

Substituting for the coefficients of the velocity ellipsoid and the Δ's according to the foregoing equations in (III) (§ 3.4), we obtain

$$\left.\begin{aligned} (\kappa_1+\kappa_2 y^2)\frac{\partial\mathfrak{V}}{\partial x}-\kappa_2 xy\frac{\partial\mathfrak{V}}{\partial y}+\frac{1}{2}x\frac{d^2\kappa_1}{dt^2}&=-\frac{1}{2}\frac{\partial\chi}{\partial x}\,,\\ (\kappa_1+\kappa_2 x^2)\frac{\partial\mathfrak{V}}{\partial y}-\kappa_2 xy\frac{\partial\mathfrak{V}}{\partial x}+\frac{1}{2}y\frac{d^2\kappa_1}{dt^2}&=-\frac{1}{2}\frac{\partial\chi}{\partial y}\,,\\ \kappa_3\frac{\partial\mathfrak{V}}{\partial z}+\tfrac{1}{2}z\frac{d^2\kappa_3}{dt^2}&=-\frac{1}{2}\frac{\partial\chi}{\partial z}\,,\\ \left(\frac{1}{2}\frac{d\kappa_1}{dt}x+\beta y\right)\frac{\partial\mathfrak{V}}{\partial x}+\left(\frac{1}{2}\frac{d\kappa_1}{dt}y-\beta x\right)\frac{\partial\mathfrak{V}}{\partial y}&\\ +\frac{1}{2}\frac{d\kappa_3}{dt}z\frac{\partial\mathfrak{V}}{\partial z}&=\frac{1}{2}\frac{\partial\chi}{\partial t}\,,\end{aligned}\right\} \qquad (3.703)$$

where, according to our assumption,

$$\mathfrak{B} \equiv \mathfrak{B}(\varpi, z, t) . \tag{3.704}$$

Let

$$\tau = \tfrac{1}{2}(x^2 + y^2) ; \qquad \zeta = \tfrac{1}{2} z^2 . \tag{3.705}$$

In terms of these variables, equations (3.703) take the simpler forms

$$\kappa_1 x \frac{\partial \mathfrak{B}}{\partial \tau} + \tfrac{1}{2} x \frac{d^2 \kappa_1}{dt^2} = -\frac{1}{2} \frac{\partial \chi}{\partial x} , \tag{3.706}$$

$$\kappa_1 y \frac{\partial \mathfrak{B}}{\partial \tau} + \tfrac{1}{2} y \frac{d^2 \kappa_1}{dt^2} = -\frac{1}{2} \frac{\partial \chi}{\partial y} , \tag{3.707}$$

$$\kappa_3 \frac{\partial \mathfrak{B}}{\partial \zeta} + \frac{1}{2} \frac{d^2 \kappa_3}{dt^2} = -\frac{1}{2} \frac{\partial \chi}{\partial \zeta} , \tag{3.708}$$

and

$$\frac{d\kappa_1}{dt} \tau \frac{\partial \mathfrak{B}}{\partial \tau} + \frac{d\kappa_3}{dt} \zeta \frac{\partial \mathfrak{B}}{\partial \zeta} = \frac{1}{2} \frac{\partial \chi}{\partial t} . \tag{3.709}$$

From equations (3.706) and (3.707) we readily conclude that

$$\chi \equiv \chi(\tau, \zeta, t) . \tag{3.710}$$

Thus, the two equations (3.706) and (3.707) are equivalent to the single equation

$$\kappa_1 \frac{\partial \mathfrak{B}}{\partial \tau} + \frac{1}{2} \frac{d^2 \kappa_1}{dt^2} = -\frac{1}{2} \frac{\partial \chi}{\partial \tau} . \tag{3.711}$$

The integrability condition resulting from equations (3.708) and (3.711) is

$$(\kappa_3 - \kappa_1) \frac{\partial^2 \mathfrak{B}}{\partial \tau \partial \zeta} = 0 . \tag{3.712}$$

Hence, *either*

$$\kappa_3 = \kappa_1 = \kappa \tag{3.713}$$

or

$$\frac{\partial^2 \mathfrak{B}}{\partial \tau \partial \zeta} = 0 . \tag{3.714}$$

We shall consider these two cases separately.

i) *The general case*, $\kappa_3 = \kappa_1 = \kappa$.—From equations (3.709) and (3.711) we now find

$$\frac{\partial}{\partial t}\left(\kappa \frac{\partial \mathfrak{B}}{\partial \tau} + \frac{1}{2} \frac{d^2 \kappa}{dt^2} \right) + \frac{d\kappa}{dt} \frac{\partial}{\partial \tau}\left(\tau \frac{\partial \mathfrak{B}}{\partial \tau} + \zeta \frac{\partial \mathfrak{B}}{\partial \zeta} \right) = 0 , \tag{3.715}$$

or, after performing the differentiations, we have

$$\kappa \frac{\partial^2 \mathfrak{V}}{\partial t \partial \tau} + \tau \frac{d\kappa}{dt} \frac{\partial^2 \mathfrak{V}}{\partial \tau^2} + \zeta \frac{d\kappa}{dt} \frac{\partial^2 \mathfrak{V}}{\partial \tau \partial \zeta} + 2 \frac{d\kappa}{dt} \frac{\partial \mathfrak{V}}{\partial \tau} + \frac{1}{2} \frac{d^3 \kappa}{dt^3} = 0 . \quad (3.716)$$

Similarly, from equations (3.708) and (3.709) we obtain

$$\kappa \frac{\partial^2 \mathfrak{V}}{\partial t \partial \zeta} + \zeta \frac{d\kappa}{dt} \frac{\partial^2 \mathfrak{V}}{\partial \zeta^2} + \tau \frac{d\kappa}{dt} \frac{\partial^2 \mathfrak{V}}{\partial \tau \partial \zeta} + 2 \frac{d\kappa}{dt} \frac{\partial \mathfrak{V}}{\partial \zeta} + \frac{1}{2} \frac{d^3 \kappa}{dt^3} = 0 . \quad (3.717)$$

Equations (3.716) and (3.717) can be written alternatively in the forms

$$\left.\begin{aligned} \frac{\partial}{\partial \tau}\left(\frac{d\kappa}{dt} \mathfrak{V} + \kappa \frac{\partial \mathfrak{V}}{\partial t} + \tau \frac{d\kappa}{dt} \frac{\partial \mathfrak{V}}{\partial \tau} + \zeta \frac{d\kappa}{dt} \frac{\partial \mathfrak{V}}{\partial \zeta} + \frac{1}{2} \frac{d^3 \kappa}{dt^3} \tau \right) &= 0 , \\ \frac{\partial}{\partial \zeta}\left(\frac{d\kappa}{dt} \mathfrak{V} + \kappa \frac{\partial \mathfrak{V}}{\partial t} + \tau \frac{d\kappa}{dt} \frac{\partial \mathfrak{V}}{\partial \tau} + \zeta \frac{d\kappa}{dt} \frac{\partial \mathfrak{V}}{\partial \zeta} + \frac{1}{2} \frac{d^3 \kappa}{dt^3} \zeta \right) &= 0 . \end{aligned}\right\} \quad (3.718)$$

From the foregoing equations it readily follows that

$$\frac{\partial}{\partial t} (\kappa \mathfrak{V}) + \frac{d\kappa}{dt} \left(\tau \frac{\partial \mathfrak{V}}{\partial \tau} + \zeta \frac{\partial \mathfrak{V}}{\partial \zeta} \right) + \frac{1}{2} \frac{d^3 \kappa}{dt^3} (\tau + \zeta) = G(t) , \quad (3.719)$$

where $G(t)$ is a function of time only. Again, since there is no loss of generality involved in setting $G(t) = 0$ (see p. 112), equation (3.719) reduces to a simple linear nonhomogeneous partial differential equation for $\kappa \mathfrak{V}$,

$$\kappa \frac{\partial F}{\partial t} + \tau \frac{d\kappa}{dt} \frac{\partial F}{\partial \tau} + \zeta \frac{d\kappa}{dt} \frac{\partial F}{\partial \zeta} + \tfrac{1}{2} (\tau + \zeta) \kappa \frac{d^3 \kappa}{dt^3} = 0 , \quad (3.720)$$

where we have written

$$\kappa \mathfrak{V} = F . \quad (3.721)$$

Equation (3.720) is seen to be the natural three-dimensional generalization of the equation encountered in our analysis of the two-dimensional problem (eq. [3.649]). As in the discussion of the earlier case (p. 113), we shall define the general solution of equation (3.720) by means of a relation not solved for F:

$$\Omega = \Omega(F, \tau, \zeta, t) = 0 . \quad (3.722)$$

Then,

$$\frac{\partial \Omega}{\partial \tau} + \frac{\partial \Omega}{\partial F} \frac{\partial F}{\partial \tau} = 0 ; \quad \frac{\partial \Omega}{\partial \zeta} + \frac{\partial \Omega}{\partial F} \frac{\partial F}{\partial \zeta} = 0 ; \quad \frac{\partial \Omega}{\partial t} + \frac{\partial \Omega}{\partial F} \frac{\partial F}{\partial t} = 0 . \quad (3.722')$$

Hence Ω satisfies the linear homogeneous equation

$$\kappa \frac{\partial \Omega}{\partial t} + \tau \frac{d\kappa}{dt} \frac{\partial \Omega}{\partial \tau} + \zeta \frac{d\kappa}{dt} \frac{\partial \Omega}{\partial \zeta} - \tfrac{1}{2}(\tau + \zeta)\kappa \frac{d^3\kappa}{dt^3} \frac{\partial \Omega}{\partial F} = 0 , \quad (3.723)$$

which can be solved by writing down the appropriate subsidiary equations

$$\frac{dt}{\kappa} = \frac{d\tau}{\tau \dfrac{d\kappa}{dt}} = \frac{d\zeta}{\zeta \dfrac{d\kappa}{dt}} = -\frac{dF}{\tfrac{1}{2}(\tau + \zeta)\kappa \dfrac{d^3\kappa}{dt^3}} . \quad (3.724)$$

The foregoing equations can be written alternatively in the forms

$$\frac{d\tau}{\tau} = \frac{d\kappa}{\kappa} ; \qquad \frac{d\zeta}{\zeta} = \frac{d\kappa}{\kappa} , \quad (3.725)$$

and

$$\frac{dF}{dt} = -\tfrac{1}{2}(\tau + \zeta) \frac{d^3\kappa}{dt^3} . \quad (3.726)$$

According to equations (3.725), we clearly have

$$\frac{\tau}{\kappa} = A = \text{constant} ; \qquad \frac{\zeta}{\kappa} = B = \text{constant} . \quad (3.727)$$

Using these integrals, equation (3.726) becomes

$$\frac{dF}{dt} = -\tfrac{1}{2}(A + B)\kappa \frac{d^3\kappa}{dt^3} , \quad (3.728)$$

in which form it admits of integration. We have (cf. eqs. [3.657]–[3.660]).

$$F + (\tau + \zeta)\phi\dddot{\phi} = \text{constant} , \quad (3.729)$$

where we have written

$$\kappa = \phi^2 . \quad (3.730)$$

Equations (3.727) and (3.729) provide three independent integrals of the subsidiary equations. Hence

$$\Omega \equiv \Omega\left(F + (\tau + \zeta)\phi\dddot{\phi}, \frac{\tau}{\phi^2}, \frac{\zeta}{\phi^2}\right) , \quad (3.731)$$

where the quantity on the right-hand side stands for an arbitrary function of the arguments specified.

Solving for F, we can express the solution (3.731) as

$$F = -(\tau + \zeta)\phi\ddot{\phi} + \mathfrak{B}_1\left(\frac{\tau}{\phi^2}, \frac{\zeta}{\phi^2}\right), \tag{3.732}$$

where $\mathfrak{B}_1$ is an arbitrary function of the arguments specified. According to equations (3.721) and (3.732) we finally have

$$\mathfrak{B} = -\frac{\ddot{\phi}}{\phi}(\tau + \zeta) + \frac{1}{\phi^2}\mathfrak{B}_1\left(\frac{\tau}{\phi^2}, \frac{\zeta}{\phi^2}\right). \tag{3.733}$$

The solutions for the coefficients of the velocity ellipsoid and the Δ's, appropriate to this case, are

$$a = \phi^2 + \kappa_2 y^2\,; \quad b = \phi^2 + \kappa_2 x^2\,; \quad c = \phi^2\,; \quad h = -\kappa_2 xy \tag{3.734}$$

and

$$\left.\begin{aligned} \Delta_1 &= aU_0 + hV_0 = \phi\dot{\phi}x + \beta y\,, \\ \Delta_2 &= hU_0 + bV_0 = \phi\dot{\phi}y - \beta x\,, \\ \Delta_3 &= cW_0 \qquad\quad\;\; = \phi\dot{\phi}z\,. \end{aligned}\right\} \tag{3.735}$$

From the foregoing equations we obtain

$$\left.\begin{aligned} U_0 &= \frac{\dot{\phi}}{\phi}x + \frac{\beta y}{\phi^2 + \kappa_2(x^2 + y^2)}\,; \\ V_0 &= \frac{\dot{\phi}}{\phi}y - \frac{\beta x}{\phi^2 + \kappa_2(x^2 + y^2)}\,; \\ W_0 &= \frac{\dot{\phi}}{\phi}z\,. \end{aligned}\right\} \tag{3.736}$$

Substituting for $\mathfrak{B}$ according to equation (3.733) in equations (3.708), (3.709), and (3.711) and remembering that for the case under consideration $\kappa_1 = \kappa_3 = \kappa = \phi^2$, we find (cf. eqs. [3.668] and [3.669])

$$\left.\begin{aligned} &\dot{\phi}^2 + \frac{1}{\phi^2}\frac{\partial\mathfrak{B}_1}{\partial(\tau/\phi^2)} = -\frac{1}{2}\frac{\partial\chi}{\partial\tau}\,; \quad \dot{\phi}^2 + \frac{1}{\phi^2}\frac{\partial\mathfrak{B}_1}{\partial(\zeta/\phi^2)} = -\frac{1}{2}\frac{\partial\chi}{\partial\zeta}\,, \\ &-2(\tau + \zeta)\dot{\phi}\ddot{\phi} + \frac{2\dot{\phi}}{\phi^3}\left(\tau\frac{\partial\mathfrak{B}_1}{\partial(\tau/\phi^2)} + \zeta\frac{\partial\mathfrak{B}_1}{\partial(\zeta/\phi^2)}\right) = \frac{1}{2}\frac{\partial\chi}{\partial t}\,. \end{aligned}\right\} \tag{3.737}$$

It is readily verified that the solution for χ which satisfies the equations (3.737) is given by

$$-\tfrac{1}{2}\chi = \dot{\phi}^2(\tau + \zeta) + \mathfrak{B}_1(\tau/\phi^2, \zeta/\phi^2) + \text{constant}\,. \tag{3.738}$$

Finally, let us consider the solution for σ. By definition (eq. [3.410])

$$-\chi = Q + \sigma = \Delta_1 U_0 + \Delta_2 V_0 + \Delta_3 W_0 + \sigma \, , \qquad (3.739)$$

or, according to equations (3.735) and (3.736), we have

$$-\chi = \frac{\beta^2(x^2+y^2)}{\phi^2 + \kappa_2(x^2+y^2)} + \dot{\phi}^2(x^2+y^2+z^2) + \sigma \, . \qquad (3.740)$$

Combining equations (3.738) and (3.740) we find

$$\sigma = -\frac{\beta^2 \varpi^2}{\phi^2 + \kappa_2 \varpi^2} + 2\mathfrak{B}_1\left(\frac{\varpi}{\phi}, \frac{z}{\phi}\right) + \text{constant} \, . \qquad (3.741)$$

ii) *Special case,* $\partial^2\mathfrak{B}/\partial\tau\partial\zeta \equiv 0$.—In this case the integrability conditions resulting from equations (3.708), (3.709), and (3.711) are seen to take the forms (cf. eqs. [3.715]–[3.717])

$$\left.\begin{aligned} \kappa_1 \frac{\partial^2 \mathfrak{B}}{\partial t \partial \tau} + \tau \frac{d\kappa_1}{dt}\frac{\partial^2 \mathfrak{B}}{\partial \tau^2} + 2\frac{d\kappa_1}{dt}\frac{\partial \mathfrak{B}}{\partial \tau} + \frac{1}{2}\frac{d^3\kappa_1}{dt^3} = 0 \, , \\ \kappa_3 \frac{\partial^2 \mathfrak{B}}{\partial t \partial \zeta} + \zeta \frac{d\kappa_3}{dt}\frac{\partial^2 \mathfrak{B}}{\partial \zeta^2} + 2\frac{d\kappa_3}{dt}\frac{\partial \mathfrak{B}}{\partial \zeta} + \frac{1}{2}\frac{d^3\kappa_3}{dt^3} = 0 \, . \end{aligned}\right\} \qquad (3.742)$$

Equations (3.742) are identical in form with equation (3.644), the general solution of which has already been found (eq. [3.664]). We can therefore write

$$\mathfrak{B} = -\frac{\ddot{\phi}_1}{\phi_1}\tau - \frac{\ddot{\phi}_2}{\phi_2}\zeta + \frac{1}{\phi_1^2}\mathfrak{B}_1\left(\frac{\tau}{\phi_1^2}\right) + \frac{1}{\phi_2^2}\mathfrak{B}_2\left(\frac{\zeta}{\phi_2^2}\right), \qquad (3.743)$$

where

$$\kappa_1 = \phi_1^2 \, ; \qquad \kappa_3 = \phi_2^2 \, , \qquad (3.744)$$

and $\mathfrak{B}_1$ and $\mathfrak{B}_2$ are arbitrary functions of the arguments specified. Further, the solutions for χ and σ appropriate to this case are clearly

$$\left.\begin{aligned} -\tfrac{1}{2}\chi &= \dot{\phi}_1^2\tau + \dot{\phi}_2^2\zeta + \mathfrak{B}_1\left(\frac{\tau}{\phi_1^2}\right) + \mathfrak{B}_2\left(\frac{\zeta}{\phi_2^2}\right) + \text{constant} \, , \\ \sigma &= -\frac{\beta^2\varpi^2}{\phi_1^2 + \kappa_2\varpi^2} + 2\mathfrak{B}_1\left(\frac{\varpi}{\phi_1}\right) + 2\mathfrak{B}_2\left(\frac{z}{\phi_2}\right) + \text{constant} \, . \end{aligned}\right\} \qquad (3.745)$$

3.8. *The physical characteristics of stellar systems with axial symmetries.*—We shall now examine somewhat more closely the physical characteristics of the systems considered in the two preceding sections.

Consider first the two-dimensional case. The results of this analysis may be expected to be valid for the consideration of stellar motions confined to the galactic plane. According to our discussion in § 3.6, the most general form for the gravitational potential (namely, eq. [3.664]) is provided when the coefficients of the velocity ellipse and the motions of the local centroids are expressible in the forms (eqs. [3.665] and [3.667])

$$a=\phi^2+\kappa_2 y^2\ ;\qquad b=\phi^2+\kappa_2 x^2\ ;\qquad h=-\kappa_2 xy\ , \tag{3.801}$$

and

$$\left.\begin{aligned} U_0&=\frac{\dot\phi}{\phi}\,x+\frac{\beta y}{\phi^2+\kappa_2(x^2+y^2)}\ ;\\ V_0&=\frac{\dot\phi}{\phi}\,y-\frac{\beta x}{\phi^2+\kappa_2(x^2+y^2)}\ .\end{aligned}\right\} \tag{3.802}$$

Corresponding to the solution (3.801) for a, b, and h, we have the fundamental quadratic form

$$\left.\begin{aligned} Q=(\phi^2+\kappa_2 y^2)(U-U_0)^2+(\phi^2+\kappa_2 x^2)(V-V_0)^2&\\ -2\kappa_2 xy(U-U_0)(V-V_0)\ .&\end{aligned}\right\} \tag{3.803}$$

We shall now refer the velocity ellipse represented by (3.803) to the radial (Π) and the transverse (Θ) directions at (x, y). The formulae appropriate to this transformation of the axes are

$$\left.\begin{aligned} x&=\varpi\cos\theta\ ; & y&=\varpi\sin\theta\ ,\\ U&=\Pi\cos\theta-\Theta\sin\theta\ ; & V&=\Pi\sin\theta+\Theta\cos\theta\ .\end{aligned}\right\} \tag{3.804}$$

Direct substitutions in the quadratic form (3.803) now reduce it to

$$Q=a_\varpi(\Pi-\Pi_0)^2+b_\theta(\Theta-\Theta_0)^2\ , \tag{3.805}$$

where we have written

$$a_\varpi=\phi^2\ ;\qquad b_\theta=\phi^2+\kappa_2\varpi^2\ . \tag{3.806}$$

Further, in equation (3.805) Π_0 and Θ_0 denote the components of the motion of the local centroid along the radial and the transverse directions, respectively. From equations (3.802) we obtain the following expressions for Π_0 and Θ_0:

$$\left.\begin{aligned} \Pi_0&=\frac{1}{\varpi}(yV_0+xU_0)=\frac{\dot\phi}{\phi}\,\varpi\ ,\\ \Theta_0&=\frac{1}{\varpi}(xV_0-yU_0)=-\frac{\beta\varpi}{\phi^2+\kappa_2\varpi^2}\ .\end{aligned}\right\} \tag{3.807}$$

(See Fig. 15 where the variation of Θ_0 with ϖ according to equation [3.807] is illustrated.)

From equation (3.805) it clearly follows that the principal axes of the velocity ellipse are along the radial and the transverse directions; further, the *ratio of the axes* is given by

$$\left(\frac{a_\varpi}{b_\theta}\right)^{1/2} = \frac{\phi}{(\phi^2 + \kappa_2\varpi^2)^{1/2}}, \tag{3.808}$$

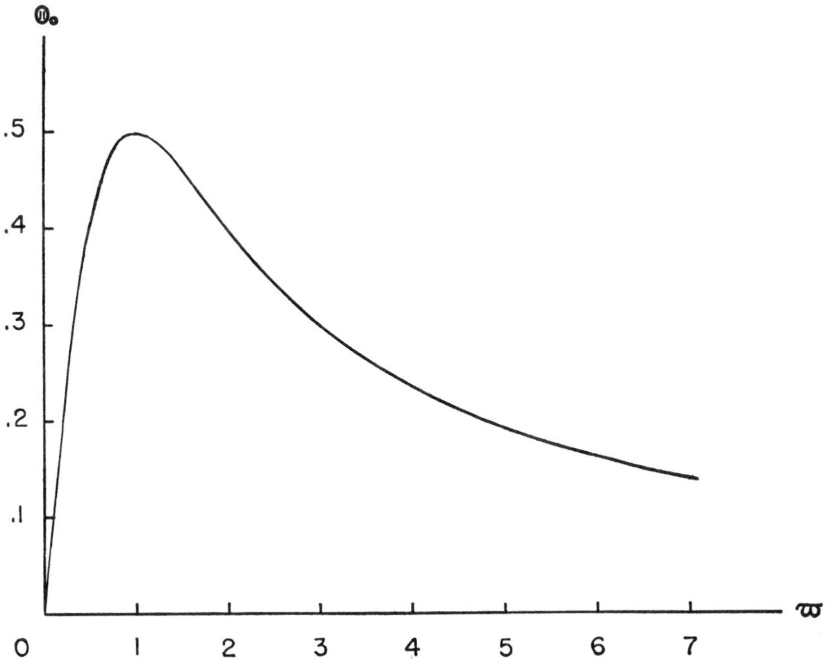

FIG. 15.—Illustrating the dependence of Θ_0 on ϖ predicted by galactic dynamics for systems with axially (or circularly) symmetrical potentials. According to the theory,

$$\Theta_0 = \text{constant}\ \frac{\varpi}{1+\varpi^2}$$

if the distance ϖ from the axis of symmetry is measured in appropriate units.

the major axis being that in the radial direction. Again, according to equation (3.807), we notice that in addition to differential rotations represented by Θ_0 we also have motions in the radial directions specified by Π_0. This field of radial motions corresponds to an expansion or contraction, depending on the sign of the rate of change of ϕ. If $\dot{\phi} > 0$, Π_0 corresponds to a general expansion proportional to the distance from the center; on the other hand, we have a similar field of contraction if $\dot{\phi} < 0$. Finally, $\Pi_0 \neq 0$ only when $\dot{\phi} \neq 0$; in other words, *the field of radial motions is directly connected with the nonsteady character of the system.* Physical considerations seem to suggest a general expansion rather than a contraction. This would imply that $\dot{\phi} \geqslant 0$.

It is of interest to evaluate explicitly the coefficients A, B, and K (§ 1.4) in the expressions for the radial velocities and proper motions due to the field of differential motions defined by equation (3.807). Since (cf. eq. [1.424])

$$\left.\begin{aligned} A &= \frac{1}{2}\left(\frac{\partial \Theta_0}{\partial \varpi} - \frac{\Theta_0}{\varpi}\right); \quad B = \frac{1}{2}\left(\frac{\partial \Theta_0}{\partial \varpi} + \frac{\Theta_0}{\varpi}\right); \\ K &= \frac{1}{2}\left(\frac{\partial \Pi_0}{\partial \varpi} + \frac{\Pi_0}{\varpi}\right), \end{aligned}\right\} \tag{3.809}$$

we find

$$A = \beta \frac{\kappa_2 \varpi^2}{(\phi^2 + \kappa_2 \varpi^2)^2}; \qquad B = -\beta \frac{\phi^2}{(\phi^2 + \kappa_2 \varpi^2)^2}; \qquad K = \frac{\dot{\phi}}{\phi}. \tag{3.810}$$

Thus, according to equation (1.416), we have a K-term proportional to the distance in the differential-motion term in the expression for the radial velocity.

From the explicit expression obtained for A and Θ_0 we derive the following relation:

$$\left.\begin{aligned} 1 + \frac{A}{(\Theta_0/\varpi)} &= 1 - \frac{\kappa_2 \varpi^2}{\phi^2 + \kappa_2 \varpi^2} = \frac{\phi^2}{\phi^2 + \kappa_2 \varpi^2} \\ &= \frac{a_\varpi}{b_\theta} = (\text{ratio of axes})^2 . \end{aligned}\right\} \tag{3.811}$$

Since, however, $B - A = \Theta_0/\varpi$, we also have

$$\frac{B}{B - A} = (\text{ratio of axes})^2 . \tag{3.812}$$

For the values of A and B quoted in chapter i (eq. [1.422]), the ratio of the axes predicted by equation (3.812) is $(13/31)^{1/2} = 0.65$; this predicted value is in general agreement with the analysis of the residual motions in the neighborhood of the sun (see Table 1, p. 12).

When we pass on to the consideration of the general three-dimensional systems, we notice that, according to equations (3.702) and (3.736), the characteristics of the motions in the galactic plane are the same as in the two-dimensional problem. The only additional features are those which refer to the motions perpendicular to the galactic plane. In the "general case" considered in § 3.7

$$c = a_{\varpi} = \phi^2\,; \qquad W_0 = \frac{\dot{\phi}}{\phi}\,z\,. \tag{3.813}$$

Hence, on this model, the third axis of the velocity ellipsoid (which is in the z-direction) is of the same length as that in the radial direction. But this is not in agreement with the results of observations which indicate, far more, a prolate form for the velocity ellipsoid. However, to a sufficient approximation, we may suppose that the motions in the z-directions are largely independent of the motions in the galactic plane. Under these circumstances, we may use the results for the "special case" ($\partial^2\mathfrak{V}/\partial\varpi\partial z \equiv 0$) considered in § 3.7. Then the third axis of the velocity ellipsoid (which is in the z-direction) will, in general, be different from that in the radial direction. Further, for this special case, W_0 is given by $(\dot{\phi}_2/\phi_2)z$, where

$$\phi_2 = c^{1/2} \qquad\qquad (\neq a_{\varpi}^{1/2} = \phi)\,.$$

Finally, we shall derive an important relation between the distributions of matter and motion predicted for the systems under consideration. The analysis of §§ 3.6 and 3.7 has disclosed the existence of a very general relation of the form (cf. eqs. [3.664], [3.673], and [3.733] and [3.741])

$$\sigma = -\frac{\beta^2\varpi^2}{\phi^2+\kappa_2\varpi^2} + \phi\ddot{\phi}\,(\varpi^2+z^2) + 2\phi^2\mathfrak{V} + \text{constant}\,. \tag{3.814}$$ [10]

Differentiating this equation partially with respect to ϖ we have

$$\frac{\partial\sigma}{\partial\varpi} = -\frac{2\phi^2}{\varpi}\left(\frac{\beta^2\varpi^2}{(\phi^2+\kappa_2\varpi^2)^2} - \varpi\,\frac{\partial\mathfrak{V}}{\partial\varpi}\right) + 2\phi\ddot{\phi}\varpi\,. \tag{3.815}$$

[10] The formula quoted is valid for the "general case" of § 3.7. But equation (3.815) and the succeeding equations, which are obtained after a partial differentiation with respect to ϖ of equation (3.814), are, however, seen to be valid, quite generally.

But, according to equation (3.312), the velocity, Θ_c, in a circular orbit of radius ϖ is given by

$$\Theta_c^2 = \varpi \frac{\partial \mathfrak{B}}{\partial \varpi} . \tag{3.816}$$

Hence, using equations (3.807) and (3.816), we can re-write equation (3.815) in the form

$$\frac{\partial \sigma}{\partial \varpi} = \frac{2\phi^2}{\varpi}(\Theta_c^2 - \Theta_0^2) + 2\phi\ddot{\phi}\varpi . \tag{3.817}$$

The physical meaning of the relation (3.817) becomes clearer when we introduce some special form for the distribution function to relate σ explicitly with the number of stars per unit volume, N. Thus, if we assume that

$$\Psi(Q+\sigma) = e^{-Q-\sigma} , \tag{3.818}$$

we have the relation (eq. [1.93])

$$N = \frac{\text{constant}}{\phi^2\sqrt{\phi^2 + \kappa_2\varpi^2}} e^{-\sigma} . \tag{3.819}$$ [11]

From equation (3.819) we obtain

$$-\frac{\partial \log N}{\partial \varpi} = \frac{\partial \sigma}{\partial \varpi} + \frac{\kappa_2 \varpi}{\phi^2 + \kappa_2\varpi^2} . \tag{3.820}$$

Combining equations (3.817) and (3.820), we have

$$\varpi \frac{\partial \log N}{\partial \varpi} + \frac{\kappa_2\varpi^2}{\phi^2 + \kappa_2\varpi^2} = 2\phi^2(\Theta_0^2 - \Theta_c^2) - 2\phi\ddot{\phi}\varpi^2 , \tag{3.821}$$

or, using equations (3.806), we alternatively have

$$\varpi \frac{\partial \log N}{\partial \varpi} + \frac{b_\theta - a_\varpi}{b_\theta} = 2a_\varpi(\Theta_0^2 - \Theta_c^2) - 2\varpi^2\sqrt{a_\varpi}\frac{d^2}{dt^2}\sqrt{a_\varpi} . \tag{3.822}$$

In the form (3.822) we recognize equation (3.817) as essentially a relation between the density gradient at any point, the characteristics of the motions, and the extent of the deviation of the system from a steady state.

3.9. *Stellar systems formed by superposition.*—So far, we have considered only stellar systems which are characterized by one set

[11] This relation is valid for the "general case" of § 3.7. For the "special case" we have N = constant $/[\phi_1\phi_2(\phi_1^2 + \kappa_2\varpi^2)^{1/2}e^{\sigma}]$.

of functions and parameters. But, as we have indicated in § 1.5, the kinematics of stellar motions in our neighborhood requires us to consider the stars as being the members of one of two subsystems—the system of the "normal" stars or the system of the high-velocity stars. The question now arises as to whether there is any general *principle of superposition for stellar systems.* We shall consider this problem from the point of view of Liouville's theorem, i.e., from the point of view of solving the equation of continuity (3.303) for the distribution function Ψ, and more particularly on the basis of an appropriate generalization of our fundamental kinematical postulates I, II, and III (pp. 89–90).

Now the equation of continuity is linear in Ψ; and consequently, if Ψ_1 and Ψ_2 are two distinct solutions of equation (3.303), then $\Psi_1 + \Psi_2$ is also a solution. To be more specific, let

$$\Psi = \Psi_i(Q_i + \sigma_i) \qquad (i = 1, \ldots, n) \quad (3.901)$$

be n distinct solutions of the equation of continuity. In equation (3.901) the Q_i's are general quadratic forms in the variables $(U - U_i)$, $(V - V_i)$, and $(W - W_i)$; further, the coefficients of the various quadratic forms, the motions (U_i, V_i, W_i) and the σ_i's are all functions of x, y, z, and t. Then

$$\Psi = \sum_{i=1}^{n} \Psi_i \quad (3.902)$$

is also a solution of the equation of continuity, provided certain *conditions of consistency* are satisfied. The reason for the existence of such conditions is easily understood: According to equation (3.902), the stellar system can be regarded as consisting of n subsystems, described, respectively, by $\Psi_1, \Psi_2, \ldots, \Psi_n$. Since, however, the motions in each of the subsystems are governed by the same gravitational potential $\mathfrak{B}(x, y, z, t)$, it is clear that there should be certain restrictions in order that there be no inconsistency resulting from the superposition of the different subsystems. The problem which thus presents itself can be formulated as follows:

What are the circumstances under which we can regard a stellar system as consisting of two or more independent subsystems, each of which satisfies our fundamental kinematical postulates? It is a relatively simple matter to give a formally complete answer to this question. But the establishment of the necessary conditions is explicitly possible only after we have first solved the problem of the compatibility of the relations III (p. 93) for a single system. Conversely, for any particular solution of the integrability equations (3.448) and (3.450) the necessary conditions for the consistent superposition of two or more such systems can be easily written down. We shall illustrate the principles involved in carrying out such a superposition by considering some examples.

Let us first consider the superposition of two systems, each of which provides for the most general form $\mathfrak{B}$ in the two-dimensional case (§ 3.6). We accordingly assume that

$$\Psi = \Psi_1(Q_1 + \sigma_1) + \Psi_2(Q_2 + \sigma_2)\,, \tag{3.903}$$

where (cf. eqs. [3.805] and [3.807])

$$\left.\begin{aligned} Q_1 + \sigma_1 &= \phi_1^2(\Pi - \Pi_1)^2 + (\phi_1^2 + \kappa_{21}\varpi^2)(\Theta - \Theta_1)^2 + \sigma_1\,,\\ Q_2 + \sigma_2 &= \phi_2^2(\Pi - \Pi_2)^2 + (\phi_2^2 + \kappa_{22}\varpi^2)(\Theta - \Theta_2)^2 + \sigma_2\,, \end{aligned}\right\} \tag{3.904}$$

$$\left.\begin{aligned} \Pi_1 &= \frac{\dot\phi_1}{\phi_1}\varpi\,; \qquad \Theta_1 = -\frac{\beta_1\varpi}{\phi_1^2 + \kappa_{21}\varpi^2}\,,\\ \Pi_2 &= \frac{\dot\phi_2}{\phi_2}\varpi\,; \qquad \Theta_2 = -\frac{\beta_2\varpi}{\phi_2^2 + \kappa_{22}\varpi^2}\,, \end{aligned}\right\} \tag{3.905}$$

where ϕ_1 and ϕ_2 are functions of time and κ_{21}, κ_{22}, β_1, and β_2 are constants. Defined in this manner, Ψ_1 and Ψ_2 are both solutions of the two-dimensional equation of continuity, provided (cf. eqs. [3.664] and [3.673], also [3.814])

$$\left.\begin{aligned} 2\mathfrak{B} &= \frac{\beta_1^2\varpi^2}{\phi_1^2(\phi_1^2 + \kappa_{21}\varpi^2)} - \frac{\ddot\phi_1}{\phi_1}\varpi^2 + \frac{\sigma_1 + c_1}{\phi_1^2}\,,\\ 2\mathfrak{B} &= \frac{\beta_2^2\varpi^2}{\phi_2^2(\phi_2^2 + \kappa_{22}\varpi^2)} - \frac{\ddot\phi_2}{\phi_2}\varpi^2 + \frac{\sigma_2 + c_2}{\phi_2^2}\,, \end{aligned}\right\} \tag{3.906}$$

where c_1 and c_2 are constants. Again, the consideration of each of the two subsystems provides for $\mathfrak{B}$ expressions of the forms (eq. [3.664])

$$\left.\begin{aligned} \mathfrak{B} &= -\frac{\ddot\phi_1}{2\phi_1}\varpi^2 + \frac{1}{\phi_1^2}\mathfrak{B}_1\left(\frac{\varpi}{\phi_1}\right),\\ \mathfrak{B} &= -\frac{\ddot\phi_2}{2\phi_2}\varpi^2 + \frac{1}{\phi_2^2}\mathfrak{B}_2\left(\frac{\varpi}{\phi_2}\right). \end{aligned}\right\} \tag{3.907}$$

From the foregoing equations it follows that, first,

$$\frac{\phi_1}{\phi_2} = \text{constant} \tag{3.908}$$

and, second,

$$\frac{1}{\phi_1^2}\left(\sigma_1 + c_1 + \frac{\beta_1^2 \varpi^2}{\phi_1^2 + \kappa_{21}\varpi^2}\right) = \frac{1}{\phi_2^2}\left(\sigma_2 + c_2 + \frac{\beta_2^2 \varpi^2}{\phi_2^2 + \kappa_{22}\varpi^2}\right). \tag{3.909}$$

Equations (3.908) and (3.909) are therefore the conditions which should be satisfied in order that the motions in the two subsystems may be governed by the same gravitational potential $\mathfrak{V}$.

The physical meaning of the relation (3.909) becomes clearer if we consider the special case

$$\Psi_1 = e^{-(Q_1+\sigma_1)}\ ; \qquad \Psi_2 = e^{-(Q_2+\sigma_2)}\ . \tag{3.910}$$

Under these circumstances

$$N_1 = \frac{\pi}{\phi_1 \sqrt{\phi_1^2 + \kappa_{21}\varpi^2}}\, e^{-\sigma_1}\ ; \qquad N_2 = \frac{\pi}{\phi_2 \sqrt{\phi_2^2 + \kappa_{22}\varpi^2}}\, e^{-\sigma_2}\ , \tag{3.911}$$

where N_1 and N_2 are the number of stars per unit area in the two subsystems. Eliminating σ_1 and σ_2 between the relations (3.909) and (3.911), we readily obtain

$$\left.\begin{aligned} &\left[\frac{N_1}{\pi}\,\phi_1 \sqrt{\phi_1^2 + \kappa_{21}\varpi^2}\ e^{-c_1 - (\beta_1^2\varpi^2)/(\phi_1^2+\kappa_{21}\varpi^2)}\right]^{1/\phi_1^2} \\ =&\left[\frac{N_2}{\pi}\,\phi_2 \sqrt{\phi_2^2 + \kappa_{22}\varpi^2}\ e^{-c_2 - (\beta_2^2\varpi^2)/(\phi_2^2+\kappa_{22}\varpi^2)}\right]^{1/\phi_2^2} . \end{aligned}\right\} \tag{3.912}$$

So far we have considered only the conditions resulting from the superposition of two subsystems. The extension to more than two systems is, of course, immediate. It is further evident that for a stellar system formed by the superposition of n distinct subsystems there will be $(n - 1)$ conditions of the form (3.908) and further $(n - 1)$ conditions of the form (3.909).

The superposition of the axially symmetrical systems treated in § 3.7 can be considered on lines exactly similar to the preceding discussion of the two-dimensional case. Thus, for the "general case" of § 3.7, we conclude from equations (3.733), (3.741), and (3.814) that we are led to relations identical in forms with equations (3.908) and (3.909). For the "special case" (§ 3.7) the situation is somewhat different. According to equations (3.743) and (3.745), we can write

$$\mathfrak{V} = \mathfrak{V}_1(\varpi, t) + \mathfrak{V}_2(z, t)\,; \qquad \sigma = \sigma_1(\varpi, t) + \sigma_2(z, t)\,, \quad (3.913)$$

where

$$\mathfrak{V}_1 = -\frac{\ddot{\phi}_1}{2\phi_1}\varpi^2 + \frac{1}{\phi_1^2}\mathfrak{B}_1\left(\frac{\varpi}{\phi_1}\right); \qquad \mathfrak{V}_2 = -\frac{\ddot{\phi}_2}{2\phi_2}z^2 + \frac{1}{\phi_2^2}\mathfrak{B}_2\left(\frac{z}{\phi_2}\right) \quad (3.914)$$

and

$$\left.\begin{aligned} \sigma_1 &= -\frac{\beta^2\varpi^2}{\phi_1^2 + \kappa_2\varpi^2} + \phi_1\ddot{\phi}_1\varpi^2 + 2\phi_1^2\mathfrak{V}_1 + c_1\,, \\ \sigma_2 &= \phi_2\ddot{\phi}_2 z^2 + 2\phi_2^2\mathfrak{V}_2 + c_2\,, \end{aligned}\right\} \quad (3.915)$$

where c_1 and c_2 are constants. For the superposition of two systems the necessary conditions are (in an obvious notation)

$$\frac{\phi_{11}}{\phi_{12}} = \text{constant}\,; \qquad \frac{\phi_{21}}{\phi_{22}} = \text{constant}\,, \quad (3.916)$$

and

$$\left.\begin{aligned} \frac{1}{\phi_{11}^2}\left(\sigma_{11} + c_{11} + \frac{\beta_1^2\varpi^2}{\phi_{11}^2 + \kappa_{21}\varpi^2}\right) &= \frac{1}{\phi_{12}^2}\left(\sigma_{12} + c_{12} + \frac{\beta_2^2\varpi^2}{\phi_{12}^2 + \kappa_{22}\varpi^2}\right), \\ \frac{1}{\phi_{21}^2}(\sigma_{21} + c_{21}) &= \frac{1}{\phi_{22}^2}(\sigma_{22} + c_{22})\,. \end{aligned}\right\} \quad (3.917)$$

We shall not continue our discussion further to enunciate any general principle of superposition for stellar systems. As we have already indicated, such an enunciation will not serve any useful purpose, since the necessary conditions can be explicitly given only after the integrability conditions have been satisfied for a single system; and the examples we have considered are sufficiently illustrative of the general method which should be adopted in any particular case.

BIBLIOGRAPHICAL NOTES

§ 3.3.—The first general application of Liouville's theorem to stellar dynamics was made by Jeans:

1. J. H. Jeans, *M.N.*, **76,** 70, 1915 (see particularly pp. 78–81). Also—

2. J. H. Jeans, *Problems of Cosmogony and Stellar Dynamics*, pp. 229–236, Cambridge, England, 1919. In particular, Jeans explicitly drew at-

tention to the fact that an immediate consequence of Liouville's theorem to stellar dynamics is that the distribution function must be of the form

$$\Psi \equiv \Psi(I_1, I_2, \ldots, I_6) ,$$

where $I_1, \ldots, I_6$ are any six independent integrals of the equations of motion and where the quantity on the right-hand side stands for an arbitrary function of the arguments specified. This result has sometimes been quoted as "Jeans's theorem." However, in a somewhat different connection the theorem was also proved by Poincaré:

3. H. POINCARÉ, *Leçons sur les hypothèses cosmogoniques*, p. 100, Paris, 1911.

The importance of the case of axial symmetry for galactic dynamics has been particularly emphasized by Lindblad. His investigations have largely centered on the problem of the spiral structure in stellar systems, and complete references to his work will be found in the next chapter. But meantime we may note the following references, which are of more immediate interest in our present connection:

4. B. LINDBLAD, *Ark. f. mat., astr., och fysik* **19A,** No. 21, 1925; **19B,** No. 7, 1926; and **21A,** No. 3, 1928, and—

5. B. LINDBLAD, *Stockholms obs. ann.*, **12,** No. 4, 1936.

§ 3.4—We may briefly record here the history of the problem formulated in § 3.4. The problem is essentially one of determining the forces acting on a system which admits an integral of a certain special form. In our case the integral is required to be a general nonhomogeneous quadratic form in the velocities (other than the energy integral). In two dimensions under steady-state circumstances the problem has been known for a long time:

6. J. BERTRAND, *J. de math.*, Ser. I, **17,** 121, 1852. Also—

7. G. DARBOUX, *Arch. Néerland.*, Ser. II, **6,** 371, 1901, and—

8. E. T. WHITTAKER, *Analytical Dynamics*, p. 331, Cambridge, England, 1937. But it appears that the problem in three dimensions and under the circumstances of a nonsteady state has not been considered except in its astronomical context.

Before the existence of differential motions in the Galaxy was recognized, it was natural to suppose that the integral required is a *homogeneous* quadratic form in the velocities (except for a possible additive function of position). The problem then reduces to finding the circumstances under which a dynamical system will admit an integral of the form

$$au^2 + bv^2 + cw^2 + 2fvw + 2gwu + 2huv + \sigma ,$$

where a, b, c, f, g, h, and σ are functions of position only. This simplified problem was first considered by Eddington:

9. A. S. Eddington, *M.N.*, **76**, 37, 1915. But, unfortunately, Eddington's treatment was based on a fundamental fallacy. He argues in the following manner:

"At any point of the system the directions of the axes of the velocity ellipsoid determine three directions at right angles. The velocity ellipsoids thus define three orthogonal families of curves, each curve being traced by moving step by step always in the direction of an axis of the velocity ellipsoid at the point reached. These curves may be regarded as the intersections of a triply orthogonal family of surfaces, which we shall call the *principal velocity surfaces*. The axes of the velocity ellipsoid at any point are normals to the three principal velocity surfaces through that point."

On these premises Eddington goes on to prove that the "principal velocity surfaces must be confocal quadrics."

The fallacy in Eddington's argumentation is clear. It is true that we can regard the directions of the principal axes of the velocity ellipsoid at any given point as being tangential to three curves which intersect orthogonally at the point considered. But it is *not* generally true that we can regard these curves as the intersections of a triply orthogonal system of *surfaces*. Consequently, the notion of the principal velocity surfaces introduces severe restrictions on the problem, which are wholly irrelevant and certainly unnecessary.

The same problem was also considered by Jeans independently of Eddington:

10. J. H. Jeans, *M.N.*, **76**, 70, 1915 (see particularly pp. 70–78). But again there are some unfortunate errors which vitiate Jeans's treatment. We may note in particular that the general solution for the coefficients of the velocity ellipsoid contains twenty constants of integration and not fifteen as Jeans finds.

With the discovery of galactic rotation, the consideration of the more general case when the quadratic form is nonhomogeneous became necessary. But the general problem was not immediately formulated. A number of special problems were, however, considered. Thus, Oort discussed the case in which the gravitational potential was characterized by an axial symmetry and under circumstances of a steady state. He further restricted himself to integrals of the form

$$a\Pi^2 + b(\Theta - \Theta_0)^2 + cZ^2 + 2f(\Theta - \Theta_0)Z + 2gZ\Pi + 2h\Pi(\Theta - \Theta_0) + \sigma .$$

11. J. H. OORT, *B.A.N.*, **4**, 269, 1928 (particularly pp. 274–80).

More recently, the general two-dimensional problem under the circumstances of a steady state and circular symmetry of $\mathfrak{V}$ has been considered by several authors:

12. S. W. SHIVESHWARKAR, *M.N.*, **95**, 655, 1935.
13. B. LINDBLAD, *M.N.*, **96**, 69, 1935.
14. O. HECKMANN, *M.N.*, **96**, 67, 1935.
15. G. L. CLARK, *M.N.*, **97**, 182, 1937.
16. B. LINDBLAD, *M.N.*, **97**, 642, 1937.

In its completely general form and under circumstances of a nonsteady state the problem was first formulated by Chandrasekhar, who also made a systematic study of the methods for obtaining the complete solution.

17. S. CHANDRASEKHAR, *Ap. J.*, **90**, 1–155, 1939 and—
18. S. CHANDRASEKHAR, *Ap. J.*, **92**, 441–642, 1940.

The rest of chapter iv (§§ 3.4–3.9) deals almost exclusively with the methods and results derived from the foregoing two papers. However, it has been found possible to simplify the analysis and the argumentation quite considerably. Also, a more direct approach to the central problems has been made in the text than in the original investigations. However, considerations of space have required a drastic restriction of the problems considered in the text. But we may refer to one general problem which has considerable practical importance.

It is clear that in any given small region of space in the neighborhood of a point (x_0, y_0, z_0) we may express the gravitational potential $\mathfrak{V}$ in the form of a Taylor expansion

$$\begin{aligned}\mathfrak{V}(x, y, z) = \mathfrak{V}(x_0, y_0, z_0) &+ \left(\frac{\partial \mathfrak{V}}{\partial x}\right)_0 (x - x_0) + \left(\frac{\partial \mathfrak{V}}{\partial y}\right)_0 (y - y_0) \\ &+ \left(\frac{\partial \mathfrak{V}}{\partial z}\right)_0 (z - z_0) + \frac{1}{2}\left\{\left(\frac{\partial^2 \mathfrak{V}}{\partial x^2}\right)_0 (x - x_0)^2 + \left(\frac{\partial^2 \mathfrak{V}}{\partial y^2}\right)_0 (y - y_0)^2\right. \\ &+ \left(\frac{\partial^2 \mathfrak{V}}{\partial z^2}\right)_0 (z - z_0)^2 + \left(\frac{\partial^2 \mathfrak{V}}{\partial x \partial y}\right)_0 (x - x_0)(y - y_0) \\ &+ \left(\frac{\partial^2 \mathfrak{V}}{\partial y \partial z}\right)_0 (y - y_0)(z - z_0) \\ &\left.+ \left(\frac{\partial^2 \mathfrak{V}}{\partial z \partial x}\right)_0 (z - z_0)(x - x_0)\right\} + \dots .\end{aligned}$$

where all the partial derivatives of $\mathfrak{V}$ (evaluated at x_0, y_0, z_0) and $\mathfrak{V}(x_0, y_0, z_0)$ may be expected to be functions of time. By a proper choice of the origin and the orientation of our co-ordinate system we can simplify the foregoing expression to the form

$$\mathfrak{V} = \mathfrak{V}_0(t) + \tfrac{1}{2}\{a_1(t)\,x^2 + a_2(t)\,y^2 + a_3(t)\,z^2\} + \ldots,$$

where $\mathfrak{V}_0$, a_1, a_2, and a_3 are functions of time. We can now proceed to discuss the integrability conditions (3.448) and (3.450), when $\mathfrak{V}$ has the form just found. This discussion has been carried out by CHANDRASEKHAR (ref. 18, see particularly pp. 523–573) and the results have some further applications to problems concerning the evolution of ellipsoidal stellar systems. In this connection we may also refer to the two following papers:

19. O. HECKMANN and H. STRASSL, *Göttingen Veröff.*, No. 41, 1934, and—

20. O. HECKMANN and H. STRASSL, *Göttingen Veröff.*, No. 43, 1935.

CHAPTER IV

GENERAL DYNAMICS OF STELLAR SYSTEMS: SPIRAL STRUCTURE

In this chapter we shall continue to discuss methods of stellar dynamics based on the assumption that the motions of the individual stars in a stellar system can be expressed in terms of a gravitational potential $\mathfrak{B}(x, y, z, t)$. As we have already shown in chapter iii, under these circumstances we can at once write down a partial differential equation for the distribution function $\Psi(x, y, z; U, V, W; t)$. The further discussion of this equation, particularly with a view to discovering the most general forms for the potential and the density distributions which are consistent with our fundamental kinematical postulates, will provide one method of approach to the *general dynamics* of stellar systems. While this method of approach will be satisfactory for obtaining information concerning the implications of the specified kinematical postulates, it yet eliminates any direct appeal to the actual character of the orbits described by the individual stars. On the other hand, it can well be argued that the state of motions obtaining in a stellar system must, in the final analysis, depend on the nature of the orbits described by the stars. This would be particularly important for the consideration of systems which are on the "verge" of stability. For this reason it would be useful to establish some general theorems on the motions of stars in given potential fields. While it would be difficult to specify $\mathfrak{B}$ without, at the same time, losing some degree of generality, it is clear that the most important case for stellar dynamics is that in which $\mathfrak{B}$ is characterized by both an axis and a plane of symmetry.

In developing the general dynamics of stellar systems, we shall therefore be primarily concerned with the following two problems: First, an investigation into the most general type of stellar system which is consistent with the notion of differential motions and, second, the nature of the orbits in a field $\mathfrak{B}$ characterized by both an axis and a plane of symmetry. As we shall see, the consideration of these two problems gives us some insight into the dynamics of extragalactic systems.

4.1. *Stellar systems described by a spherical distribution of the residual velocities.*—To determine the most general type of potential fields consistent with our fundamental kinematical postulates, we first notice that, according to the integrability conditions (3.448) and (3.450), our freedom to specify $\mathfrak{V}$ is restricted by our solution for the coefficients of the velocity ellipsoid. More particularly, the greater the degree of arbitrariness we wish to have in the specification of the potential $\mathfrak{V}$, the less, in general, is the arbitrariness we are left with in the specification of the velocity ellipsoid, and conversely. Consequently, it would appear that we should impose the maximum restrictions on the coefficients of the velocity ellipsoid in order that we may have the maximum generality for the form of $\mathfrak{V}(x, y, z, t)$. Since we cannot restrict the form of the velocity ellipsoid to a greater extent than to suppose that it is a sphere, the problem which suggests itself is the following:

What are the characteristics of a stellar system which is described by a spherical distribution of the residual velocities?

Now, a spherical distribution of the residual velocities implies that the distribution function Ψ has the form

$$\Psi \equiv \Psi\{a[(U-U_0)^2+(V-V_0)^2+(W-W_0)^2]+\sigma\}, \quad (4.101)$$

where a, U_0, V_0, W_0, and σ are, in the first instance, arbitrary functions of x, y, z, and t. On the other hand, according to our general solution for the coefficients of the velocity ellipsoid (eqs. [3.423], [3.429], and [3.430]), it follows that

$$a \equiv \kappa(t), \quad (4.102)$$

where, as the notation implies, κ is a function of time only. Again, according to equations (3.409), (3.439), and (3.443), we have

$$\left.\begin{aligned} \Delta_1 &= \kappa U_0 = \frac{1}{2}\frac{d\kappa}{dt}x+\beta_3 y-\beta_2 z+\delta_1, \\ \Delta_2 &= \kappa V_0 = \frac{1}{2}\frac{d\kappa}{dt}y+\beta_1 z-\beta_3 x+\delta_2, \\ \Delta_3 &= \kappa W_0 = \frac{1}{2}\frac{d\kappa}{dt}z+\beta_2 x-\beta_1 y+\delta_3, \end{aligned}\right\} \quad (4.103)$$

where β_1, β_2, β_3, δ_1, δ_2, and δ_3 are all functions of time only. We can write (4.103) in the form of a single vector equation, as

$$\boldsymbol{\Delta} = \frac{1}{2}\frac{d\kappa}{dt}\boldsymbol{r} + \boldsymbol{r} \times \boldsymbol{\beta} + \boldsymbol{\delta}\,, \tag{4.104}$$

where $\boldsymbol{\Delta}$, $\boldsymbol{\beta}$, and $\boldsymbol{\delta}$ denote the vectors $(\Delta_1, \Delta_2, \Delta_3)$, $(\beta_1, \beta_2, \beta_3)$, and $(\delta_1, \delta_2, \delta_3)$, respectively. It may be further noted that $\boldsymbol{\Delta}$ is proportional to the vector (U_0, V_0, W_0) defining the motion of the local centroid. Finally, equations (3.448) and (3.450) now reduce to

$$\kappa \operatorname{grad} \mathfrak{B} + \frac{\partial \boldsymbol{\Delta}}{\partial t} = -\tfrac{1}{2}\operatorname{grad} \chi \tag{4.105}$$

and

$$\boldsymbol{\Delta} \cdot \operatorname{grad} \mathfrak{B} = \frac{1}{2}\frac{\partial \chi}{\partial t}\,, \tag{4.106}$$

where χ stands for (cf. eq. [3.410])

$$-\chi = \mathfrak{Q}_0 + \sigma = \kappa\,(U_0^2 + V_0^2 + W_0^2) + \sigma\,. \tag{4.107}$$

Taking the curl of equation (4.105), we obtain

$$\frac{\partial}{\partial t}(\operatorname{curl} \boldsymbol{\Delta}) = 0\,. \tag{4.108}$$

But, according to equation (4.104),

$$\operatorname{curl} \boldsymbol{\Delta} = -2\boldsymbol{\beta}\,. \tag{4.109}$$

Hence,

$$\frac{d\boldsymbol{\beta}}{dt} = 0\,; \tag{4.110}$$

in other words, $\boldsymbol{\beta}$ is a *constant vector*.

Consider next the integrability condition resulting from equations (4.105) and (4.106). We have

$$\operatorname{grad}(\boldsymbol{\Delta} \cdot \operatorname{grad} \mathfrak{B}) + \frac{\partial}{\partial t}(\kappa \operatorname{grad} \mathfrak{B}) + \frac{\partial^2 \boldsymbol{\Delta}}{\partial t^2} = 0\,. \tag{4.111}$$

Substituting for $\boldsymbol{\Delta}$ according to equation (4.104) in the foregoing equation and remembering that $\boldsymbol{\beta}$ is a constant vector, we have

$$\operatorname{grad}(\boldsymbol{\Delta} \cdot \operatorname{grad} \mathfrak{B}) + \frac{\partial}{\partial t}(\kappa \operatorname{grad} \mathfrak{B}) + \frac{1}{2}\frac{d^3\kappa}{dt^3}\boldsymbol{r} + \frac{d^2\boldsymbol{\delta}}{dt^2} = 0\,. \tag{4.112}$$

It is readily verified that equation (4.112) is equivalent to

$$\operatorname{grad}\left\{\boldsymbol{\Delta}\cdot\operatorname{grad}\mathfrak{B}+\frac{\partial}{\partial t}(\kappa\mathfrak{B})+\frac{1}{4}\frac{d^3\kappa}{dt^3}r^2+\frac{d^2\boldsymbol{\delta}}{dt^2}\cdot\boldsymbol{r}\right\}=0\,. \tag{4.113}$$

Hence,

$$\boldsymbol{\Delta}\cdot\operatorname{grad}\mathfrak{B}+\frac{\partial}{\partial t}(\kappa\mathfrak{B})+\frac{1}{4}\frac{d^3\kappa}{dt^3}r^2+\frac{d^2\boldsymbol{\delta}}{dt^2}\cdot\boldsymbol{r}=G(t)\,, \tag{4.114}$$

where $G(t)$ is an arbitrary function of time only.

In considering equation (4.114), there is no loss of generality if we set $G(t) = 0$. For, if we write

$$\mathfrak{B}=\mathfrak{B}_1(x,y,z,t)+\frac{1}{\kappa}\int^t G(t)\,dt\,, \tag{4.115}$$

it readily follows that $\mathfrak{B}_1$ satisfies the differential equation

$$\boldsymbol{\Delta}\cdot\operatorname{grad}\mathfrak{B}+\frac{\partial}{\partial t}(\kappa\mathfrak{B})+\frac{1}{4}\frac{d^3\kappa}{dt^3}r^2+\frac{d^2\boldsymbol{\delta}}{dt^2}\cdot\boldsymbol{r}=0\,. \tag{4.116}$$

Substituting for $\boldsymbol{\Delta}$ according to equation (4.104), equation (4.116) takes explicitly the form

$$\left.\begin{aligned}\left(\frac{1}{2}\frac{d\kappa}{dt}\boldsymbol{r}+\boldsymbol{r}\times\boldsymbol{\beta}+\boldsymbol{\delta}\right)\cdot\operatorname{grad}\mathfrak{B}+\frac{\partial}{\partial t}(\kappa\mathfrak{B})+\frac{1}{4}\frac{d^3\kappa}{dt^3}r^2&\\+\frac{d^2\boldsymbol{\delta}}{dt^2}\cdot\boldsymbol{r}=0\,.&\end{aligned}\right\} \tag{4.117}$$

Equation (4.117) is a linear nonhomogeneous partial differential equation for $\mathfrak{B}$, and it is on this equation that the solution to our problem hinges.

i) *Solution of the differential equation for* $\mathfrak{B}$.—Since $\boldsymbol{\beta}$ is a constant vector, we can choose the z-axis of our co-ordinate system to lie along the $\boldsymbol{\beta}$-direction. With this choice of the orientation of the co-ordinate system, the vector $\boldsymbol{\beta}$ has the form $(0, 0, \beta)$, and equation (4.117) reduces to

$$\left.\begin{aligned}&\left(\frac{1}{2}\frac{d\kappa}{dt}x+\beta y+\delta_1\right)\frac{\partial F}{\partial x}+\left(\frac{1}{2}\frac{d\kappa}{dt}y-\beta x+\delta_2\right)\frac{\partial F}{\partial y}\\&\quad+\left(\frac{1}{2}\frac{d\kappa}{dt}z+\delta_3\right)\frac{\partial F}{\partial z}+\kappa\frac{\partial F}{\partial t}+\tfrac{1}{4}(x^2+y^2+z^2)\kappa\frac{d^3\kappa}{dt^3}\\&\quad+(x\ddot{\delta}_1+y\ddot{\delta}_2+z\ddot{\delta}_3)\kappa=0\end{aligned}\right\} \tag{4.118}$$

where we have written

$$\kappa \mathfrak{V} = F . \tag{4.119}$$

Equation (4.118) is seen to be a linear nonhomogeneous partial differential equation for F, and, following the standard procedure for solving such equations, we express the general solution of equation (4.118) in terms of an equation not solved for F:

$$\Omega = \Omega(F, x, y, z, t) = 0 , \tag{4.120}$$

where the function Ω of the five variables F, x, y, z, and t is now the unknown function. Equation (4.118) now becomes a homogeneous equation for Ω (cf. the similar transformation of eq. [3.720]):

$$\left.\begin{aligned}&\left(\frac{1}{2}\frac{d\kappa}{dt}x + \beta y + \delta_1\right)\frac{\partial \Omega}{\partial x} + \left(\frac{1}{2}\frac{d\kappa}{dt}y - \beta x + \delta_2\right)\frac{\partial \Omega}{\partial y}\\ &\quad + \left(\frac{1}{2}\frac{d\kappa}{dt}z + \delta_3\right)\frac{\partial \Omega}{\partial z} + \kappa\frac{\partial \Omega}{\partial t} - \left\{\tfrac{1}{4}(x^2+y^2+z^2)\,\kappa\frac{d^3\kappa}{dt^3}\right.\\ &\quad \left. + (x\ddot{\delta}_1 + y\ddot{\delta}_2 + z\ddot{\delta}_3)\,\kappa\right\}\frac{\partial \Omega}{\partial F} = 0 .\end{aligned}\right\} \tag{4.121}$$

To solve equation (4.121), we first write down the appropriate subsidiary equations, which are

$$\left.\begin{aligned}&\frac{dx}{\frac{1}{2}\frac{d\kappa}{dt}x + \beta y + \delta_1} = \frac{dy}{\frac{1}{2}\frac{d\kappa}{dt}y - \beta x + \delta_2} = \frac{dz}{\frac{1}{2}\frac{d\kappa}{dt}z + \delta_3} = \frac{dt}{\kappa}\\ &\qquad = -\frac{dF}{\tfrac{1}{4}(x^2+y^2+z^2)\,\kappa\frac{d^3\kappa}{dt^3} + \kappa(x\ddot{\delta}_1 + y\ddot{\delta}_2 + z\ddot{\delta}_3)} .\end{aligned}\right\} \tag{4.122}$$

These equations can be expressed alternatively as

$$\left.\begin{aligned}\kappa\frac{dx}{dt} &= \frac{1}{2}\frac{d\kappa}{dt}x + \beta y + \delta_1 ,\\ \kappa\frac{dy}{dt} &= \frac{1}{2}\frac{d\kappa}{dt}y - \beta x + \delta_2 ,\\ \kappa\frac{dz}{dt} &= \frac{1}{2}\frac{d\kappa}{dt}z + \delta_3 ,\end{aligned}\right\} \tag{4.123}$$

and

$$\frac{dF}{dt} + \tfrac{1}{4}(x^2+y^2+z^2)\frac{d^3\kappa}{dt^3} + (x\ddot{\delta}_1 + y\ddot{\delta}_2 + z\ddot{\delta}_3) = 0 . \tag{4.124}$$

We shall first consider the equations (4.123). We notice that these equations can be re-written more simply in the forms

$$\left.\begin{aligned} \kappa^{3/2}\frac{d}{dt}\left(\frac{x}{\sqrt{\kappa}}\right) &= \beta y + \delta_1 , \\ \kappa^{3/2}\frac{d}{dt}\left(\frac{y}{\sqrt{\kappa}}\right) &= -\beta x + \delta_2 , \\ \kappa^{3/2}\frac{d}{dt}\left(\frac{z}{\sqrt{\kappa}}\right) &= \delta_3 . \end{aligned}\right\} \tag{4.125}$$

The following change of variables now suggests itself:

$$\xi = \frac{x}{\phi} ; \qquad \eta = \frac{y}{\phi} ; \qquad \zeta = \frac{z}{\phi} ; \qquad \kappa = \phi^2 . \tag{4.126}$$

In terms of these variables, equations (4.125) reduce to

$$\phi^2 \frac{d\xi}{dt} = \beta\eta + \frac{\delta_1}{\phi} , \qquad \phi^2 \frac{d\eta}{dt} = -\beta\xi + \frac{\delta_2}{\phi} , \qquad \phi^2 \frac{d\zeta}{dt} = \frac{\delta_3}{\phi} . \tag{4.127}$$

We shall now introduce a new independent variable ι, defined according to the relation

$$d\iota = \frac{dt}{\phi^2} ; \qquad \iota = \int_{t_0}^{t} \frac{dt}{\phi^2} , \tag{4.128}$$

where t_0 corresponds to an appropriately chosen origin of time. Equations (4.127) now take the simplified forms

$$\frac{d\xi}{d\iota} = \beta\eta + \frac{\delta_1}{\phi} ; \qquad \frac{d\eta}{d\iota} = -\beta\xi + \frac{\delta_2}{\phi} , \tag{4.129}$$

and

$$\frac{d\zeta}{d\iota} = \frac{\delta_3}{\phi} . \tag{4.130}$$

Equations (4.129) can be solved by the method of the variation of the parameters. The solution of the associated homogeneous system

$$\frac{d\xi}{d\iota} = \beta\eta ; \qquad \frac{d\eta}{d\iota} = -\beta\xi , \tag{4.131}$$

is

$$\left.\begin{aligned} \xi &= A \cos\beta\iota + B \sin\beta\iota , \\ \eta &= -A \sin\beta\iota + B \cos\beta\iota , \end{aligned}\right\} \tag{4.132}$$

where A and B are constants. For solving the nonhomogeneous system (4.129), we assume that the solution is of the form (4.132), where A and B are now no longer regarded as constants but as functions of ι. Introducing equations (4.132) in equations (4.129), we obtain

$$\left.\begin{aligned} \frac{dA}{d\iota}\cos\beta\iota+\frac{dB}{d\iota}\sin\beta\iota=\frac{\delta_1}{\phi}\,; \\ -\frac{dA}{d\iota}\sin\beta\iota+\frac{dB}{d\iota}\cos\beta\iota=\frac{\delta_2}{\phi}\,, \end{aligned}\right\} \tag{4.133}$$

or, solving for $dA/d\iota$ and $dB/d\iota$, we have

$$\left.\begin{aligned} \frac{dA}{d\iota}=\frac{1}{\phi}\,(\delta_1\cos\beta\iota-\delta_2\sin\beta\iota)\,, \\ \frac{dB}{d\iota}=\frac{1}{\phi}\,(\delta_1\sin\beta\iota+\delta_2\cos\beta\iota)\,. \end{aligned}\right\} \tag{4.134}$$

Integrating the foregoing equations, we have

$$A=A_0+J_1\,;\qquad B=B_0+J_2\,, \tag{4.135}$$

where A_0 and B_0 are arbitrary constants and

$$\left.\begin{aligned} J_1=\int\frac{1}{\phi}\,(\delta_1\cos\beta\iota-\delta_2\sin\beta\iota)\,d\iota\,, \\ J_2=\int\frac{1}{\phi}\,(\delta_1\sin\beta\iota+\delta_2\cos\beta\iota)\,d\iota\,. \end{aligned}\right\} \tag{4.136}$$

In equations (4.136), the integrals on the right-hand side are indefinite integrals. Combining equations (4.132) and (4.135), we obtain the required solutions for ξ and η. We have

$$\left.\begin{aligned} \xi-\xi_0=A_0\cos\beta\iota+B_0\sin\beta\iota\,, \\ \eta-\eta_0=-A_0\sin\beta\iota+B_0\cos\beta\iota\,, \end{aligned}\right\} \tag{4.137}$$

where

$$\left.\begin{aligned} \xi_0=J_1\cos\beta\iota+J_2\sin\beta\iota\,, \\ \eta_0=-J_1\sin\beta\iota+J_2\cos\beta\iota\,. \end{aligned}\right\} \tag{4.138}$$

From equations (4.137) we derive two first integrals of the subsidiary equations (4.122). According to equations (4.137), we clearly have

$$(\xi-\xi_0)^2+(\eta-\eta_0)^2=A_0^2+B_0^2=\text{constant}\,, \tag{4.139}$$

which is one first integral. Again, according to equations (4.137), we have

$$\frac{\eta-\eta_0}{\xi-\xi_0}=\frac{-A_0\sin\beta\iota+B_0\cos\beta\iota}{A_0\cos\beta\iota+B_0\sin\beta\iota}\,, \tag{4.140}$$

or, alternatively, as

$$\frac{\eta-\eta_0}{\xi-\xi_0}=\frac{\tan\Sigma-\tan\beta\iota}{1+\tan\Sigma\tan\beta\iota}=\tan(\Sigma-\beta\iota)\,, \tag{4.141}$$

where

$$\tan\Sigma=\frac{B_0}{A_0}=\text{constant}\,. \tag{4.142}$$

From equation (4.141) it now follows that

$$\vartheta+\beta\iota=\text{constant}\,, \tag{4.143}$$

where

$$\vartheta=\tan^{-1}\frac{\eta-\eta_0}{\xi-\xi_0}\,. \tag{4.144}$$

Equation (4.143) is another first integral of the subsidiary equations.

Consider, next, equation (4.130). This equation admits of immediate integration, and we have

$$\zeta-\zeta_0=\text{constant}\,, \tag{4.145}$$

where

$$\zeta_0=\int\frac{\delta_3}{\phi}\,d\iota\,. \tag{4.146}$$

Finally, to integrate equation (4.124), we proceed as follows: Introducing the variables ξ, η, and ζ (cf. eq. [4.126]), this equation becomes

$$\frac{dF}{dt}+\tfrac{1}{4}(\xi^2+\eta^2+\zeta^2)\phi^2\frac{d^3}{dt^3}\phi^2+\phi(\xi\ddot{\delta}_1+\eta\ddot{\delta}_2+\zeta\ddot{\delta}_3)=0\,. \tag{4.147}$$

Since

$$\phi^2\frac{d^3}{dt^3}\phi^2=\frac{d}{dt}\left(\phi^2\frac{d^2}{dt^2}\phi^2-\frac{1}{2}\left[\frac{d}{dt}\phi^2\right]^2\right)=2\frac{d}{dt}(\phi^3\ddot{\phi}) \tag{4.148}$$

and remembering that $dt=\phi^2 d\iota$ (eq. [4.128]), we can re-write equation (4.147) in the form

$$\frac{dF}{d\iota}+\tfrac{1}{2}(\xi^2+\eta^2+\zeta^2)\frac{d}{d\iota}(\phi^3\ddot{\phi})+\phi^3(\xi\ddot{\delta}_1+\eta\ddot{\delta}_2+\zeta\ddot{\delta}_3)=0\,. \tag{4.149}$$

We have

$$\frac{d}{dt}=\frac{1}{\phi^2}\frac{d}{d\iota}\,;\qquad \frac{d^2}{dt^2}=\frac{1}{\phi^4}\frac{d^2}{d\iota^2}-\frac{2}{\phi^3}\dot{\phi}\frac{d}{d\iota}\,. \tag{4.150}$$

On the other hand, since we can write

$$\ddot{\delta}_1=\frac{d^2}{dt^2}\left(\phi\frac{\delta_1}{\phi}\right)=\phi\frac{d^2}{dt^2}\left(\frac{\delta_1}{\phi}\right)+2\dot{\phi}\frac{d}{dt}\left(\frac{\delta_1}{\phi}\right)+\ddot{\phi}\frac{\delta_1}{\phi}\,, \tag{4.151}$$

we have (according to eqs. [4.150])

$$\ddot{\delta}_1 = \frac{1}{\phi^3}\frac{d^2}{d\iota^2}\left(\frac{\delta_1}{\phi}\right) + \ddot{\phi}\,\frac{\delta_1}{\phi}\,. \tag{4.152}$$

We have similar relations for $\ddot{\delta}_2$ and $\ddot{\delta}_3$. Introducing these expressions for $\ddot{\delta}_1$, $\ddot{\delta}_2$, and $\ddot{\delta}_3$ into equation (4.149), we have

$$\left.\begin{aligned} &\frac{dF}{d\iota} + \tfrac{1}{2}(\xi^2+\eta^2+\zeta^2)\frac{d}{d\iota}(\phi^3\ddot{\phi}) + \phi^3\ddot{\phi}\left(\xi\,\frac{\delta_1}{\phi} + \eta\,\frac{\delta_2}{\phi} + \zeta\,\frac{\delta_3}{\phi}\right) \\ &\qquad + \xi\,\frac{d^2}{d\iota^2}\left(\frac{\delta_1}{\phi}\right) + \eta\,\frac{d^2}{d\iota^2}\left(\frac{\delta_2}{\phi}\right) + \zeta\,\frac{d^2}{d\iota^2}\left(\frac{\delta_3}{\phi}\right) = 0\,. \end{aligned}\right\} \tag{4.153}$$

From the equations (4.129) and (4.130) we readily find that

$$\xi\,\frac{\delta_1}{\phi} + \eta\,\frac{\delta_2}{\phi} + \zeta\,\frac{\delta_3}{\phi} = \frac{1}{2}\frac{d}{d\iota}(\xi^2+\eta^2+\zeta^2)\,. \tag{4.154}$$

Combining equations (4.153) and (4.154), we have

$$\left.\begin{aligned} &\frac{dF}{d\iota} + \frac{1}{2}\frac{d}{d\iota}([\xi^2+\eta^2+\zeta^2]\,\phi^3\ddot{\phi}) + \xi\,\frac{d^2}{d\iota^2}\left(\frac{\delta_1}{\phi}\right) \\ &\qquad + \eta\,\frac{d^2}{d\iota^2}\left(\frac{\delta_2}{\phi}\right) + \zeta\,\frac{d^2}{d\iota^2}\left(\frac{\delta_3}{\phi}\right) = 0\,. \end{aligned}\right\} \tag{4.155}$$

Again, using equations (4.129), we find

$$\left.\begin{aligned} &\xi\,\frac{d^2}{d\iota^2}\left(\frac{\delta_1}{\phi}\right) + \eta\,\frac{d^2}{d\iota^2}\left(\frac{\delta_2}{\phi}\right) \\ &= \xi\,\frac{d^2}{d\iota^2}\left(\frac{d\xi}{d\iota} - \beta\eta\right) + \eta\,\frac{d^2}{d\iota^2}\left(\frac{d\eta}{d\iota} + \beta\xi\right) \\ &= \xi\,\frac{d^3\xi}{d\iota^3} + \eta\,\frac{d^3\eta}{d\iota^3} - \beta\left(\xi\,\frac{d^2\eta}{d\iota^2} - \eta\,\frac{d^2\xi}{d\iota^2}\right) \\ &= \frac{d}{d\iota}\left\{\xi\,\frac{d^2\xi}{d\iota^2} - \frac{1}{2}\left(\frac{d\xi}{d\iota}\right)^2 + \eta\,\frac{d^2\eta}{d\iota^2} - \frac{1}{2}\left(\frac{d\eta}{d\iota}\right)^2 - \beta\xi\,\frac{d\eta}{d\iota}\right. \\ &\qquad\qquad \left. + \beta\eta\,\frac{d\xi}{d\iota}\right\} \\ &= \frac{d}{d\iota}\left\{\xi\,\frac{d}{d\iota}\left(\frac{d\xi}{d\iota} - \beta\eta\right) + \eta\,\frac{d}{d\iota}\left(\frac{d\eta}{d\iota} + \beta\xi\right) - \frac{1}{2}\left(\frac{d\xi}{d\iota}\right)^2\right. \\ &\qquad\qquad \left. - \frac{1}{2}\left(\frac{d\eta}{d\iota}\right)^2\right\} \\ &= \frac{d}{d\iota}\left\{\xi\,\frac{d}{d\iota}\left(\frac{\delta_1}{\phi}\right) + \eta\,\frac{d}{d\iota}\left(\frac{\delta_2}{\phi}\right) - \frac{1}{2}\left(\beta\eta + \frac{\delta_1}{\phi}\right)^2\right. \\ &\qquad\qquad \left. - \frac{1}{2}\left(-\beta\xi + \frac{\delta_2}{\phi}\right)^2\right\}. \end{aligned}\right\} \tag{4.156}$$

Similarly, we find that

$$\left.\begin{aligned}\zeta\frac{d^2}{d\iota^2}\left(\frac{\delta_3}{\phi}\right)=\zeta\frac{d^3\zeta}{d\iota^3}&=\frac{d}{d\iota}\left\{\zeta\frac{d^2\zeta}{d\iota^2}-\frac{1}{2}\left(\frac{d\zeta}{d\iota}\right)^2\right\}\\&=\frac{d}{d\iota}\left\{\zeta\frac{d}{d\iota}\left(\frac{\delta_3}{\phi}\right)-\frac{1}{2}\left(\frac{\delta_3}{\phi}\right)^2\right\}.\end{aligned}\right\}\quad(4.157)$$

Combining equations (4.155), (4.156), and (4.157), we have

$$\left.\begin{aligned}\frac{dF}{d\iota}+\frac{1}{2}\frac{d}{d\iota}\{(\xi^2+\eta^2+\zeta^2)\phi^3\ddot{\phi}\}+\frac{d}{d\iota}\Big\{\xi\frac{d}{d\iota}\left(\frac{\delta_1}{\phi}\right)+\eta\frac{d}{d\iota}\left(\frac{\delta_2}{\phi}\right)&\\+\zeta\frac{d}{d\iota}\left(\frac{\delta_3}{\phi}\right)-\frac{1}{2}\left(\beta\eta+\frac{\delta_1}{\phi}\right)^2&\\-\frac{1}{2}\left(-\beta\xi+\frac{\delta_2}{\phi}\right)^2-\frac{1}{2}\left(\frac{\delta_3}{\phi}\right)^2\Big\}=0\,.&\end{aligned}\right\}\quad(4.158)$$

Equation (4.158) can be integrated as it stands, and we have

$$\left.\begin{aligned}F+\tfrac{1}{2}(\xi^2+\eta^2+\zeta^2)\phi^3\ddot{\phi}+\xi\frac{d}{d\iota}\left(\frac{\delta_1}{\phi}\right)+\eta\frac{d}{d\iota}\left(\frac{\delta_2}{\phi}\right)+\zeta\frac{d}{d\iota}\left(\frac{\delta_3}{\phi}\right)&\\-\frac{1}{2}\left(\beta\eta+\frac{\delta_1}{\phi}\right)^2-\frac{1}{2}\left(-\beta\xi+\frac{\delta_2}{\phi}\right)^2-\frac{1}{2}\left(\frac{\delta_3}{\phi}\right)^2=\text{constant}\,.&\end{aligned}\right\}\quad(4.159)$$

Equation (4.159) can be expressed more conveniently in terms of the vectors

$$\boldsymbol{\rho}=(\xi,\eta,\zeta)\,;\qquad\boldsymbol{\delta}=(\delta_1,\delta_2,\delta_3)\,;\qquad\boldsymbol{\beta}=(0,0,\beta)\,.\quad(4.160)$$ [1]

We readily verify that equation (4.159) is equivalent to

$$F+\tfrac{1}{2}\phi^3\ddot{\phi}|\boldsymbol{\rho}|^2+\boldsymbol{\rho}\cdot\frac{d}{d\iota}\left(\frac{\boldsymbol{\delta}}{\phi}\right)-\frac{1}{2}\left|\boldsymbol{\rho}\times\boldsymbol{\beta}+\frac{\boldsymbol{\delta}}{\phi}\right|^2=\text{constant}\,.\quad(4.161)$$

Equations (4.139), (4.143), (4.145), and (4.161) represent the general solution of the subsidiary equations (4.122) and define the necessary first integrals. Consequently, the general solution of the partial differential equation (4.121) can be written as

$$\left.\begin{aligned}(F,\xi,\eta,\zeta,\iota)\equiv\Omega\Big\{F+\tfrac{1}{2}\phi^3\ddot{\phi}|\boldsymbol{\rho}|^2+\boldsymbol{\rho}\cdot\frac{d}{d\iota}\left(\frac{\boldsymbol{\delta}}{\phi}\right)-\frac{1}{2}\left|\boldsymbol{\rho}\times\boldsymbol{\beta}+\frac{\boldsymbol{\delta}}{\phi}\right|^2;&\\(\xi-\xi_0)^2+(\eta-\eta_0)^2\,;\ \tan^{-1}\frac{\eta-\eta_0}{\xi-\xi_0}+\beta\iota\,;\ \zeta-\zeta_0\Big\}\,,&\end{aligned}\right\}\quad(4.162)$$

[1] It will be recalled that, according to the choice of the orientation of our system of co-ordinates, the axis of rotation defined by the vector $\boldsymbol{\beta}$ is along the z-direction (cf. p. 138).

where the quantity on the right-hand side stands for an arbitrary function of the arguments specified.

It is now clear that according to equations (4.120) and (4.162), we can express our solution for F in the form

$$\left.\begin{aligned} F+\tfrac{1}{2}\phi^3\ddot{\phi}|\boldsymbol{\rho}|^2+\boldsymbol{\rho}\cdot\frac{d}{d\iota}\left(\frac{\boldsymbol{\delta}}{\phi}\right)-\frac{1}{2}\left|\boldsymbol{\rho}\times\boldsymbol{\beta}+\frac{\boldsymbol{\delta}}{\phi}\right|^2 \\ =\mathfrak{V}_1\{(\xi-\xi_0)^2+(\eta-\eta_0)^2\,;\;\vartheta+\beta\iota\,;\;\zeta-\zeta_0\}\,, \end{aligned}\right\} \tag{4.163}$$

where $\mathfrak{V}_1$ stands for an arbitrary function of the arguments specified. Hence,

$$\left.\begin{aligned} \mathfrak{V}(\xi,\eta,\zeta,\iota)&=\frac{1}{\phi^2}F(\xi,\eta,\zeta,\iota) \\ &=-\tfrac{1}{2}\phi\ddot{\phi}|\boldsymbol{\rho}|^2-\frac{\boldsymbol{\rho}}{\phi^2}\cdot\frac{d}{d\iota}\left(\frac{\boldsymbol{\delta}}{\phi}\right)+\frac{1}{2\phi^2}\left|\boldsymbol{\rho}\times\boldsymbol{\beta}+\frac{\boldsymbol{\delta}}{\phi}\right|^2 \\ &\quad+\frac{1}{\phi^2}\mathfrak{V}_1\{(\xi-\xi_0)^2+(\eta-\eta_0)^2\,;\;\vartheta+\beta\iota\,;\;\zeta-\zeta_0\}\,, \end{aligned}\right\} \tag{4.164}$$

or, somewhat differently, as (cf. eqs. [4.126] and [4.128])

$$\left.\begin{aligned} \mathfrak{V}=-\frac{1}{2}\frac{\ddot{\phi}}{\phi}r^2-\frac{1}{\phi}\frac{d}{dt}\left(\frac{\boldsymbol{\delta}}{\phi}\right)\cdot\boldsymbol{r}+\frac{1}{2\phi^4}|\boldsymbol{r}\times\boldsymbol{\beta}+\boldsymbol{\delta}|^2 \\ +\frac{1}{\phi^2}\mathfrak{V}_1\{(\xi-\xi_0)^2+(\eta-\eta_0)^2\,;\;\vartheta+\beta\iota\,;\;\zeta-\zeta_0\}\,. \end{aligned}\right\} \tag{4.165}$$

ii) *The solution for the density function,* σ.—We shall now obtain the appropriate solutions for χ and σ. Explicitly, equation (4.105) takes the form

$$-\tfrac{1}{2}\operatorname{grad}\chi=\kappa\operatorname{grad}\mathfrak{V}+\frac{1}{2}\frac{d^2\kappa}{dt^2}\boldsymbol{r}+\frac{d\boldsymbol{\delta}}{dt}\,; \tag{4.166}$$

or, solving directly for χ, we have

$$-\tfrac{1}{2}\chi=\kappa\mathfrak{V}+\frac{1}{4}\frac{d^2\kappa}{dt^2}r^2+\frac{d\boldsymbol{\delta}}{dt}\cdot\boldsymbol{r}-\tfrac{1}{2}\chi_0(t) \tag{4.167}$$

where $\chi_0(t)$ is an arbitrary function of time only. We can suppose without any loss of generality that in equation (4.167) $\mathfrak{V}$ denotes the general solution of equation (4.116). For, since the general solution of equation (4.116) differs from the general solution of equation (4.114) only through an arbitrary function of time, we can allow for this by redefining χ_0; or, in other words, we can absorb the additive function of time in equation (4.115) in our definition of χ_0.

From equation (4.167) it follows that

$$-\frac{1}{2}\frac{\partial\chi}{\partial t}=\frac{\partial}{\partial t}(\kappa\mathfrak{V})+\frac{1}{4}\frac{d^3\kappa}{dt^3}r^2+\frac{d^2\boldsymbol{\delta}}{dt^2}\cdot\boldsymbol{r}-\frac{1}{2}\frac{d\chi_0}{dt}. \qquad (4.168)$$

Combining equations (4.106) and (4.168), we have

$$\frac{1}{2}\frac{d\chi_0}{dt}=\boldsymbol{\Delta}\cdot\operatorname{grad}\mathfrak{V}+\frac{\partial}{\partial t}(\kappa\mathfrak{V})+\frac{1}{4}\frac{d^3\kappa}{dt^3}r^2+\frac{d^2\boldsymbol{\delta}}{dt^2}\cdot\boldsymbol{r}. \qquad (4.169)$$

Since $\mathfrak{V}$ satisfies the differential equation (4.116), the right-hand side of the foregoing equation vanishes identically, and we conclude that χ_0 is a constant. Hence, our solution for χ is

$$-\tfrac{1}{2}\chi=\kappa\mathfrak{V}+\frac{1}{4}\frac{d^2\kappa}{dt^2}r^2+\frac{d\boldsymbol{\delta}}{dt}\cdot\boldsymbol{r}+\text{constant}, \qquad (4.170)$$

or, alternatively, in terms of ϕ,

$$-\tfrac{1}{2}\chi=\phi^2\mathfrak{V}+\tfrac{1}{2}(\dot{\phi}^2+\phi\ddot{\phi})r^2+\dot{\boldsymbol{\delta}}\cdot\boldsymbol{r}+\text{constant}. \qquad (4.171)$$

The solution for σ is now readily obtained, since

$$Q_0=\kappa(U_0^2+V_0^2+W_0^2)=\left|\frac{\boldsymbol{\Delta}}{\phi}\right|^2 \qquad (4.172)$$

we have (cf. eq. [4.104])

$$Q_0=\left|\dot{\phi}\boldsymbol{r}+\frac{1}{\phi}(\boldsymbol{r}\times\boldsymbol{\beta})+\frac{\boldsymbol{\delta}}{\phi}\right|^2. \qquad (4.173)$$

Expanding the right-hand side of the foregoing equation, we find that

$$Q_0=\dot{\phi}^2r^2+\frac{1}{\phi^2}|\boldsymbol{r}\times\boldsymbol{\beta}+\boldsymbol{\delta}|^2+2\frac{\dot{\phi}}{\phi}\boldsymbol{\delta}\cdot\boldsymbol{r}. \qquad (4.174)$$

According to equations (4.107), (4.171), and (4.174), we now have

$$\left.\begin{aligned}\tfrac{1}{2}\sigma=\phi^2\mathfrak{V}+\tfrac{1}{2}\phi\ddot{\phi}r^2-\frac{1}{2\phi^2}|\boldsymbol{r}\times\boldsymbol{\beta}+\boldsymbol{\delta}|^2+\dot{\boldsymbol{\delta}}\cdot\boldsymbol{r}\\ -\frac{\dot{\phi}}{\phi}\boldsymbol{\delta}\cdot\boldsymbol{r}+\text{constant}.\end{aligned}\right\} \qquad (4.175)$$

Simplifying the last two terms in equation (4.175), we have

$$\left.\begin{aligned}\tfrac{1}{2}\sigma=\phi^2\mathfrak{V}+\tfrac{1}{2}\phi\ddot{\phi}r^2-\frac{1}{2\phi^2}|\boldsymbol{r}\times\boldsymbol{\beta}+\boldsymbol{\delta}|^2\\ +\phi\frac{d}{dt}\left(\frac{\boldsymbol{\delta}}{\phi}\right)\cdot\boldsymbol{r}+\text{constant}.\end{aligned}\right\} \qquad (4.176)$$

Finally, substituting for $\mathfrak{B}$ is solution (eq. [4.165]), we find

$$\tfrac{1}{2}\sigma = \mathfrak{B}_1\{(\xi-\xi_0)^2+(\eta-\eta_0)^2;\ \vartheta+\beta t;\ \zeta-\zeta_0\}+\text{constant}\,. \quad (4.177)$$

4.2. *Physical characteristics of stellar systems described by a spherical distribution of the residual velocities.*—In § 4.1 we obtained the complete formal solution to the problem of stellar systems described by a spherical distribution of the residual velocities. We shall now consider in some detail the physical characteristics of the solution obtained.

We shall begin this discussion by recalling that our *only* assumption has been the restriction to a distribution function of the form

$$\Psi \equiv \Psi\{a[(U-U_0)^2+(V-V_0)^2+(W-W_0)^2]+\sigma\}\,, \quad (4.201)$$

where a, U_0, V_0, W_0, and σ are all functions of x, y, z, and t and arbitrary in the first instance; further, Ψ is itself an arbitrary function of the argument specified. Again, it may be pointed out that this assumption concerning Ψ has been made primarily with a view to discovering the most general types of potential and density distributions that are consistent with the notion of differential motions.

The equation of continuity now allows us to derive the following rigorous consequences of the assumed spherical form for the distribution function:

i) We have

$$a = \phi^2\,, \quad (4.202)$$

where ϕ is an arbitrary function of time.

ii) According to equations (4.103), (4.104), and (4.110), we have

$$(U_0, V_0, W_0) = \frac{\dot{\phi}}{\phi}\boldsymbol{r}+\frac{1}{\phi^2}(\boldsymbol{r}\times\boldsymbol{\beta})+\frac{\boldsymbol{\delta}}{\phi^2}\,, \quad (4.203)$$

where $\boldsymbol{\beta}$ is a constant vector and $\boldsymbol{\delta}$ an arbitrary function of time. The three terms which occur in this expression for (U_0, V_0, W_0) have simple interpretations. The first term corresponds to a radial expansion (or contraction) of amount

$$\mathrm{P}_0 = \frac{\dot{\phi}}{\phi}\,r\,; \quad (4.204)$$

the second term corresponds to a rotation Θ_0 about an axis through the origin and parallel to the $\boldsymbol{\beta}$-direction given by

$$\Theta_0 = -\frac{|\boldsymbol{\beta}|}{\phi^2}\,\varpi\,; \quad (4.204')$$

and, finally, the third term corresponds to a general translation which is a function of time.

Since $\boldsymbol{\beta}$ is a constant vector, we can arrange that the z-axis of our co-ordinate system is along the $\boldsymbol{\beta}$-direction. With this choice of the orientation of the co-ordinate system $\boldsymbol{\beta}$ has the form $(0, 0, \beta)$, and equation (4.203) gives

$$\left.\begin{aligned} U_0 &= \frac{\dot{\phi}}{\phi}x+\frac{1}{\phi^2}(\beta y+\delta_1)\,; \qquad V_0=\frac{\dot{\phi}}{\phi}y+\frac{1}{\phi^2}(-\beta x+\delta_2)\,;\\ W_0 &= \frac{\dot{\phi}}{\phi}z+\frac{\delta_3}{\phi^2}\,. \end{aligned}\right\} \tag{4.205}$$

iii) The gravitational potential $\mathfrak{V}$ must be expressible in the form (eq. [4.165])

$$\left.\begin{aligned} \mathfrak{V} = &-\frac{1}{2}\frac{\ddot{\phi}}{\phi}r^2-\frac{1}{\phi}\frac{d}{dt}\left(\frac{\boldsymbol{\delta}}{\phi}\right)\cdot\boldsymbol{r}+\frac{1}{2\phi^4}|\boldsymbol{r}\times\boldsymbol{\beta}+\boldsymbol{\delta}|^2\\ &+\frac{1}{\phi^2}\mathfrak{V}_1\{(\xi-\xi_0)^2+(\eta-\eta_0)^2\,;\ \vartheta+\beta\iota\,;\ \zeta-\zeta_0\}\,, \end{aligned}\right\} \tag{4.206}$$

where

$$x=\xi\phi\,; \qquad y=\eta\phi\,; \qquad z=\zeta\phi\,; \qquad \iota=\int^t\frac{dt}{\phi^2}\,, \tag{4.207}$$

and $\mathfrak{V}_1$ is an arbitrary function of the arguments specified. Further, according to equations (4.136), (4.138), (4.143)–(4.146), we have

$$\left.\begin{aligned} \xi_0 = &\left\{\int\left(\frac{\delta_1}{\phi}\cos\beta\iota-\frac{\delta_2}{\phi}\sin\beta\iota\right)d\iota\right\}\cos\beta\iota\\ &+\left\{\int\left(\frac{\delta_1}{\phi}\sin\beta\iota+\frac{\delta_2}{\phi}\cos\beta\iota\right)d\iota\right\}\sin\beta\iota\,, \end{aligned}\right\} \tag{4.208}$$

$$\left.\begin{aligned} \eta_0 = &-\left\{\int\left(\frac{\delta_1}{\phi}\cos\beta\iota-\frac{\delta_2}{\phi}\sin\beta\iota\right)d\iota\right\}\sin\beta\iota\\ &+\left\{\int\left(\frac{\delta_1}{\phi}\sin\beta\iota+\frac{\delta_2}{\phi}\cos\beta\iota\right)d\iota\right\}\cos\beta\iota\,, \end{aligned}\right\} \tag{4.209}$$

$$\zeta_0=\int\frac{\delta_3}{\phi}\,d\iota\,, \tag{4.210}$$

and

$$\vartheta=\tan^{-1}\frac{\eta-\eta_0}{\xi-\xi_0}\,. \tag{4.211}$$

iv) Finally, the solution for σ is given by (eq. [4.177])

$$\sigma = 2\mathfrak{B}_1\{(\xi-\xi_0)^2+(\eta-\eta_0)^2;\ \vartheta+\beta\iota;\ \zeta-\zeta_0\}+\text{constant}\ . \qquad (4.212)$$

If we now specialize the general spherical distribution (eq. [4.201]) to a Maxwellian distribution, then

$$\Psi(Q+\sigma)=e^{-(Q+\sigma)}=e^{-\phi^2\{(U-U_0)^2+(V-V_0)^2+(W-W_0)^2\}-\sigma}\ . \qquad (4.213)$$

On integrating the foregoing equation, we obtain for the number of stars, N, per unit volume the expression

$$N(x,y,z,t)=\frac{\pi^{3/2}}{\phi^3}\,e^{-\sigma}\ . \qquad (4.214)$$

According to equation (4.212), we can express N in the form

$$N=\frac{1}{\phi^3}\,N_1\{(\xi-\xi_0)^2+(\eta-\eta_0)^2;\ \vartheta+\beta\iota;\ \zeta-\zeta_0\}\ , \qquad (4.215)$$

where N_1 is a function of the arguments specified.

We may also note that the physical meaning of ϕ is that its reciprocal is a measure of the dispersion of the residual velocities. For a Maxwellian distribution the mean residual speed in any given direction is given by $\pi^{-1/2}\phi^{-1}$. Thus,

$$\overline{|U-U_0|}=\overline{|V-V_0|}=\overline{|W-W_0|}=\frac{1}{\pi^{1/2}\phi}\ . \qquad (4.216)$$

We shall now consider an important characteristic of the function σ.[2] According to equation (4.212), σ involves the time only *implicitly* through the functions ϕ, ξ_0, η_0, and ζ_0. The nature of this dependence of σ on t (or ι) is best understood by considering the locus of points at which σ takes some preassigned value as the time varies, i.e., by considering the *trajectories* of points of constant σ. Assuming that σ is a single-valued function of its arguments, it follows that such trajectories will be described parametrically by relations of the form

$$\left.\begin{aligned}(\xi-\xi_0)^2+(\eta-\eta_0)^2&=c_1^2\ ,\\ \vartheta=\tan^{-1}\frac{\eta-\eta_0}{\xi-\xi_0}&=c_2-\beta\iota\ ,\end{aligned}\right\} \qquad (4.217)$$

and

$$\zeta-\zeta_0=c_3\ , \qquad (4.218)$$

[2] The remarks which follow apply equally well also to the function N_1 (eq. [4.215]).

where c_1, c_2, and c_3 are constants. In the foregoing equations ξ_0, η_0, and ζ_0 are themselves functions of ι (eqs. [4.208]–[4.210]). From equations (4.217) and (4.218) it appears that the motions perpendicular to, and respectively parallel to, the ζ-direction can be considered separately.

Consider, first, the projection of the trajectory in the (ξ, η) plane. This is a curve defined parametrically by the relations (4.217). This locus (4.217) has a simple geometrical interpretation (see Fig. 16).

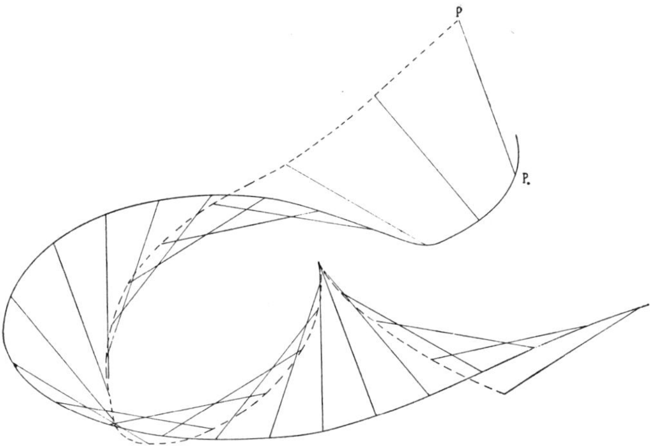

FIG. 16.—The geometrical construction for deriving the trajectories of points of constant σ in the (ξ, η) plane from a basic (ξ_0, η_0) locus. While P_0 describes the (ξ_0, η_0) locus (the full line curve) the "arm" $P_0\,P$ rotates about P_0 at a constant rate and traces a possible trajectory (the dotted curve).

According to equations (4.208) and (4.209), the point (ξ_0, η_0) will describe some locus (as ι varies) in the (ξ, η) plane. The explicit form which this locus will take will depend on δ_1 and δ_2; but when δ_1 and δ_2 are known as functions of ι, the (ξ_0, η_0) locus will be uniquely determined. We can regard this (ξ_0, η_0) locus as being described by a moving representative point, P_0. The locus (4.217) can be derived from the (ξ_0, η_0) locus by attaching to the representative point P_0 an "arm" P_0P of length c_1 and allowing it to rotate about P_0 with a constant angular velocity,[3] $-\beta$. The curve described by P in this manner is the required locus.

[3] This, in a measure of "time" according to ι,

From the geometrical construction given in the preceding paragraph it follows that the locus defined by the equations (4.217) is a transcendental curve of the same general nature as an epitrochoid or a hypotrochoid.[4] To transform these loci in the (ξ, η) plane into trajectories in the (x, y) plane we should apply the transformation (eq. [4.207])

$$x = \xi\phi\ ; \qquad y = \eta\phi\ , \tag{4.219}$$

where ϕ is itself a function of ι. The result of this transformation will be that the trajectories in the (x, y) plane will belong to a general class of spirals which may have kinks or may even interpenetrate themselves.

Considering next the motion in the ζ-direction, it follows from equation (4.210) that in the (ξ, η, ζ) space the points of constant σ always remain at a constant distance from ζ_0. To obtain the corresponding motion in the (x, y, z) space, we should apply the transformation

$$z = \zeta\phi\ ; \qquad \phi^2 = \frac{dt}{d\iota}\,. \tag{4.220}$$

On the other hand, from equations (4.205) it follows that for "flat" systems the motions in the z-direction are quite small compared to the much larger rotational motions present in the (x, y) plane.

To interpret physically the trajectories described by points of constant σ we need a relation expressing σ in terms of other physical parameters. Such a relation will, however, depend on the explicit form of $\Psi(Q + \sigma)$. While there is this arbitrariness, it is probable that the most important case arises when we have a Maxwellian distribution of the residual velocities. Then (eq. [4.214])

$$N = \frac{\text{constant}}{\phi^3}\, e^{-\sigma}\ , \tag{4.221}$$

where N denotes the number of stars per unit volume. According to this equation, the dependence of N on the spatial co-ordinates is governed solely by σ. Thus the regions of maximum (or minimum) density are determined by grad $N = 0$; but this condition is clearly equivalent to grad $\sigma = 0$. Consequently, the orbits described by

[4] A useful reference for information concerning these classical transcendental curves is H. Lamb, *Infinitesimal Calculus*, chaps. ix and x, pp. 284–367, Cambridge, England, 1938.

regions of maximum or minimum density will be the same as appropriately selected trajectories of points of constant σ. More generally, we may say that *the trajectories of points of constant σ are essentially the trajectories of points of constant relative density.* As we have already indicated, these trajectories belong to a very wide class of spirals derived from a general family of epicyclical or trochoidal curves.

It thus appears that the present theory can be used as a basis for interpreting, in a general way, the spiral and other structural features of extragalactic nebulae. In suggesting this, we are guided by the following circumstances: (i) the occurrence of quite general spiral orbits for points of constant relative density, (ii) the degree of permanence which is attributed to the spiral structure, and (iii) the linearity of the rotational velocity (eq. [4.204′]) with distance which is in general agreement with the velocity-curve derived by Babcock for the Andromeda nebula (see Fig. 11). In this connection we should particularly emphasize the fact that the class of spiral orbits predicted is so wide that it would not be difficult to interpret almost every structural feature of nebulae on the basis of trajectories derived from suitable (ξ_0, η_0) loci.[5] Indeed, in this very generality lies the inherent weakness of the present interpretation as providing an *explicit* theory of spiral structure in nebulae; thus the theory gives no definite indications why certain forms of spiral orbits are preferred to the exclusion of others. But it should be remembered that we were not looking for a theory of spiral structure when we began the study of stellar systems described by a spherical distribution of the residual velocities. We were interested, far more, in discovering the most general type of stellar systems consistent with the notion of differential motions. And the analysis has disclosed that the solution to the problem of spiral and other structural features of nebulae is not beyond the range of our fundamental kinematical postulates.

4.3. *Circular orbits and nearly circular orbits in an axially symmetrical potential field with a plane of symmetry,* $\mathfrak{V}(\varpi, z) \equiv \mathfrak{V}(\varpi, -z)$. —We shall now consider some general theorems on the orbits described by stars in a potential field which is characterized by both

[5] For further information on these and related matters see S. Chandrasekhar, *Ap. J.*, **92**, 441, 1940 (particularly pp. 611–628).

an axis and a plane of symmetry. Our assumption concerning $\mathfrak{B}$ can be expressed analytically by the equations

$$\mathfrak{B}(x, y, z) \equiv \mathfrak{B}(\varpi, z) \tag{4.301}$$

and

$$\mathfrak{B}(\varpi, +z) \equiv \mathfrak{B}(\varpi, -z) , \tag{4.302}$$

where the co-ordinate system has been so chosen that the (x, y) plane and the z-axis are the plane and the axis of symmetry, respectively. (We may remark in this connection that, according to our current ideas, the galactic plane is supposed to be an approximate plane of symmetry for the Galaxy.) Equation (4.302) implies that

$$\frac{\partial \mathfrak{B}}{\partial z} = \frac{\partial^2 \mathfrak{B}}{\partial \varpi \partial z} = 0 \qquad (z = 0) . \tag{4.303}$$

The equations of motion are (eqs. [3.312]–[3.314])

$$\frac{d^2 \varpi}{dt^2} = \varpi \dot{\theta}^2 - \frac{\partial \mathfrak{B}}{\partial \varpi} , \tag{4.304}$$

$$\frac{d}{dt}(\varpi^2 \dot{\theta}) = -\frac{\partial \mathfrak{B}}{\partial \theta} = 0 , \tag{4.305}$$

and

$$\frac{d^2 z}{dt^2} = -\frac{\partial \mathfrak{B}}{\partial z} . \tag{4.306}$$

These equations admit, of course, *the energy integral*

$$\tfrac{1}{2} I_1 = \tfrac{1}{2}(\dot{\varpi}^2 + \varpi^2 \dot{\theta}^2 + \dot{z}^2) + \mathfrak{B} = \text{constant} , \tag{4.307}$$

and the *angular-momentum integral*

$$I_2 = \varpi^2 \dot{\theta} = \varpi \Theta = h = \text{constant} . \tag{4.308}$$

In equation (4.308) h is the so-called constant of areas.

We may notice that, according to equations (4.303), orbits lying entirely in the (x, y) plane are possible. For, if at any time, $z = 0$ and $\dot{z} = 0$, then, according to equations (4.303) and (4.306), $\ddot{z} = 0$ and hence all the higher derivatives also vanish. Thus z vanishes identically, and the orbit always remains in the (x, y) plane.

i) *Circular orbits.*—According to equations (4.304) and (4.306), circular orbits in the (x, y) plane represent possible solutions of the equations of motion, i.e.,

$$\varpi = \varpi_0 = \text{constant} ; \qquad z = 0 \tag{4.309}$$

provided

$$\varpi_0 \dot{\theta}_c^2 = \left(\frac{\partial \mathfrak{B}}{\partial \varpi}\right)_0 ; \qquad \varpi_0^2 \dot{\theta}_c = \varpi_0 \Theta_c = h_c , \tag{4.310}$$

where we have used Θ_c to denote the circular rotational velocity and the subscript "0" to signify that the quantity in parenthesis is to be evaluated at $\varpi = \varpi_0$ and $z = 0$. From equations (4.310) we obtain

$$\Theta_c^2 = \left(\varpi \frac{\partial \mathfrak{B}}{\partial \varpi}\right)_0 ; \qquad h_c^2 = \left(\varpi^3 \frac{\partial \mathfrak{B}}{\partial \varpi}\right)_0 . \tag{4.311}$$

Also, if ω_c denotes the angular velocity in the circular orbit, then

$$\dot{\theta}_c^2 = \omega_c^2 = \left(\frac{1}{\varpi} \frac{\partial \mathfrak{B}}{\partial \varpi}\right)_0 = \frac{h_c^2}{\varpi_0^4} . \tag{4.312}$$

ii) *Nearly circular orbits and their stability.*—Having shown the existence of circular orbits in the (x, y) plane, we shall now consider nearly circular orbits, i.e., orbits for which we can write

$$\varpi = \varpi_0 + \varpi_1 ; \qquad \varpi_1 \ll \varpi_0 , \tag{4.313}$$

where ϖ_0 is a constant, and which do not also deviate very appreciably from the (x, y) plane. Using equation (4.303), we find that equations (4.304) and (4.306) become

$$\frac{d^2 \varpi_1}{dt^2} = (\varpi_0 + \varpi_1)\, \dot{\theta}^2 - \left(\frac{\partial \mathfrak{B}}{\partial \varpi}\right)_0 - \varpi_1 \left(\frac{\partial^2 \mathfrak{B}}{\partial \varpi^2}\right)_0 , \tag{4.314}$$

$$\frac{d^2 z}{dt^2} = -\left(\frac{\partial^2 \mathfrak{B}}{\partial z^2}\right)_0 z , \tag{4.315}$$

where we have retained only quantities of the first order of smallness in ϖ_1 and z. Further, we have the angular-momentum integral

$$(\varpi_0 + \varpi_1)^2 \dot{\theta} = h . \tag{4.316}$$

Eliminating $\dot{\theta}$ between equations (4.314) and (4.316), we have

$$\frac{d^2 \varpi_1}{dt^2} = \frac{h^2}{\varpi_0^3}\left(1 - 3\,\frac{\varpi_1}{\varpi_0}\right) - \left(\frac{\partial \mathfrak{B}}{\partial \varpi}\right)_0 - \varpi_1 \left(\frac{\partial^2 \mathfrak{B}}{\partial \varpi^2}\right)_0 . \tag{4.317}$$

So far, we have not restricted ϖ_0 to have any particular value. We shall now suppose that ϖ_0 has been so chosen that the constant of areas for the circular orbit of radius ϖ_0 is h, i.e., according to equations (4.311) and (4.312), we arrange to have

$$h^2 = h_c^2 = \left(\varpi^3 \frac{\partial \mathfrak{B}}{\partial \varpi}\right)_0 = (\varpi_0^2 \dot{\theta}_c)^2 . \tag{4.318}$$

Equation (4.317) now reduces to

$$\frac{d^2\varpi_1}{dt^2} = -\left(\frac{\partial^2 \mathfrak{B}}{\partial \varpi^2} + \frac{3}{\varpi}\frac{\partial \mathfrak{B}}{\partial \varpi}\right)_0 \varpi_1 . \tag{4.319}$$

Again, if we write

$$\theta = \theta_c + \theta_1 \tag{4.320}$$

where θ_c denotes the position angle on the circular orbit, (ϖ_0, h_c), then from equations (4.316) and (4.318) we derive

$$(\varpi_0 + \varpi_1)^2 (\dot{\theta}_c + \dot{\theta}_1) = h_c = \varpi_0^2 \dot{\theta}_c ; \tag{4.321}$$

or, on expanding the expression on the left-hand side and retaining only quantities of the first order of smallness, we obtain

$$\dot{\theta}_1 = -2 \frac{\varpi_1}{\varpi_0} \dot{\theta}_c = -2 \frac{\Theta_c}{\varpi_0^2} \varpi_1 . \tag{4.322}$$

The equations of motion for nearly circular orbits are therefore given by equations (4.319), (4.322), and (4.315). From the first of these equations, we are at once able to draw an important conclusion:

Nearly circular orbits represent stable solutions of the equations of motion only provided that

$$\frac{\partial^2 \mathfrak{B}}{\partial \varpi^2} + \frac{3}{\varpi}\frac{\partial \mathfrak{B}}{\partial \varpi} > 0 . \tag{4.323}$$

The condition (4.323) for the stability of the circular orbits can be expressed alternatively in the form

$$\frac{\partial}{\partial \varpi}\left(\varpi^3 \frac{\partial \mathfrak{B}}{\partial \varpi}\right) > 0 ; \tag{4.324}$$

or, in words: *a circular orbit of radius ϖ in the (x, y) plane is stable if and only if the gravitational attraction at ϖ decreases more slowly than an inverse cube law of force.* [This theorem is actually a very special case of a much more general theorem proved in Appen. II.]

Let us assume that the condition for the stability of circular orbits (eq. [4.323]) is satisfied. Then the solution of equation (4.319) can be written in the form

$$\varpi_1 = \varpi_{10} \sin n_1 (t - t_1) \qquad (\varpi_{10} \ll \varpi_0) , \qquad (4.325)$$

where ϖ_{10} and t_1 are constants of integration and

$$n_1^2 = \left(\frac{\partial^2 \mathfrak{V}}{\partial \varpi^2} + \frac{3}{\varpi} \frac{\partial \mathfrak{V}}{\partial \varpi} \right)_0 . \qquad (4.326)$$

An alternative expression for n_1^2 may be noted. From the relation $\Theta_c^2 = \varpi_0 (\partial \mathfrak{V} / \partial \varpi)_0$ we obtain

$$n_1^2 = 2 \frac{\Theta_c}{\varpi_0} \left(\frac{\partial \Theta_c}{\partial \varpi} + \frac{\Theta_c}{\varpi} \right)_0 . \qquad (4.327)$$

Using equation (4.325), we can write equation (4.322) as

$$\dot{\theta}_1 = -2 \frac{\Theta_c}{\varpi_0^2} \varpi_{10} \sin n_1 (t - t_1) ; \qquad (4.328)$$

or, after integrating this equation,

$$\theta_1 = 2 \frac{\Theta_c}{\varpi_0^2 n_1} \varpi_{10} \cos n_1 (t - t_1) + \theta_{10} \qquad (4.329)$$

where θ_{10} is a constant. On the other hand, since θ_1 must tend to zero identically as $\varpi_{10} \to 0$, it follows that $\theta_{10} = 0$. Hence,

$$\theta_1 = 2 \frac{\Theta_c}{\varpi_0^2 n_1} \varpi_{10} \cos n_1 (t - t_1) . \qquad (4.330)$$

Finally, from equation (4.315) we obtain the solution

$$z = z_{10} \sin n_2 (t - t_2) , \qquad (4.331)$$

where

$$n_2^2 = \left(\frac{\partial^2 \mathfrak{V}}{\partial z^2} \right)_0 , \qquad (4.332)$$

and z_{10} and t_2 are two constants.

iii) *Nearly circular orbits referred to a rotating frame of reference.*— We shall now refer the orbit considered in (ii) above to a frame of reference, $(\mathfrak{X}, \mathfrak{Y}, \mathfrak{Z})$, rotating with the angular velocity ω_c and with its origin at a distance ϖ_0 from the center. Further, let the $\mathfrak{X}$, $\mathfrak{Y}$, and $\mathfrak{Z}$ axes be in the radial, transverse, and z-directions, respectively (see Fig. 17). Then for a nearly circular orbit we have (cf. eqs. [4.325], [4.330], and [4.331])

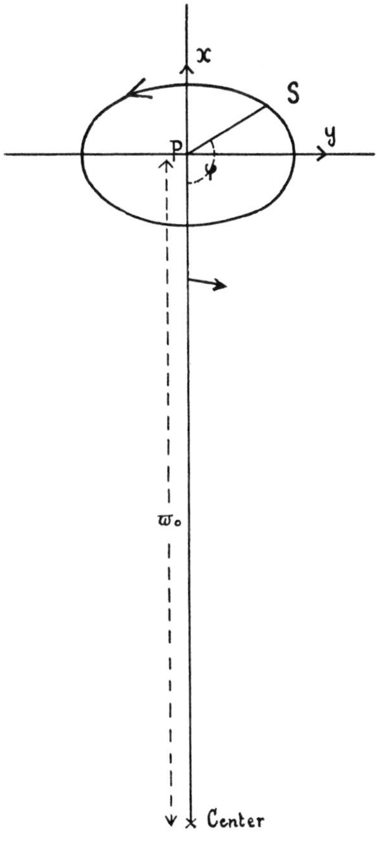

FIG. 17

$$\mathfrak{X} = \varpi_1 \quad = \varpi_{10} \sin n_1 (t - t_1) , \tag{4.333}$$

$$\mathfrak{Y} = \varpi_0 \theta_1 = 2 \frac{\Theta_c}{\varpi_0 n_1} \varpi_{10} \cos n_1 (t - t_1) , \tag{4.334}$$

and

$$\mathfrak{Z} = z \quad = z_{10} \sin n_2 (t - t_2) . \tag{4.335}$$

Thus, in the rotating frame of reference the projection of the orbit in the $(\mathcal{X}, \mathcal{Y})$ plane is an ellipse:

$$\mathcal{X}^2 + \frac{\varpi_0^2 n_1^2}{4\Theta_c^2} \mathcal{Y}^2 = \varpi_{10}^2 , \tag{4.336}$$

or, using equation (4.327),

$$\mathcal{X}^2 + \frac{\varpi_0}{2\Theta_c} \left(\frac{\partial \Theta_c}{\partial \varpi} + \frac{\Theta_c}{\varpi} \right)_0 \mathcal{Y}^2 = \varpi_{10}^2 . \tag{4.337}$$

In the nonrotating frame of reference the motion in the galactic plane (i.e., the $[x, y]$ plane) is therefore an *elliptical epicycle*.

iv) *Motions in the epicyclical orbits.*—Let Θ and Π denote the transverse and the radial components of motion in an epicyclical orbit. Then

$$\Theta = (\varpi_0 + \varpi_1)\, (\dot{\theta}_c + \dot{\theta}_1) \simeq \varpi_0 \dot{\theta}_c + \varpi_0 \dot{\theta}_1 + \varpi_1 \dot{\theta}_c , \tag{4.338}$$

or, using equations (4.322) and (4.333),

$$\Theta = \Theta_c - \frac{\Theta_c}{\varpi_0} \mathcal{X} . \tag{4.339}$$

Again, from equations (4.325) and (4.334), we obtain

$$\Pi = \dot{\varpi}_1 = \varpi_{10} n_1 \cos n_1 (t - t_1) = \frac{n_1^2 \varpi_0}{2\Theta_c} \mathcal{Y} , \tag{4.340}$$

or, using the expression (4.327) for n_1^2, we have

$$\Pi = \left(\frac{\partial \Theta_c}{\partial \varpi} + \frac{\Theta_c}{\varpi} \right)_0 \mathcal{Y} . \tag{4.341}$$

Finally, the z-component of the motion is

$$Z = \dot{z} = z_{10} n_2 \cos n_2 (t - t_2) . \tag{4.342}$$

Let S be the point $(\mathcal{X}, \mathcal{Y}, \mathcal{Z})$ and S_0 the point $(\mathcal{X}, \mathcal{Y}, 0)$ on the epicycle in the galactic plane. We shall now refer the motion at S to the circular orbit passing through S_0. The Π-, Θ-, and Z-components of the motion in this circular orbit are

$$\Pi_c (S_0) = 0 ; \qquad \Theta_c (S_0) = \Theta_c + \left(\frac{\partial \Theta_c}{\partial \varpi} \right)_0 \mathcal{X} ; \qquad Z_c (S_0) = 0 . \tag{4.343}$$

The required relative motion has, therefore, the components

$$\left.\begin{aligned} \Pi - \Pi_c(S_0) &= +\left(\frac{\partial\Theta_c}{\partial\varpi}+\frac{\Theta_c}{\varpi}\right)_0 \mathcal{Y}\,,\\ \Theta - \Theta_c(S_0) &= -\left(\frac{\partial\Theta_c}{\partial\varpi}+\frac{\Theta_c}{\varpi}\right)_0 \mathcal{X}\,,\\ Z - Z_c(S_0) &= n_2\sqrt{\mathcal{Z}_{10}^2-\mathcal{Z}^2}\,. \end{aligned}\right\} \tag{4.344}$$

From the foregoing expressions for $\Pi - \Pi_c(S_0)$ and $\Theta - \Theta_c(S_0)$ and equation (4.337) we obtain

$$[\Theta-\Theta_c(S_0)]^2+\frac{\varpi_0}{2\Theta_c}\left(\frac{\partial\Theta_c}{\partial\varpi}+\frac{\Theta_c}{\varpi}\right)_0[\Pi-\Pi_c(S_0)]^2=\text{constant}\,. \tag{4.345}$$

To the order of accuracy in which we are working, we can clearly evaluate Θ_c and its derivatives (which occur in equations [4.344] and [4.345]) at S_0 instead of at the origin of the system ($\mathcal{X}$, $\mathcal{Y}$, $\mathcal{Z}$). We can therefore re-write equation (4.345) as

$$\left.\begin{aligned} [\Theta-\Theta_c(S_0)]^2+\left\{\frac{\varpi}{2\Theta_c}\left(\frac{\partial\Theta_c}{\partial\varpi}+\frac{\Theta_c}{\varpi}\right)\right\}_{S_0}[\Pi-\Pi_c(S_0)]^2&\\ =\text{constant}\,.& \end{aligned}\right\} \tag{4.346}$$

The interpretation of equation (4.346) is the following: If we consider the various epicyclical orbits passing through a given point, S_0, and refer the motions in these orbits to the circular orbit passing through S_0, then the components of the motions in the radial and the transverse directions must satisfy a relation of the form (4.346). The ratio of the axes of this *velocity ellipse* (4.346) is given by

$$(\text{ratio of axes})^2=\left\{\frac{\varpi}{2\Theta_c}\left(\frac{\partial\Theta_c}{\partial\varpi}+\frac{\Theta_c}{\varpi}\right)\right\}_{S_0}. \tag{4.347}$$

If we now let (cf. eqs. [1.428])

$$A=\frac{1}{2}\left(\frac{\partial\Theta_c}{\partial\varpi}-\frac{\Theta_c}{\varpi}\right)_{S_0};\qquad B=\frac{1}{2}\left(\frac{\partial\Theta_c}{\partial\varpi}+\frac{\Theta_c}{\varpi}\right)_{S_0}, \tag{4.348}$$

the relation (4.347) can be expressed alternatively in the form

$$(\text{ratio of axes})^2=\frac{B}{B-A}\,, \tag{4.349}$$

an equation which is identical in form with equation (3.812), which we derived from the general theory of differential motions in an axially symmetrical system.

Again, according to equations (4.327) and (4.348), we have

$$n_1 = 2\sqrt{B(B-A)}\ . \tag{4.350}$$

If we use in equation (4.350) the values of A and B quoted in chapter i (eqs. [1.422]), we find for the period of description of the ellipse (4.337), the time

$$\frac{2\pi}{n_1} = \frac{\pi}{\sqrt{B(B-A)}} = 1.5 \times 10^8 \text{ years}\ . \tag{4.351}$$

v) *On a minimal property of the circular orbits.*—We have already seen that in the field $\mathfrak{B}(\varpi, z)$ the equations of motion, trivially, admit the two integrals

$$I_1 = \Pi^2 + \Theta^2 + Z^2 + 2\mathfrak{B}(\varpi, z) = \text{constant}\ , \tag{4.352}$$

and

$$I_2 = \varpi\Theta = \text{constant}\ . \tag{4.353}$$

Lindblad has now proved the following theorem:

Among all the orbits with a given constant of areas in an axially symmetrical field with a plane of symmetry, that which has the least energy is the circular orbit in the plane of symmetry, provided this orbit is stable.

In other words, this theorem states that among the orbits with a given I_2, the circular orbit, if stable, has the minimum I_1. To prove this, we write I_1 in the form

$$I_1 = \Pi^2 + Z^2 + \frac{I_2^2}{\varpi^2} + 2\mathfrak{B}\ , \tag{4.354}$$

and minimize it for fixed I_2.

First, the conditions for being stationary are

$$\frac{\partial I_1}{\partial \Pi} = \frac{\partial I_1}{\partial Z} = \frac{\partial I_1}{\partial z} = \frac{\partial I_1}{\partial \varpi} = 0\ . \tag{4.355}$$

These conditions require, respectively,

$$\Pi = 0\ ; \qquad Z = 0\ ; \qquad \frac{\partial \mathfrak{B}}{\partial z} = 0\ , \tag{4.356}$$

and

$$\frac{\partial \mathfrak{B}}{\partial \varpi} - \frac{I_2^2}{\varpi^3} = 0\ . \tag{4.357}$$

Equation (4.357) can be written alternatively as

$$\Theta^2 = \varpi \frac{\partial \mathfrak{V}}{\partial \varpi} . \tag{4.358}$$

The conditions (4.356) and (4.358) clearly imply a circular orbit in the (x, y) plane. But for this circular orbit, I_1 will be a true minimum only if all the second derivatives with respect to Π, Z, z, and ϖ are positive. The only one of these second derivatives which requires consideration is

$$\frac{\partial^2 I_1}{\partial \varpi^2} = 2\left(\frac{\partial^2 \mathfrak{V}}{\partial \varpi^2} + 3\,\frac{I_2^2}{\varpi^4}\right), \tag{4.359}$$

or, using equation (4.357),

$$\frac{\partial^2 I_1}{\partial \varpi^2} = 2\left(\frac{\partial^2 \mathfrak{V}}{\partial \varpi^2} + \frac{3}{\varpi}\frac{\partial \mathfrak{V}}{\partial \varpi}\right); \tag{4.360}$$

but the condition for this to be positive is precisely the condition for the stability of the circular orbit (eq. [4.323]). This proves the theorem.

We may note that the minimum value of I_1 for the given value of I_2 is

$$I_1\,(\text{min}) = \left(\frac{I_2^2}{\varpi^2} + 2\mathfrak{V}\right)_{\varpi=\varpi_0;\; z=0} = \left(\varpi\,\frac{\partial \mathfrak{V}}{\partial \varpi} + 2\mathfrak{V}\right)_{\varpi=\varpi_0;\; z=0} . \tag{4.361}$$

Thus, in the (I_1, I_2) plane, the locus defining these minima is the curve defined parametrically by the relations

$$\left.\begin{aligned} I_1 &= \left(\varpi\,\frac{\partial \mathfrak{V}}{\partial \varpi} + 2\mathfrak{V}\right)_{z=0} , \\ I_2^2 &= \left(\varpi^3\,\frac{\partial \mathfrak{V}}{\partial \varpi}\right)_{z=0} . \end{aligned}\right\} \tag{4.362}$$

This locus is sometimes called the "*characteristic envelope*."[6] The usefulness of this locus in a general discussion of the orbits in the given potential field $\mathfrak{V}(\varpi, z)$ will become apparent in the following sections.

4.4. *The characteristic envelope.*—We shall now consider the orbits described in an axially symmetrical field more generally than in § 4.3.

[6] For the significance of "envelope" in this expression see § 4.4.

Consider an orbit which passes through a given point (ϖ, θ, z). The permissible values of I_1 and I_2 for such an orbit are clearly restricted by the inequality (eq. [4.354])

$$I_1 - 2\mathfrak{V}(\varpi, z) = \Pi^2 + Z^2 + \frac{I_2^2}{\varpi^2} \geqslant \frac{I_2^2}{\varpi^2}, \tag{4.401}$$

or, alternatively, by

$$I_2^2 \leqslant \varpi^2 [I_1 - 2\mathfrak{V}(\varpi, z)]. \tag{4.402}$$

In other words, the possible values of I_1 and I_2 are limited by the parabola

$$I_2^2 = \varpi^2 [I_1 - 2\mathfrak{V}(\varpi, z)] \tag{4.403}$$

in the (I_1, I_2) plane.

For the purposes of our present discussion there is clearly no loss of generality if we restrict ourselves to positive values of I_2 only. Again, if we consider only those orbits which are permanently in the finite part of the space, then I_1 must take only negative values. Under these circumstances the possible values of I_1 and I_2 for an orbit passing through (ϖ, θ, z) must be limited by the negative I_1-axis, the positive I_2-axis, and the associated *characteristic parabola* ([eq. 4.403]). The vertex of this parabola is at $[2\mathfrak{V}(\varpi, z), 0]$ and the *latus rectum* is ϖ^2.

Consider, now, the class of orbits passing through points lying on an equipotential surface. From equation (4.403) it is evident that the associated characteristic parabolae all have the same vertex but different *latera recta*. Suppose now that the stellar system under consideration is a flattened one. We should then expect that the maximum abscissa on any given equipotential surface will be attained on the galactic plane. We shall assume that this is the case. Then, among the characteristic parabolae associated with any particular equipotential surface, that which has the maximum *latus rectum* is the one for which $z = 0$:

$$I_2^2 = \varpi_0^2 [I_1 - 2\mathfrak{V}(\varpi_0, 0)], \tag{4.404}$$

where the subscript "0" denotes that the equipotential surface,

$$\mathfrak{V}(\varpi, z) = \mathfrak{V}(\varpi_0, 0) = \text{constant}, \tag{4.405}$$

is under consideration. It is further clear that all the other characteristic parabolae associated with the surface (4.405) must lie inside the curve (4.404). Hence, the possible values of I_1 and I_2 for an orbit passing through a point on the equipotential surface (4.405) must, a fortiori, be limited by the parabola (4.404), and the I_2-axis.

Consider, finally, *any* orbit in the given potential field. The possible values of I_1 and I_2 for the orbit must evidently be limited by the envelope to the parabolae,

$$I_2^2 = \varpi^2 [\, I_1 - 2\mathfrak{V}(\varpi, 0)\,] \,. \tag{4.406}$$

This envelope has been called by Lindblad the *characteristic envelope* associated with the given field.

The equation of the characteristic envelope is found by eliminating ϖ between equation (4.406) and the equation derived from this by differentiating it partially with respect to ϖ, i.e., by the eliminant of the relations

$$\left.\begin{aligned} I_2^2 - \varpi^2 (I_1 - 2\mathfrak{V}_0) &= 0 \,, \\ -2\varpi (I_1 - 2\mathfrak{V}_0) + 2\varpi^2 \frac{\partial \mathfrak{V}_0}{\partial \varpi} &= 0 \,, \end{aligned}\right\} \tag{4.407}$$

where we have used $\mathfrak{V}_0$ to denote the function $\mathfrak{V}(\varpi, 0)$. After some further reductions we find that the characteristic envelope is defined parametrically by the relations

$$\left.\begin{aligned} I_1 &= \varpi \frac{\partial \mathfrak{V}_0}{\partial \varpi} + 2\mathfrak{V}_0 \,, \\ I_2^2 &= \varpi^3 \frac{\partial \mathfrak{V}_0}{\partial \varpi} \,. \end{aligned}\right\} \tag{4.408}$$

On comparing equations (4.362) and (4.408) we notice that the characteristic envelope and the locus defining the minimum values of I_1 for given I_2 are both the same. This identity is clearly necessary.

We shall now consider some geometrical properties of the characteristic envelope. According to equations (4.408) we have

$$\left.\begin{aligned} \frac{dI_1}{d\varpi} &= \varpi \frac{\partial^2 \mathfrak{V}_0}{\partial \varpi^2} + 3 \frac{\partial \mathfrak{V}_0}{\partial \varpi} = \frac{1}{\varpi^2} \frac{\partial}{\partial \varpi} \left(\varpi^3 \frac{\partial \mathfrak{V}_0}{\partial \varpi} \right) , \\ 2I_2 \frac{dI_2}{d\varpi} &= \frac{\partial}{\partial \varpi} \left(\varpi^3 \frac{\partial \mathfrak{V}_0}{\partial \varpi} \right) . \end{aligned}\right\} \tag{4.409}$$

From these equations and equation (4.324) we conclude that $dI_1/d\varpi$ and $dI_2/d\varpi$ are both positive for values of ϖ for which the circular orbits are stable. Similarly, both these derivatives are negative when the corresponding circular orbits are unstable. Thus, along the characteristic envelope, I_1 and I_2 both increase or decrease together, depending on the stability or otherwise of the circular orbits. Again, for values of ϖ for which the circular orbit just becomes unstable or ceases to be unstable, the characteristic envelope has "*turning-points.*"

From equations (4.409) we also have

$$\frac{dI_1}{dI_2} = 2\frac{I_2}{\varpi^2} = 2\left(\frac{\Theta_c}{\varpi}\right) = 2\omega_c\,, \tag{4.410}$$

where ω_c denotes the angular velocity in the circular orbit. Hence, at the turning-points, the slope of the characteristic envelope must change continuously.

4.5. *The instability of circular orbits at the peripheries of highly spheroidal systems.*—We shall now illustrate the application and the usefulness of the method of the characteristic envelopes to practical problems.

i) *Characteristic envelope for a homogeneous oblate spheroid. The regions of instability of the circular orbits.*—We shall consider first the motions in the field of a homogeneous oblate spheroid. According to elementary potential theory, the potential inside the spheroid can be written as[7]

$$\left.\begin{aligned}\mathfrak{B} = \frac{3GM}{4a^3e^2}\left(\frac{1}{e}\sin^{-1}e - \sqrt{1-e^2}\right)\varpi^2 + \frac{3GM}{2a^3e^2}\Big(\frac{1}{\sqrt{1-e^2}}\\ -\frac{1}{e}\sin^{-1}e\Big)z^2 - \frac{3GM}{2ae}\sin^{-1}e\,,\end{aligned}\right\} \tag{4.501}$$

where M, a, and e denote the mass, the major axis, and the eccentricity of the spheroid. For motions in the (x, y) plane, the potential reduces to

$$\left.\begin{aligned}\mathfrak{B}_0 = \frac{3GM}{4a^3e^2}\left(\frac{1}{e}\sin^{-1}e - \sqrt{1-e^2}\right)\varpi^2\\ -\frac{3GM}{2ae}\sin^{-1}e \qquad (\varpi\leqslant a)\,.\end{aligned}\right\} \tag{4.502}$$

[7] E. J. Routh, *Analytical Statics*, **2**, 106–116, Cambridge, England, 1922.

Similarly, the external potential in the (x, y) plane is given by

$$\left.\begin{aligned}\mathfrak{V}_0 = \frac{3GM}{4ae}\bigg[\left(\frac{\varpi^2}{a^2e^2}-2\right)\sin^{-1}\frac{ae}{\varpi} \\ -\frac{\varpi}{ae}\sqrt{1-\frac{a^2e^2}{\varpi^2}}\bigg] \qquad (\varpi \geqslant a)\,.\end{aligned}\right\} \quad (4.503)$$

We shall now construct the appropriate characteristic envelope. According to equations (4.502) and (4.503), we find

$$\frac{\partial \mathfrak{V}_0}{\partial \varpi} = \frac{3GM}{2a^2e^2}\left(\frac{1}{e}\sin^{-1}e - \sqrt{1-e^2}\right)\frac{\varpi}{a} \qquad (\varpi \leqslant a) \quad (4.504)$$

and

$$\frac{\partial \mathfrak{V}_0}{\partial \varpi} = \frac{3GM}{2a^2e^2}\left(\frac{\varpi}{ae}\sin^{-1}\frac{ae}{\varpi} - \sqrt{1-\frac{a^2e^2}{\varpi^2}}\right) \qquad (\varpi \geqslant a)\,. \quad (4.505)$$

From equations (4.408) and (4.502)–(4.505) we obtain

$$\left.\begin{aligned} I_1 &= 3\frac{GM}{ae^2}\left(\frac{1}{e}\sin^{-1}e - \sqrt{1-e^2}\right)\left(\frac{\varpi}{a}\right)^2 \\ &\qquad - 3\frac{GM}{ae}\sin^{-1}e \qquad (\varpi \leqslant a)\,, \\ &= 3\frac{GM}{ae}\bigg[\left(\frac{\varpi^2}{a^2e^2}-1\right)\sin^{-1}\frac{ae}{\varpi} \\ &\qquad -\frac{\varpi}{ae}\sqrt{1-\frac{a^2e^2}{\varpi^2}}\bigg] \qquad (\varpi \geqslant a)\,,\end{aligned}\right\} \quad (4.506)$$

and

$$\left.\begin{aligned} I_2^2 &= \frac{3GMa}{2e^2}\left(\frac{1}{e}\sin^{-1}e - \sqrt{1-e^2}\right)\left(\frac{\varpi}{a}\right)^4 \qquad (\varpi \leqslant a)\,, \\ &= \frac{3GMae}{2}\left(\frac{\varpi}{ae}\sin^{-1}\frac{ae}{\varpi} - \sqrt{1-\frac{a^2e^2}{\varpi^2}}\right)\left(\frac{\varpi}{ae}\right)^3 \qquad (\varpi \geqslant a)\,.\end{aligned}\right\} \quad (4.507)$$

The foregoing equations defining the characteristic envelope can be expressed more conveniently as follows: For $\varpi \leqslant a$, we clearly have

$$\left.\begin{aligned} I_1 &= \sqrt{\frac{6GM}{a^3e^2}\left(\frac{1}{e}\sin^{-1}e - \sqrt{1-e^2}\right)}\, I_2 \\ &\qquad - \frac{3GM}{ae}\sin^{-1}e \qquad (\varpi \leqslant a)\,.\end{aligned}\right\} \quad (4.508)$$

Hence the part of the characteristic envelope associated with the motions inside the spheroid is a straight line. There is no such simple relation for points outside the spheroid. But the characteristic envelope for these regions can be expressed parametrically by the relations

$$\left.\begin{aligned} I_1 &= 3\,\frac{GM}{ae}\left[(y^2-1)\sin^{-1}\frac{1}{y}-\sqrt{y^2-1}\right] \\ I_2^2 &= \tfrac{3}{2}GMae\left[y^4\sin^{-1}\frac{1}{y}-y^2\sqrt{y^2-1}\right] \end{aligned}\quad \begin{pmatrix} (\varpi \geqslant a) \\ (y \geqslant e^{-1}) \end{pmatrix},\right\} \tag{4.509}$$

where we have written

$$\varpi = aey\,, \tag{4.510}$$

so that $y = e^{-1}$ at $\varpi = a$. The characteristic envelope as defined by equations (4.508) and (4.509) is illustrated in Figure 18.

We shall now show that under certain circumstances the part of the characteristic envelope defined by the equations (4.509) has turning-points. As we have already shown in § 4.4, the appearance of turning-points depends on the existence of regions of instability of the circular orbits. Inside the spheroid the circular orbits are clearly stable. Consequently, turning-points can occur only on or outside the spheroid. Thus the condition for the appearance of turning-points is

$$\frac{\partial}{\partial\varpi}\left(\varpi^3\,\frac{\partial\mathfrak{B}_0}{\partial\varpi}\right) \leqslant 0 \qquad (\varpi \geqslant a)\,, \tag{4.511}$$

for $\mathfrak{B}_0$ give by equation (4.503). Explicitly, this condition is (cf. eqs. [4.409] and [4.509])

$$\frac{d}{dy}\left(y^4\sin^{-1}\frac{1}{y}-y^2\sqrt{y^2-1}\right) \leqslant 0 \qquad (y \geqslant e^{-1})\,, \tag{4.512}$$

or, after performing the required differentiation,

$$4y^3\sin^{-1}\frac{1}{y}-\frac{4y^3-2y}{\sqrt{y^2-1}} \leqslant 0 \qquad (y \geqslant e^{-1})\,, \tag{4.513}$$

or

$$\sin^{-1}\frac{1}{y}-\frac{\dfrac{1}{y}-\dfrac{1}{2y^3}}{\sqrt{1-\dfrac{1}{y^2}}} \leqslant 0 \qquad (y \geqslant e^{-1})\,. \tag{4.514}$$

Hence, the instability of the circular orbits at the periphery of the spheroid requires

$$\sin^{-1} e - \frac{e - \frac{1}{2} e^3}{\sqrt{1 - e^2}} \leqslant 0 . \tag{4.515}$$

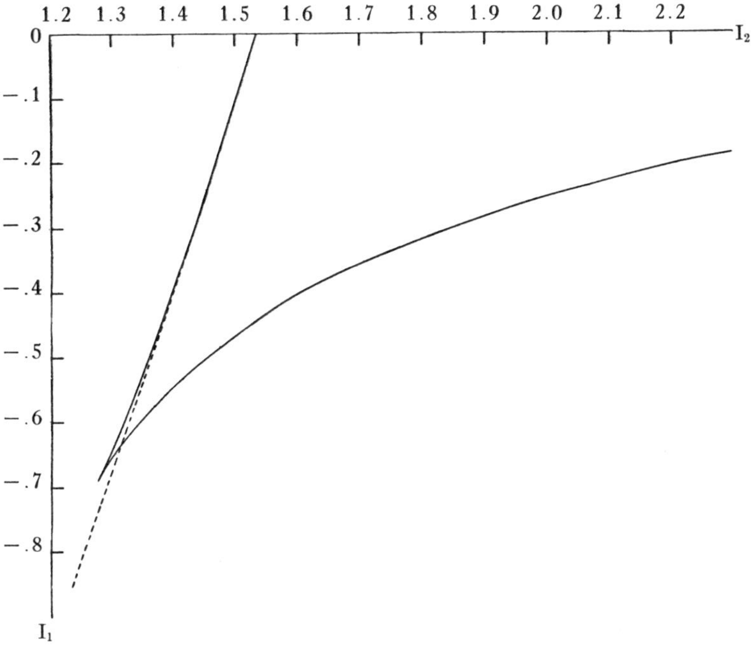

FIG. 18.—The characteristic envelope for homogeneous spheroids. The fully drawn curve represents the (I_1, I_2) locus, determined parametrically by equations (4.509). (I_1 and I_2 are measured in units of $[GM]/[ae]$ and $[GMae]^{1/2}$, respectively.) The turning-point occurs for $y = 1.199$ corresponding to the solution $e_1 = 0.834$ of equation (4.517). The dotted curve (which is a straight line), represents the part of the characteristic envelope for the inside of a spheroid with an eccentricity $e = 0.983$.

The inequality (4.515) is clearly equivalent to

$$e \geqslant e_1 , \tag{4.516}$$

where e_1 is defined by

$$\sin^{-1} e_1 - \frac{e_1 - \frac{1}{2} e_1^3}{\sqrt{1 - e_1^2}} = 0 . \tag{4.517}$$

Numerically, it is found that

$$e_1 = 0.834 . \tag{4.518}$$

Thus the circular orbit at the periphery of an oblate spheroid within an eccentricity greater than e_1 is unstable. The associated characteristic envelope has a turning-point at $\varpi = a$. Further, according to equations (4.510), (4.514), and (4.517), it follows that the region of the instability extends from $\varpi = a$ to $\varpi = (ae/e_1)$. Hence, for

$$a \leqslant \varpi \leqslant a \frac{e}{e_1} \tag{4.519}$$

the circular orbits are unstable.

We can summarize the main conclusions of the foregoing analysis as follows:

The characteristic envelope associated with the field of a homogeneous oblate spheroid has no turning-points for e $\leqslant$ $e_1(= 0.834)$; *for* e $>$ e_1 *there are two turning-points: the first occurs at the periphery of the spheroid, where the circular orbits are unstable, and the second at* $\varpi = ae/e_1$, *where the circular orbits just cease to be unstable.*

ii) *The regions of instability of the circular orbits in the field of a homogeneous spheroid and a central mass.*—The appearance of the instability of circular orbits in the outer regions of spheroidal systems of sufficient eccentricity can be extended to more general types of systems. Thus, let us consider the case where the gravitational field arises from a central mass together with a homogeneous oblate spheroid. We can then write

$$\mathfrak{B}_0 = \mathfrak{B}_s - \mu \frac{GM}{\varpi}, \tag{4.520}$$

where the first term on the right-hand side represents the gravitational field of the spheroid, and the second term the field due to the central mass. In equation (4.520) μ denotes the ratio of the central mass to the mass of the spheroid. The characteristic envelope associated with the field (4.520) is readily found. We have (cf. eqs. [4.506], [4.507], and [4.509])

$$\left.\begin{aligned} I_1 &= 3\frac{GM}{a e^2}\left(\frac{1}{e}\sin^{-1} e - \sqrt{1-e^2}\right)\left(\frac{\varpi}{a}\right)^2 \\ &\qquad - \mu\frac{GM}{\varpi} - 3\frac{GM}{a e}\sin^{-1} e, \\ I_2^2 &= \frac{3GMa}{2e^2}\left(\frac{1}{e}\sin^{-1} e - \sqrt{1-e^2}\right)\left(\frac{\varpi}{a}\right)^4 \\ &\qquad + \mu GM\varpi, \end{aligned}\right\} (\varpi \leqslant a) \tag{4.521}$$

and

$$\left.\begin{aligned} I_1 &= 3\,\frac{GM}{a\,e}\left[(y^2-1)\sin^{-1}\frac{1}{y}-\sqrt{y^2-1}\right] \\ &\qquad\qquad -\mu\,\frac{GM}{a\,e}\,\frac{1}{y}\,, \\ I_2^2 &= \tfrac{3}{2}GM\,a\,e\left[y^4\sin^{-1}\frac{1}{y}-y^2\sqrt{y^2-1}\right] \\ &\qquad\qquad +\mu GM\,a\,e\,y\,, \end{aligned}\right\}\quad (\varpi\geqslant a,\ y\geqslant e^{-1})\qquad (4.522)$$

where we have written $y = \varpi/ae$.

The condition for the appearance of turning-points on the characteristic envelope becomes (cf. eq. [4.512])

$$\frac{d}{dy}\left(y^4\sin^{-1}\frac{1}{y}-y^2\sqrt{y^2-1}+\tfrac{2}{3}\mu y\right)\leqslant 0\qquad (y\geqslant e^{-1})\,.\quad (4.523)$$

After some further reductions the foregoing inequality becomes (cf. eq. [4.513])

$$4y^3\sin^{-1}\frac{1}{y}-\frac{4y^3-2y}{\sqrt{y^2-1}}+\tfrac{2}{3}\mu\leqslant 0\qquad (y\geqslant e^{-1})\,.\quad (4.524)$$

Hence the condition for the appearance of instability at the periphery of the spheroid is (remembering that at $\varpi = a$, $y = 1/e$)

$$\sin^{-1}e-\frac{e-\frac{1}{2}e^3}{\sqrt{1-e^2}}+\tfrac{1}{6}\mu e^3\leqslant 0\,.\qquad (4.525)$$

Let $e(\mu)$ be such that

$$\sin^{-1}e(\mu)-\frac{e(\mu)-\frac{1}{2}e^3(\mu)}{\sqrt{1-e^2(\mu)}}+\tfrac{1}{6}\mu e^3(\mu)=0\,;\qquad (4.526)$$

then, for $e \geqslant e(\mu)$, the circular orbit at the periphery of the spheroid is unstable, and the region of instability extends from $\varpi = a$ to $\varpi = ae/e(\mu)$. (We may note that, according to Lindblad, $e(\mu) = 0.90$ for $\mu = 0.9$.)

iii) *The condition for the appearance of turning-points on the characteristic envelope in terms of the density gradient.*—The appearance of the instability of the circular orbits at the edges of flattened spheroidal systems which we have found is seen to be directly correlated with the relatively steep density gradients prevailing in these regions. Indeed, it can be shown, conversely, that, given a sufficiently steep density gradient, we should expect the instability of the circular orbits in these regions and the corresponding appearance of turning-points in the characteristic envelope. To show this we first note that quite generally the density at a point must be related to the potential by Poisson's equation

$$\nabla^2 \mathfrak{B} = 4\pi G \rho \, , \tag{4.527}$$

or, in cylindrical co-ordinates,

$$\frac{\partial^2 \mathfrak{B}}{\partial \varpi^2} + \frac{1}{\varpi} \frac{\partial \mathfrak{B}}{\partial \varpi} + \frac{\partial^2 \mathfrak{B}}{\partial z^2} = 4\pi G \rho \, . \tag{4.528}$$

We shall now apply this equation for a point on the galactic plane. Assuming, as we have done hitherto, that the galactic plane is a plane of symmetry, we can write

$$\mathfrak{B} = \frac{1}{2} \left(\frac{\partial^2 \mathfrak{B}}{\partial z^2} \right)_0 z^2 + \text{constant} \qquad (z \to 0) \, , \tag{4.529}$$

where the subscript "0" indicates that the quantity in parentheses is to be evaluated on the plane $z = 0$. We can re-write equation (4.529) alternatively in the form

$$\mathfrak{B} = 2\pi G \bar{\rho} z^2 + \text{constant} \qquad (z \to 0) \, , \tag{4.530}$$

where we have *defined* $\bar{\rho}$ by the equation

$$\left(\frac{\partial^2 \mathfrak{B}}{\partial z^2} \right)_0 = 4\pi G \bar{\rho} \, . \tag{4.531}$$

We can, therefore, interpret $\bar{\rho}$ as an *average density* appropriate for, and relevant to, the discussion of motions in the region under consideration. In a general way, it is clear that for the averaging required to obtain $\bar{\rho}$ we might have to include regions which may be appreciably distant from the particular region to which ρ refers.

According to equation (4.530), we can re-write Poisson's equation in the form

$$\frac{\partial^2 \mathfrak{B}_0}{\partial \varpi^2} + \frac{1}{\varpi} \frac{\partial \mathfrak{B}_0}{\partial \varpi} = 4\pi G (\rho - \bar{\rho}) \, , \tag{4.532}$$

where, as in § 4.4, $\mathfrak{B}_0$ denotes the function $\mathfrak{B}(\varpi, 0)$. Now the condition for the instability of the circular orbit is

$$\frac{\partial^2 \mathfrak{B}_0}{\partial \varpi^2} + \frac{3}{\varpi} \frac{\partial \mathfrak{B}_0}{\partial \varpi} \leqslant 0 \, . \tag{4.533}$$

Combining equations (4.532) and (4.533), we have the inequality

$$4\pi G(\rho - \bar{\rho}) + \frac{2}{\varpi}\frac{\partial \mathfrak{B}_0}{\partial \varpi} \leqslant 0 \qquad (4.534)$$

or, somewhat differently,

$$\bar{\rho} - \rho \geqslant \frac{1}{2\pi G}\frac{1}{\varpi}\frac{\partial \mathfrak{B}}{\partial \varpi} = \frac{\omega_c^2}{2\pi G}. \qquad (4.535)$$

In this form, the criterion for the instability of circular orbits is due to Lindblad.

Since $\bar{\rho}$ refers to the average over a relatively large neighborhood, the inequality (4.535) is essentially the requirement of a sufficiently steep gradient of density for the appearance of the instability of the circular orbits in the region considered.

4.6. *Lindblad's theory of spiral structure in nebulae.*—The considerations of the previous sections have formed the starting-point for a specific theory of spiral structure in nebulae due to Lindblad. In this theory the phenomenon of the instability of the circular orbits, which has been found to be present at the edges of flattened spheroidal systems, is regarded as providing the basic reason for the initial development of spiral structure in nebulae. As evidence for this suggestion we might refer to the fact that early spirals are highly elliptical objects and, further, that at the edges of these systems we may expect precisely those conditions to prevail as would provide for the necessary density gradients to secure the instability of the circular orbits. In other words, it would appear that if we follow the variation of $(\bar{\rho} - \rho)$ from the center outward[8] we will reach a point where this quantity will just become equal to $\omega_c^2/2\pi G$ (cf. eq. [4.535]). At this point there will occur a turning-point on the characteristic envelope and, according to our discussion in §§ 4.4 and 4.5, the stars just inside this point will be describing orbits close to instability. Consequently, we may expect that as a result of accidental disturbances some of these stars may be "ejected" into the region where the circular orbits are definitely unstable. The first question which arises is therefore concerned with the nature of these orbits. We shall start our discussion of Lindblad's theory with the consideration of this matter.

[8] For the definition of $\bar{\rho}$ see § 4.5 (eq. [4.531]).

i) *Spiral orbits in the equatorial plane of highly oblate systems.*— We shall consider the orbits described in the field of an oblate spheroid together with a central mass. According to equations (4.304), (4.305), (4.505), and (4.520), the equations of motion for an orbit confined to the (x, y) plane are

$$\frac{d^2\varpi}{dt^2} - \frac{h^2}{\varpi^3} = -\frac{3}{2}\frac{GM}{a^2 e^2}\left(\frac{\varpi}{a e}\sin^{-1}\frac{a e}{\varpi} - \sqrt{1 - \frac{a^2 e^2}{\varpi^2}} + \tfrac{2}{3}\mu\frac{a^2 e^2}{\varpi^2}\right) \quad (4.601)$$

and

$$\varpi^2 \dot{\theta} = h = \text{constant} . \quad (4.602)$$

Following the standard procedure for treating the motions described under the action of a central field of force, we first introduce $1/\varpi$ as the variable. We then find

$$\left.\begin{aligned}\frac{d^2}{d\theta^2}\left(\frac{1}{\varpi}\right) + \frac{1}{\varpi} = \frac{3}{2}\frac{GM}{h^2}\left(\frac{\varpi}{a e}\right)^2 \Big(\frac{\varpi}{a e}\sin^{-1}\frac{a e}{\varpi} \\ - \sqrt{1 - \frac{a^2 e^2}{\varpi^2}} + \tfrac{2}{3}\mu\frac{a^2 e^2}{\varpi^2}\Big).\end{aligned}\right\} \quad (4.603)$$

Introduce the new variable u, defined by

$$u = \frac{a e}{\varpi} . \quad (4.604)$$

Equation (4.603) becomes

$$\frac{d^2 u}{d\theta^2} + u = \frac{3GM a e}{2h^2}\frac{1}{u^2}\left(\frac{1}{u}\sin^{-1} u - \sqrt{1 - u^2} + \tfrac{2}{3}\mu u^2\right) , \quad (4.605)$$

which is the general equation for the determination of the orbit.

We shall first consider those orbits which are *asymptotic to the circular orbits* at the periphery of the spheroid. We should then require that the constant of areas h in equation (4.605) be the same as that for the circular orbit $\varpi = a$. Since

$$e = u \qquad \text{for} \qquad \varpi = a , \quad (4.606)$$

we conclude from equation (4.605) that the constant of areas must be so chosen that

$$e = \frac{3GM a e}{2h^2}\left(\tfrac{2}{3}\mu + \frac{1}{e^3}\sin^{-1} e - \frac{1}{e^2}\sqrt{1 - e^2}\right) . \quad (4.607)$$

Equation (4.605) now reduces to

$$\left.\begin{aligned}\frac{d^2u}{d\theta^2}+u=&\frac{e^4}{\frac{2}{3}\mu e^3+\sin^{-1} e-e\sqrt{1-e^2}}\\&\times\left(\tfrac{2}{3}\mu+\frac{1}{u^3}\sin^{-1} u-\frac{1}{u^2}\sqrt{1-u^2}\right).\end{aligned}\right\} \quad (4.608)$$

A first integral of the foregoing equation can be obtained by multiplying throughout by $du/d\theta$ and integrating. We find

$$\left.\begin{aligned}\left(\frac{du}{d\theta}\right)^2+u^2=&\frac{e^4}{\frac{2}{3}\mu e^3+\sin^{-1} e-e\sqrt{1-e^2}}\Big[\tfrac{4}{3}\mu u\\&+\left(2-\frac{1}{u^2}\right)\sin^{-1} u+\frac{1}{u}\sqrt{1-u^2}\Big]+c_0\,,\end{aligned}\right\} \quad (4.609)$$

where c_0 is a constant of integration. Again, for orbits asymptotic to the circular orbit $\varpi = a$, c_0 is determinate. For we should clearly require that

$$\left.\begin{aligned}e^2=&\frac{e^4}{\frac{2}{3}\mu e^3+\sin^{-1} e-e\sqrt{1-e^2}}\Big[\tfrac{4}{3}\mu e\\&+\left(2-\frac{1}{e^2}\right)\sin^{-1} e+\frac{1}{e}\sqrt{1-e^2}\Big]+c_0\end{aligned}\right\} \quad (4.610)$$

or

$$c_0 = 2e^2\,\frac{(1-e^2)\sin^{-1} e-e\sqrt{1-e^2}-\frac{1}{3}\mu e^3}{\sin^{-1} e-e\sqrt{1-e^2}+\frac{2}{3}\mu e^3}. \quad (4.611)$$

Substituting (4.611) in equation (4.609), we finally obtain

$$\left.\begin{aligned}\left(\frac{du}{d\theta}\right)^2+u^2=&\frac{e^4}{\frac{2}{3}\mu e^3+\sin^{-1} e-e\sqrt{1-e^2}}\Big[\tfrac{4}{3}\mu u\\&+\left(2-\frac{1}{u^2}\right)\sin^{-1} u+\frac{1}{u}\sqrt{1-u^2}\\&+\frac{2}{e^2}(1-e^2)\sin^{-1} e-\frac{2}{e}\sqrt{1-e^2}-\tfrac{2}{3}\mu e\Big].\end{aligned}\right\} \quad (4.612)$$

The integration of equation (4.612) for different values of μ and e ($e > e[\mu]$, where $e[\mu]$ is given by eq. [4.526]), will be sufficient for obtaining a general view of these orbits. Lindblad has numerically integrated equation (4.612) for several values of μ and e. In Figure 19 we reproduce some of his orbits.

As we have already indicated (p. 171), we expect that stars describing orbits originally nearly circular and just inside the edges of flattened systems are "ejected" on account of accidental disturbances which may cause changes in their energies and/or constant of areas. Consequently, the orbits resulting from such disturbed circular motion are of greater interest. Figures 20 and 21 taken from a paper by Rosseland[9] illustrate such orbits.

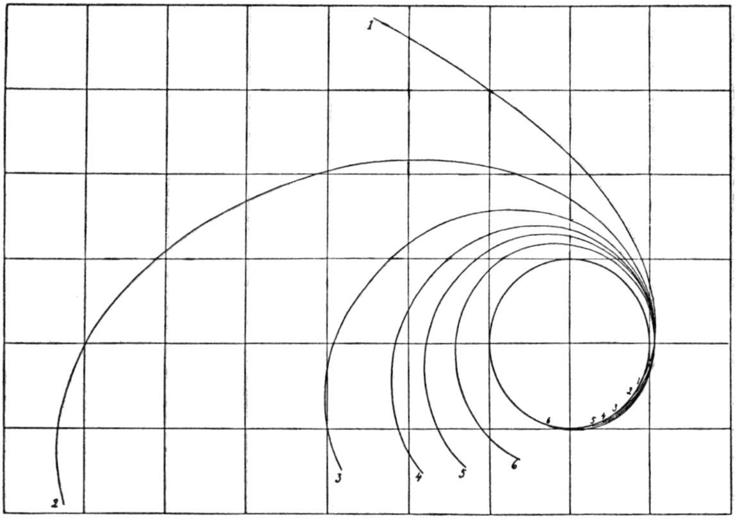

FIG. 19.—Orbits asymptotic to the edge of a homogeneous spheroid derived from equation (4.612) with $\mu = 0$. The curves marked 1, ... , 6 are for values of $e = 1.000$, 0.995, 0.980, 0.965, 0.950, and 0.920, respectively (Lindblad, *Kungl. Svenska vetensk. handl.*, Tredje serien, **4**, No. 7, 1927).

ii) *The process of ejection.*—We shall now examine in a general way the manner in which we may expect the ejection of matter from the edges of flattened systems to lead to the formation of spiral arms.

As we have already seen, when a mass of material leaves the region where the instability of the circular orbits is just beginning, it will depart along orbits of the form illustrated in Figures 19–21. Since the ejected mass was originally characterized by approximately the same constant of areas as the matter at the edge of the system,

[9] *Naturwiss.*, **27**, 729, 1939.

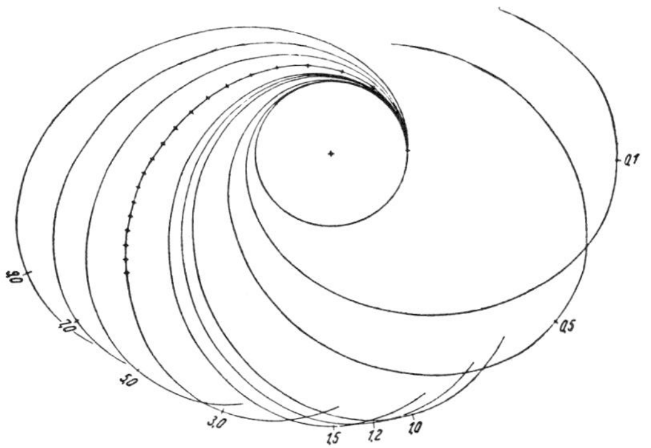

Fig. 20

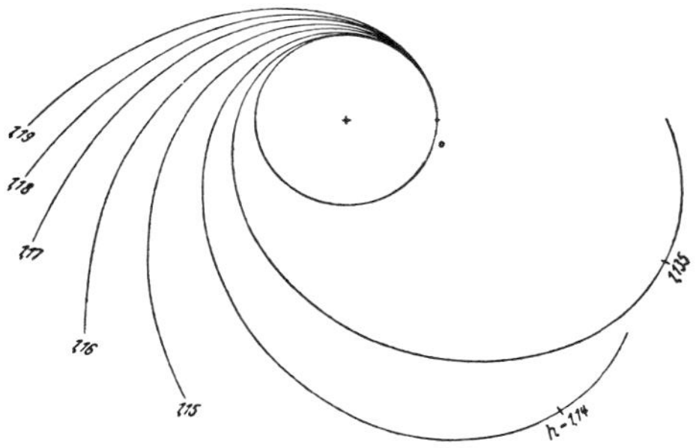

Fig. 21

FIGS. 20–21.—Orbits in the equatorial plane of a highly flattened spheroid which are asymptotic to its edge. The orbits illustrated in Figures 20 and 21 are all derived from an orbit, originally circular, by perturbations of radial (Fig. 20) or tangential (Fig. 21) character. The markings on the curve "3,0" in Figure 20 denote the positions occupied after equal intervals of time (Rosseland, *Naturwiss.*, **27**, 729, 1939).

it follows that on account of its greater distance from the center it will lag behind the point from which ejection took place. This ejected matter will in turn cause a deviation in $\mathfrak{V}$ along the radius vector joining it to the center. It is seen that this deviation will consist principally in decreasing the circular angular velocity for the material immediately beneath it. Consequently, if the equation

$$\bar{\rho} - \rho = \frac{\omega_c^2}{2\pi G} \tag{4.613}$$

was originally valid, we should expect that at the later time

$$\bar{\rho} - \rho_0 > \frac{\omega_c^2}{2\pi G} \tag{4.614}$$

for the material directly below the ejected mass. In other words, the region of the instability of the circular orbits will begin nearer the center beneath the ejected mass than elsewhere. Thus, while the orbit described by this mass must originally have been on the verge of stability, it will later become definitely unstable on account of the tidal effects of the mass already ejected. Hence this mass will also depart from the edge of the system. In this manner more and more of the material will be drawn out, and we anticipate the slow formation of spiral arms.

In following this gradual disintegration of the central system, we may ask whether under suitable circumstances a state of continuous and steady ejection can prevail. To examine this we shall introduce a rotating frame of reference moving with the angular velocity ω_c characterizing the circular motion at the edge of the system. From our remarks in the preceding paragraph it follows that in this frame of reference the point at which ejection takes place must move with an angular velocity of sign opposite to that of ω_c. It is clear that the angular velocity actually selected will depend not only on the kind of tidal field which begins to operate as a consequence of this velocity but also on the extent to which this disturbing action is in resonance with the free oscillations of the system. As we have seen in § 4.3, the frequency of this oscillation is $n_1/2\pi$ where (cf. eq. [4.327])

$$n_1^2 = 2\,\frac{\Theta_c}{\varpi_0}\left(\frac{\partial\Theta_c}{\partial\varpi} + \frac{\Theta_c}{\varpi}\right)_0 . \tag{4.615}$$

For $\Theta_c \propto \varpi$, $n_1 = 2\omega_c$. If we now suppose that the disturbance is in resonance with this oscillation, any of its effects may be developed in the form of a Fourier series

$$\Sigma\{A_n \cos(2\omega_c t + n\theta) + B_n \sin(2\omega_c t + n\theta)\} . \quad (4.616)$$

For a disturbance propagated against the direction of rotation, n takes only positive values. The term $n = 1$ in the foregoing expansion corresponds to a disturbance which has only one maximum along the circumference and is propagated with an angular velocity $-2\omega_c$. According to Lindblad, a disturbance of this character will not be very effective in disintegrating the system. On the other hand, when $n = 2$, we have a disturbance with two opposite maxima propagated with an angular velocity $-\omega_c$. In other words, for disturbances of this character the point of ejection remains *fixed in space*. For higher values of n the disturbance becomes increasingly complicated, but it appears that the tidal force is most effective for $n = 2$.

Now an ejection process to be of interest in our present connection must increase, rather than decrease, with time. Consequently, we should require the conditions to be such as to favor the instability of the system to disturbances which lead to ejection. It is clear that such conditions will be provided by a considerable flattening of the system. For, according to Bryan, Maclaurin spheroids first become unstable at an eccentricity $e = 0.9529$ for sectorial harmonic waves which have two opposite maxima—in other words, for disturbances similar to those we have considered as suitable in the preceding paragraph. We may thus expect that the ejection of the kind contemplated will continue only for systems with eccentricities greater than 0.95. This corresponds to a ratio of the axis of about 3.1, and this value is in agreement with the upper limit to the ellipticities of elliptical nebulae (§ 1.6).

In the case where the spiral arms are relatively thin, we may neglect the decrease in size and mass of the central system. In such cases the spiral arms must approximate to the orbits of individual stars. The nebula M 81 is an example of a fairly well-resolved spiral with thin arms, and we should expect the simple theory to apply to this case. In Figure 22 we have made, following Lindblad, a comparison of the form of this nebula with the orbits asymptotic to the edge of a homogeneous spheroid with an eccentricity $e = 0.965$. It is seen that the agreement is satisfactory. For the cases where the arms are "heavy" such a simple and direct comparison will not be possible. Lindblad has extended his theory to include these cases as well. However, we shall not go further into these matters but

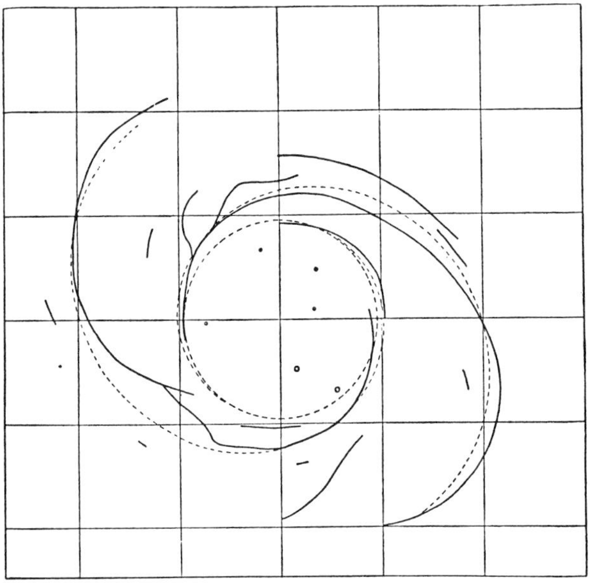

FIG. 22.—Comparison of the arms of Messier 81 with the theoretical orbits in the equatorial plane and asymptotic to the edge of a homogeneous spheroid of eccentricity $e = 0.965$ (Lindblad, *Kungl. svenska vetensk. handl.*, Tredje serien, **4**, No. 7, 1927).

refer the reader to the investigations quoted in the "Bibliographical Notes" at the end of the chapter.

iii) *The sense of rotation.*—It will be seen that on Lindblad's theory the direction of the winding of the spiral arms is such that they are described *outward* in the direction of rotation. A confirmation of this predicted sense of the winding of the spirals with respect to the direction of rotation is, of course, of crucial importance. For objects with visible spiral arms and with spectrographically measured rotation this question depends on the true orientation of the plane of the nebula in space. Several attempts have been made to solve this question by means of the absorption effects of the dark matter in the nebulae. In the case of objects in which the inclination of the fundamental plane of symmetry to the line of sight is so small that the winding of the spirals is no longer clearly visible, we often observe well-defined absorption bands as in NGC 4594 (see Pl. III). In such cases there can hardly be any doubt as to the obscuring material's being situated on the near side of the edge. With increasing angle of inclination, however, the effect of the obscuring material on the distribution of the luminosity does not lend itself to any such direct interpretation. Indeed, any attempt at interpretation must depend on the detailed distribution of the absorbing and emissive material in the nebulae. While this is still a matter largely of

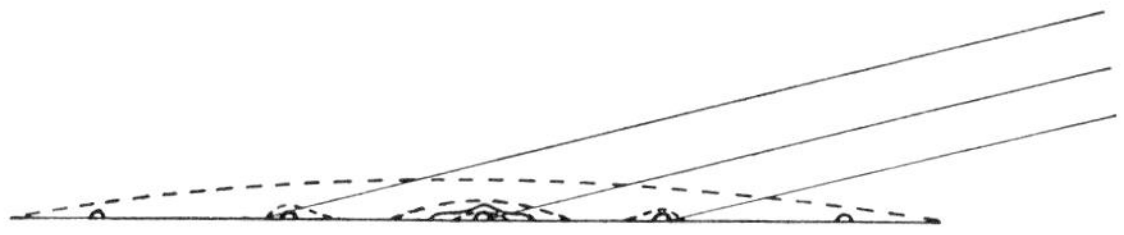

FIG. 23.—Schematic vertical section, according to Lindblad, of the luminous and dark material in an extragalactic nebula of small central mass. The fully drawn curves represent the intersections with the luminous material, while the dotted curves represent the corresponding intersections with the dark material. The oblique lines indicate the line of sight.

one's personal judgment, Lindblad suggests a distribution of the material indicated in Figure 23, where the full-drawn curves denote the luminous material, and the dotted curves the obscuring material. Though the dark matter may have a strong concentration toward the equatorial plane, it seems probable that the obscuring material will extend to quite considerable heights over this plane. The effect of the longer optical path through this absorbing medium on the far side will produce a much more effective darkening on this side than on the near side. In this connection it must be remembered that, if the absorbing medium consists of fine material particles (as in our own Galaxy), the effect of the *phase function* in scattering will also become important in the sense that forward scattering is more efficient than backward scattering. This would further accentuate the difference in brightness between the near and the far side in favor of the former.

According to Lindblad, the disposition of the absorbing and the emissive matter which he suggests finds confirmation in his photometric investigation of NGC 7331 in different colors. It appears that in the obscured regions of this nebula the color is nearly uniform and the decrease of intensity from the nucleus outward in these regions is nearly the same in the different colors. On the other hand, close to the nucleus on the brighter side of the nebula, a spiral arm is clearly visible in the ultraviolet light, while it is hardly perceptible in red light and seems to merge into the "amorphous" central regions. In other words, on the brighter side of the nebula the decrease in intensity from the nucleus outward is much more rapid in red light than in ultraviolet light. It is seen that these effects become readily intelligible on the distribution of obscuring and luminous matter according to Figure 23.

Finally, if we accept Lindblad's interpretation of the dark lanes in nebulae, it appears that both in the case of the Andromeda nebula and in the case of M 33 the predicted and observed senses of rotation with respect to the winding of the spirals agree. We should, however, point out that this important matter is far from being settled and that considerable divergence of views still persists. Thus, as we have already remarked in § 1.7, in the case of NGC 3190 Hubble and Mayall suggest a sense of rotation for this object which is contrary to Lindblad's theory. The final decision in this matter must await future investigations.

4.7. *Critical remarks on Lindblad's theory. Some alternative suggestions.*—According to Lindblad's theory outlined in § 4.6, the fully resolved spiral pattern is regarded as an advanced state which all nebulae will eventually reach in the course of their evolution. On this view, elliptical nebulae represent early stages from which spiral arms begin to form on account of the instability of the circular orbits setting in at the edges of the systems. As a criticism of this view it has been pointed out that the abundance and the distribution of elliptical nebulae relative to those of the spirals do not suggest any difference in their ages. It has been particularly noted in this connection that clusters of nebulae like the Virgo cluster generally contain nebulae of all classes with the same order of luminosity. Also, in spite of Lindblad's attempts to the contrary, it appears diffi-

PLATE VI

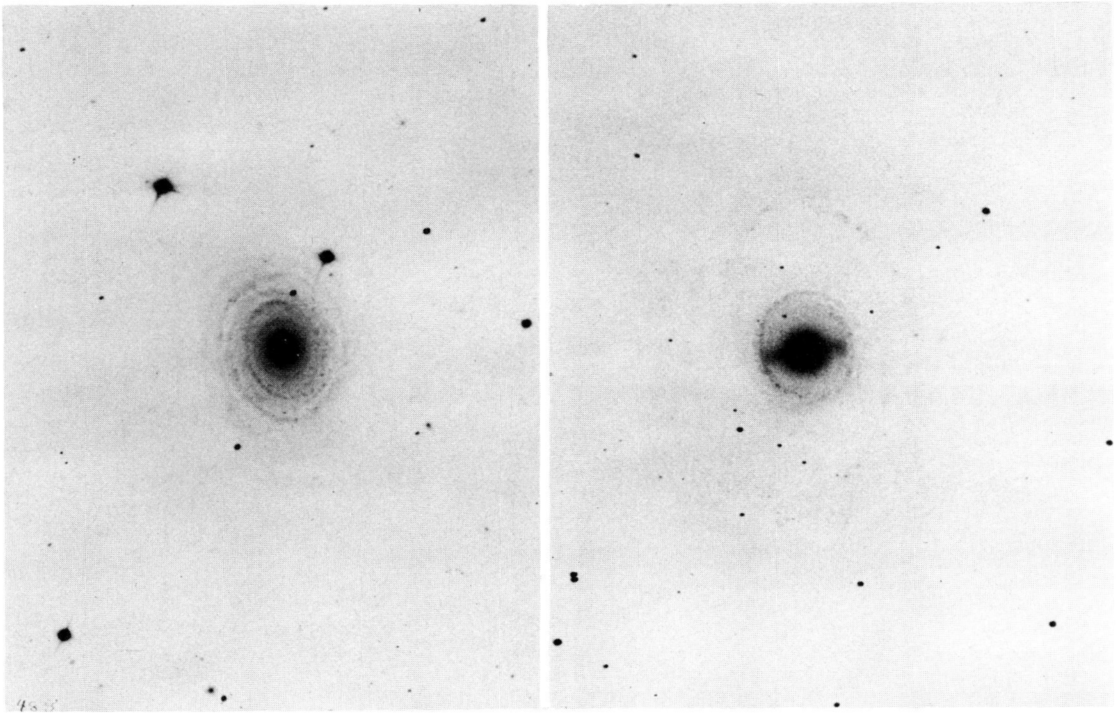

Mount Wilson Observatory

INTERMEDIATE SPIRALS

Left: NGC 488, a normal spiral. *Right:* NGC 1398, a barred spiral. The spiral patterns are well developed, but the nuclear regions remain unresolved (negative print).

cult to understand how the greater part of the material in a nebula can find its way to the arms against the gravitational forces from the original densely packed state. It should be remarked in this connection that many spirals do give indications that a large part of the mass is in the arms. Again, it has been argued that the "ejection" of arms from a rotating central body does not provide a sufficiently broad basis for the complete understanding of the wide variety of forms which nebulae show. Thus a frequent type of object which differs radically from both spirals and elliptical nebulae are the barred spirals (see Frontispiece and Pl. II). The characteristic feature of these objects is the appearance of a straight bar which crosses the central regions, with spiral arms emerging perpendicularly from the ends of the bar. Sometimes the arms form a circular ring with the bar as a diameter. It is difficult to see how these configurations can be interpreted directly in terms of the instability of the circular orbits, which forms the basis of Lindblad's theory.

In suggesting an alternative view, both Randers and Hubble emphasize the fact that a *ring* or a *system of rings* appears to be a rather general feature of most types of nebulae. Thus there exist spirals in which the impression is one of a set of concentric rings (see Pl. VI). Again, there are instances of single rings centered on dense nuclei and also transition types showing characteristics of both spirals and rings. Accordingly, it is a justifiable point of view to regard the formation of a *ring pattern* as an essential step in the evolution of nebulae. But the manner in which this is to be accomplished is not so evident. What is needed is a mechanism which will "gather" the material in the system in certain rings. It has been suggested by Randers that viscous forces might provide the necessary agency. We shall presently see that it is extremely difficult to define the concept of viscosity in stellar systems. But we shall return to this matter after describing how this supposed viscosity is expected to operate.

Consider a system in simple differential rotation. The assumed existence of viscous forces will introduce in such a system tangential forces (in the transverse directions) of amount

$$F = \mu \frac{d}{d\varpi}\left(\frac{1}{\varpi}\frac{d}{d\varpi}\varpi\Theta_0\right), \tag{4.71}$$

where μ denotes the "coefficient of viscosity" and $\Theta_0(\varpi)$ the field of differential rotation.

When the force F is positive, the angular velocity of the matter at the point under consideration will increase; similarly, if F is negative, the angular velocity will decrease; in both cases radial motions will be induced which will be directed outward in the former case and inward in the latter. For any specified distribution of Θ_0, equation (4.71) will enable us to fix the direction of motion.

To determine the circumstances under which F is positive, zero, or negative, assume for Θ_0 the form

$$\Theta_0 = k\varpi^n \qquad (k > 0)\,, \tag{4.72}$$

where k is a constant. The expression for F now becomes

$$F = \mu k\,(n^2 - 1)\,\varpi^{n-2}\,. \tag{4.73}$$

Consequently,

$$\left.\begin{array}{ll} F > 0 & |n| > 1\,, \\ F = 0 & |n| = 1\,, \\ F < 0 & |n| < 1\,. \end{array}\right\} \tag{4.74}$$

We therefore conclude that the radial motion resulting from the force F is outward if Θ_0/ϖ increases outward or decreases more rapidly than ϖ^{-2}. (The latter case [$n = -1$] corresponds to a situation in which the circular orbits are unstable; for, according to equation [4.311], in an inverse-cube field of force $\Theta_c \propto \varpi^{-1}$.) Similarly, F will induce inward motions if Θ_0/ϖ decreases less rapidly than ϖ^{-2}.

Hence, if the angular velocity increases outward, the matter will tend to move outward until it arrives at a point where the angular velocity attains its maximum. And when $\omega_0(=\Theta_0/\varpi)$ begins to decrease slowly, after passing through the maximum, the motions will be directed inward, i.e., again toward the region of maximum ω_0. At the point where the instability of the circular orbits sets in, the matter will begin to be "repelled" from the region of the preceding maximum of ω_0.

The effects we have described in the foregoing paragraph are reversed in the neighborhood of a region of minimum ω_0, the matter being directed away from this region on both sides.

From our discussion in the preceding paragraphs it follows that a tangential force of the form (4.71) will essentially tend to collect the material in regions where ω_c tends to constancy near maxima. Such a tendency would clearly be in the direction of producing a ring pattern. We shall not continue this discussion further but return to the difficulty mentioned at the outset, namely, the impossibility of giving an adequately satisfactory meaning to the concept of viscosity in a stellar system.

According to the formulae developed in § 2.5, the mean free path for a star (with average velocity) is given by

$$\left.\begin{aligned}\lambda_1(\bar{v}_2) &= 1.77\\ &\times 10^8 \frac{\bar{v}_2^4}{N m_1^2 \log_{10}[9.31\times 10^4 D_0 \bar{v}_2^2/(m_1+m_2)]}\text{ parsecs },\end{aligned}\right\} \tag{4.75}$$

where the mass, $\bar{v}_2$, D_0, and N are expressed in units of solar mass, 20 km/sec, parsec, and number per cubic parsec, respectively.

As representative of the typical conditions to be expected in a Galaxy, we shall assume that

$$\left.\begin{aligned}\bar{v}_2 &= 1.5\,(=30\text{ km/sec})\,; & m &= 0.5\odot\\ N &= 0.1\text{ stars/(parsec)}^3\,; & D_0 &= 2.7\text{ parsecs }.\end{aligned}\right\} \tag{4.76}$$

From equation (4.75) we find

$$\lambda_1(\bar{v}_2) = 6\times 10^9\text{ parsecs }, \tag{4.77}$$

which is at least several thousand times the dimensions of the Galaxy.

Again, as representative of the extreme possible conditions in a Galaxy, we shall assume that

$$\left.\begin{aligned}\bar{v}_2 &= 0.5\,(=10\text{ km/sec})\,; & m_1 &= 1\odot\,,\\ N &= 100\text{ stars/(parsec)}^3\,; & D_0 &= 0.27\text{ parsecs }.\end{aligned}\right\} \tag{4.78}$$

Equation (4.75) now gives

$$\lambda_1(\bar{v}_2) = 3\times 10^4\text{ parsecs }, \tag{4.79}$$

which is of the order of the diameter of the Galaxy.

It is very unlikely that the conditions in the Galaxy or in the extragalactic systems were at any time more extreme than those represented by equation (4.78). It therefore appears that the notion of viscosity cannot be introduced into stellar dynamics without a very much more careful discussion than has been made so far. One can reach the same conclusion by a somewhat different line of argument as follows: From the nature of the physical problem it is clear that the forces which we normally associate with the concept of viscosity, to become effective, must operate for times which are long compared to the time of relaxation of the system. On the other hand, according to our discussion in § 3.1, in galactic and extragalactic systems, we encounter systems with very long times of relaxation (of the order of 10^{14} years). Consequently, the transfer to such systems of notions valid only for systems averaged over times which are long compared with its time of relaxation becomes physically without content. While it is therefore of interest to note that the introduction of tangential forces depending on the gradient of the angular velocity will favor the development of a ring pattern in the system, the idea, even as regards the nature of these forces, is still too rudimentary to form an adequate basis for a satisfactory theory.

Summarizing, we can say that the general theory of stellar systems described by a spherical distribution of the residual velocities does provide a basis wide enough for the interpretation of the structural features of the nebulae. But the very generality of this scheme precludes it as a specific theory. Lindblad's theory, on the other hand, while it draws attention to the undoubtedly important part which the instability of the circular orbits at the edges of flattened systems must play in their evolution, yet fails in its further developments, if the highest standards of rigor are demanded. Finally, attention may also be drawn to the role which the development of a ring structure might play in the evolution of these objects.

4.8. *The equations of stellar hydrodynamics.*—In our discussions of the equation of continuity in chapter iii and in §§ 4.1 and 4.2 the emphasis has mainly been on seeking explicit solutions of this equation. It is, however, possible to obtain some general relations which have considerable practical importance. These are the *hydrodynamical equations* obtained by integrating the equation of continuity over the momentum variables after having multiplied the equation by appropriate factors. We shall now obtain these equations.

i) *The equations of stellar hydrodynamics in Cartesian co-ordinates.* —The equation of continuity in Cartesian co-ordinates is (eq. [3.303])

$$\left.\begin{aligned}\frac{\partial\Psi}{\partial t}+U\frac{\partial\Psi}{\partial x}+V\frac{\partial\Psi}{\partial y}+W\frac{\partial\Psi}{\partial z}-\frac{\partial\mathfrak{B}}{\partial x}\frac{\partial\Psi}{\partial U}&\\-\frac{\partial\mathfrak{B}}{\partial y}\frac{\partial\Psi}{\partial V}-\frac{\partial\mathfrak{B}}{\partial z}\frac{\partial\Psi}{\partial W}=0\,.&\end{aligned}\right\}\quad(4.801)$$

Integrate this equation over all the velocities. Since

$$\left.\begin{aligned}&\iiint\frac{\partial\Psi}{\partial t}\,dU\,dV\,dW=\frac{\partial}{\partial t}\iiint\Psi\,dU\,dV\,dW=\frac{\partial N}{\partial t}\,,\\&\iiint\frac{\partial\Psi}{\partial x}\,U\,dU\,dV\,dW\\&\qquad=\frac{\partial}{\partial x}\iiint\Psi U\,dU\,dV\,dW=\frac{\partial}{\partial x}(N\bar{U})\;;\text{ etc.},\\&\iiint\frac{\partial\Psi}{\partial U}\,dU\,dV\,dW=\iint[\Psi]_{U=-\infty}^{U=+\infty}dV\,dW=0\;;\text{ etc.},\end{aligned}\right\}\quad(4.802)$$

we obtain

$$\frac{\partial N}{\partial t}+\frac{\partial}{\partial x}(N\bar{U})+\frac{\partial}{\partial y}(N\bar{V})+\frac{\partial}{\partial z}(N\bar{W})=0\,,\quad(4.803)$$

where $\bar{U}$, $\bar{V}$, and $\bar{W}$ denote the average values of these quantities.[10] Equation (4.803) clearly expresses the conservation of numbers; it represents, therefore, the *macroscopic equation of continuity.*

Next, multiply the equation of continuity (4.801) successively by $UdUdVdW$, $VdUdVdW$, and $WdUdVdW$ and integrate over all the velocities. In view of

$$\left.\begin{aligned}&\iiint\frac{\partial\Psi}{\partial U}\,U\,dU\,dV\,dW=\iint[\Psi U]_{U=-\infty}^{U=+\infty}dV\,dW\\&\qquad\qquad-\iiint\Psi\,dU\,dV\,dW=-N\,,\\&\iiint\frac{\partial\Psi}{\partial U}\,V\,dU\,dV\,dW=\iint[\Psi]_{U=-\infty}^{U=+\infty}V\,dV\,dW=0\,,\end{aligned}\right\}\quad(4.804)$$

[10] These averages are clearly functions of position and time.

and similar relations obtained by cyclically permuting U, V, and W, we obtain

$$\left.\begin{aligned}\frac{\partial}{\partial t}(N\bar{U})+\frac{\partial}{\partial x}(N\overline{U^2})+\frac{\partial}{\partial y}(N\overline{UV})+\frac{\partial}{\partial z}(N\overline{UW})&=-N\frac{\partial\mathfrak{B}}{\partial x}\,,\\ \frac{\partial}{\partial t}(N\bar{V})+\frac{\partial}{\partial x}(N\overline{VU})+\frac{\partial}{\partial y}(N\overline{V^2})+\frac{\partial}{\partial z}(N\overline{VW})&=-N\frac{\partial\mathfrak{B}}{\partial y}\,,\\ \frac{\partial}{\partial t}(N\bar{W})+\frac{\partial}{\partial x}(N\overline{WU})+\frac{\partial}{\partial y}(N\overline{WV})+\frac{\partial}{\partial z}(N\overline{W^2})&=-N\frac{\partial\mathfrak{B}}{\partial z}\,,\end{aligned}\right\}\quad(4.805)$$

where we have used a bar to denote the average of the corresponding quantity.

Equations (4.805) represent the macroscopic equations for *mass motions*. These hydrodynamical equations are of greatest interest for axially symmetrical systems. However, in this case, the equations are most conveniently expressed in cylindrical co-ordinates, (ϖ, θ, z). It would be possible to obtain the required equations in this system of co-ordinates by a direct transformation of the variables. But they are more conveniently derived by first expressing the equation of continuity in these co-ordinates and then effecting the appropriate integrations. For this purpose we shall first obtain the equation of continuity in these co-ordinates.

ii) *The equation of continuity in cylindrical co-ordinates.*—In § 3.2 we proved Liouville's theorem in an arbitrary system of canonical variables. Thus, if q_1, q_2, and q_3 are any set of generalized co-ordinates and p_1, p_2, and p_3 the corresponding set of conjugate momenta, the distribution function $\Psi^*(q_1, q_2, q_3, p_1, p_2, p_3)$ satisfies the differential equation (eq. [3.26])

$$\frac{\partial\Psi^*}{\partial t}+\sum_{s=1}^{3}\left(\frac{\partial\mathfrak{H}}{\partial p_s}\frac{\partial\Psi^*}{\partial q_s}-\frac{\partial\mathfrak{H}}{\partial q_s}\frac{\partial\Psi^*}{\partial p_s}\right)=0\,.\qquad(4.806)$$

We now choose q_1, q_2, and q_3 to be ϖ, θ, and z, respectively. Then, according to equation (3.309),

$$\left.\begin{aligned}p_\varpi&=\frac{\partial\mathfrak{L}}{\partial\dot{\varpi}}=\dot{\varpi}=\Pi\,,\\ p_\theta&=\frac{\partial\mathfrak{L}}{\partial\dot{\theta}}=\varpi^2\dot{\theta}=\varpi\Theta\,,\\ p_z&=\frac{\partial\mathfrak{L}}{\partial\dot{z}}=\dot{z}=Z\,,\end{aligned}\right\}\qquad(4.807)$$

and the Hamiltonian is

$$\mathfrak{H}=\frac{1}{2}\left(p_{\varpi}^{2}+\frac{p_{\theta}^{2}}{\varpi^{2}}+p_{z}^{2}\right)+\mathfrak{V}\,. \tag{4.808}$$

In this system of co-ordinates, equation (4.806) therefore becomes

$$\left.\begin{aligned}\frac{\partial\Psi^*}{\partial t}+p_{\varpi}\frac{\partial\Psi^*}{\partial\varpi}+\frac{p_\theta}{\varpi^2}\frac{\partial\Psi^*}{\partial\theta}+p_z\frac{\partial\Psi^*}{\partial z}-\left(\frac{\partial\mathfrak{V}}{\partial\varpi}-\frac{p_\theta^2}{\varpi^3}\right)\frac{\partial\Psi^*}{\partial p_\varpi}&\\ -\frac{\partial\mathfrak{V}}{\partial\theta}\frac{\partial\Psi^*}{\partial p_\theta}-\frac{\partial\mathfrak{V}}{\partial z}\frac{\partial\Psi^*}{\partial p_z}=0\,.&\end{aligned}\right\} \tag{4.809}$$

Instead of p_ϖ, p_θ, and p_z it is more convenient to use the components of linear velocity Π, Θ, and Z as the variables. Let Ψ denote the corresponding distribution function. The relation between Ψ^* and Ψ is

$$\left.\begin{aligned}&\Psi(\varpi,\ \theta,\ z;\Pi,\Theta,Z;\,t)\,\varpi d\varpi d\theta dz d\Pi d\Theta dZ\\ &=\Psi^*(\varpi,\ \theta,\ z;\ p_\varpi,\ p_\theta,\ p_z;\,t)\,d\varpi d\theta dz dp_\varpi dp_\theta dp_z\,.\end{aligned}\right\} \tag{4.810}$$

We accordingly have

$$\left.\begin{aligned}\frac{\partial\Psi}{\partial\varpi}&=\frac{\partial\Psi^*}{\partial\varpi}+\frac{\partial\Psi^*}{\partial p_\theta}\frac{\partial p_\theta}{\partial\varpi}=\frac{\partial\Psi^*}{\partial\varpi}+\Theta\frac{\partial\Psi^*}{\partial p_\theta}\,,\\ \frac{\partial\Psi}{\partial\Theta}&=\frac{\partial\Psi^*}{\partial p_\theta}\frac{\partial p_\theta}{\partial\Theta}=\varpi\frac{\partial\Psi^*}{\partial p_\theta}\,.\end{aligned}\right\} \tag{4.811}$$

From equations (4.807), (4.809), and (4.811) we now obtain

$$\left.\begin{aligned}\frac{\partial\Psi}{\partial t}+\Pi\frac{\partial\Psi}{\partial\varpi}+\frac{\Theta}{\varpi}\frac{\partial\Psi}{\partial\theta}+Z\frac{\partial\Psi}{\partial z}-\left(\frac{\partial\mathfrak{V}}{\partial\varpi}-\frac{\Theta^2}{\varpi}\right)\frac{\partial\Psi}{\partial\Pi}&\\ -\left(\frac{1}{\varpi}\frac{\partial\mathfrak{V}}{\partial\theta}+\frac{\Pi\Theta}{\varpi}\right)\frac{\partial\Psi}{\partial\Theta}-\frac{\partial\mathfrak{V}}{\partial z}\frac{\partial\Psi}{\partial Z}=0\,.&\end{aligned}\right\} \tag{4.812}$$

iii) *The equations of stellar hydrodynamics in cylindrical co-ordinates.*—Multiply equation (4.812) by $d\Pi d\Theta dZ$ and integrate over these variables. Since

$$\left.\begin{aligned}\iiint\Pi\Theta\frac{\partial\Psi}{\partial\Theta}\,d\Pi d\Theta dZ&=\iint\left[\Theta\Psi\right]_{\Theta=-\infty}^{\Theta=+\infty}\Pi d\Pi dZ\\ &\qquad-\iiint\Pi\Psi d\Pi d\Theta dZ\\ &=-N\overline{\Pi}\end{aligned}\right\} \tag{4.813}$$

we readily obtain

$$\frac{\partial N}{\partial t}+\frac{\partial}{\partial \varpi}(N\bar{\Pi})+\frac{1}{\varpi}\frac{\partial}{\partial \theta}(N\bar{\Theta})+\frac{\partial}{\partial z}(N\bar{Z})+\frac{1}{\varpi}N\bar{\Pi}=0\,. \tag{4.814}$$

Next, multiply equation (4.812) by $\Pi d\Pi d\Theta dZ$ and integrate over these variables. Since

$$\left.\begin{aligned}\iiint \Pi\frac{\partial\Psi}{\partial\Pi}d\Pi d\Theta dZ &= -\iiint \Psi d\Pi d\Theta dZ=-N\,,\\ \iiint \Pi\Theta^2\frac{\partial\Psi}{\partial\Pi}d\Pi d\Theta dZ &= -\iiint \Theta^2\Psi d\Pi d\Theta dZ=-N\overline{\Theta^2}\,,\\ \iiint \Pi^2\Theta\frac{\partial\Psi}{\partial\Theta}d\Pi d\Theta dZ &= -\iiint \Pi^2\Psi d\Pi d\Theta dZ=-N\overline{\Pi^2}\,,\end{aligned}\right\} \tag{4.815}$$

we obtain

$$\left.\begin{aligned}\frac{\partial}{\partial t}(N\bar{\Pi})+\frac{\partial}{\partial \varpi}(N\overline{\Pi^2})+\frac{1}{\varpi}\frac{\partial}{\partial \theta}(N\overline{\Pi\Theta})+\frac{\partial}{\partial z}(N\overline{\Pi Z})&\\ +\frac{1}{\varpi}N(\overline{\Pi^2}-\overline{\Theta^2})=-N\frac{\partial\mathfrak{B}}{\partial\varpi}&\,.\end{aligned}\right\} \tag{4.816}$$

Similarly, by multiplying equation (4.812) and $\Theta d\Pi d\Theta dZ$ and $Zd\Pi d\Theta dZ$ and integrating over all the velocities we obtain, respectively,

$$\left.\begin{aligned}\frac{\partial}{\partial t}(N\bar{\Theta})+\frac{\partial}{\partial \varpi}(N\overline{\Theta\Pi})+\frac{1}{\varpi}\frac{\partial}{\partial \theta}(N\overline{\Theta^2})+\frac{\partial}{\partial z}(N\overline{\Theta Z})&\\ +\frac{2}{\varpi}N\overline{\Theta\Pi}=-N\frac{1}{\varpi}\frac{\partial\mathfrak{B}}{\partial\theta}&\end{aligned}\right\} \tag{4.817}$$

and

$$\left.\begin{aligned}\frac{\partial}{\partial t}(N\bar{Z})+\frac{\partial}{\partial \varpi}(N\overline{Z\Pi})+\frac{1}{\varpi}\frac{\partial}{\partial \theta}(N\overline{Z\Theta})+\frac{\partial}{\partial z}(N\overline{Z^2})&\\ +\frac{1}{\varpi}N\overline{Z\Pi}=-N\frac{\partial\mathfrak{B}}{\partial z}&\,.\end{aligned}\right\} \tag{4.818}$$

iv) *The equations of stellar hydrodynamics for axially symmetrical systems in steady states.*—We shall now consider axially symmetrical systems in steady states. Assuming further that

$$\bar{\Pi}=\bar{Z}=\overline{\Pi\Theta}=\overline{\Theta Z}=\overline{Z\Pi}=0\,, \tag{4.819}$$

equations (4.814) and (4.816)–(4.818) reduce to the pair of equations

$$\frac{\partial}{\partial \varpi}(N\overline{\Pi^2})+\frac{1}{\varpi}N(\overline{\Pi^2}-\overline{\Theta^2})=-N\frac{\partial \mathfrak{V}}{\partial \varpi}, \tag{4.820}$$

$$\frac{\partial}{\partial z}(N\overline{Z^2})=-N\frac{\partial \mathfrak{V}}{\partial z}. \tag{4.821}$$

We can express equation (4.820) somewhat differently as follows: multiplying this equation throughout by $(\varpi/N\overline{\Pi^2})$, we have

$$\varpi\frac{\partial}{\partial \varpi}(\log N\overline{\Pi^2})+1+\frac{\Theta_c^2-\overline{\Theta^2}}{\overline{\Pi^2}}=0, \tag{4.822}$$

where we have written

$$\Theta_c^2=\varpi\frac{\partial \mathfrak{V}}{\partial \varpi}. \tag{4.823}$$

On the other hand, since

$$\Theta=\Theta_0+(\Theta-\Theta_0), \tag{4.824}$$

where Θ_0 represents the motion of the local standard of rest, we have

$$\overline{\Theta^2}=\Theta_0^2+\overline{(\Theta-\Theta_0)^2}. \tag{4.825}$$

Equation (4.822) now becomes

$$\varpi\frac{\partial}{\partial \varpi}(\log N\overline{\Pi^2})+1-\frac{\overline{(\Theta-\Theta_0)^2}}{\overline{\Pi^2}}=\frac{\Theta_0^2-\Theta_c^2}{\overline{\Pi^2}}; \tag{4.826}$$

in this form we recognize the equation as equivalent to equation (3.822), if we remember that, according to equations (3.805) and (3.818), $\overline{\Pi^2}$ is independent of ϖ and

$$\frac{a_\varpi}{b_\theta}=\frac{\overline{(\Theta-\Theta_0)^2}}{\overline{\Pi^2}}; \qquad 2a_\varpi=\frac{1}{\overline{\Pi^2}}. \tag{4.827}$$

v) *Motions perpendicular to the galactic plane.*—According to equation (4.821)

$$\frac{\partial}{\partial z}(N\overline{Z^2})=-N\frac{\partial \mathfrak{V}}{\partial z}. \tag{4.828}$$

If $\overline{Z^2}$ is independent of z, the foregoing equation can be integrated to give

$$N(\varpi, z)=N(\varpi, 0)\,e^{-\mathfrak{V}/\overline{Z^2}}, \tag{4.829}$$

which is essentially *the law of isothermal atmospheres.*

If we consider the galactic plane as a plane of symmetry and restrict ourselves to regions not far from this plane, we can write, approximately (cf. eqs. [4.530] and [4.531]),

$$\mathfrak{B} = 2\pi G\bar{\rho}\, z^2 , \tag{4.830}$$

where $\bar{\rho}$ is a certain average density at (ϖ, 0). Equation (4.829) now becomes

$$N(\varpi, z) = N(\varpi, 0)\, e^{-2\pi G\bar{\rho} z^2/\overline{Z^2}} . \tag{4.831}$$

From this equation it follows that from the observed distribution of the stars perpendicular to the galactic plane and from a knowledge of their mean motions in the z-direction, we should be able to deduce a value of $\bar{\rho}$. This is the principle underlying Oort's analysis of the distribution of stars in the z-direction. He finds that in the neighborhood of the sun the value of $\bar{\rho}$ is 0.1 solar masses per cubic parsec.

In our present connection it is worth remarking that in the scheme of approximation leading to equation (4.830) the equations of motion perpendicular to the galactic plane can be integrated to give (cf. eqs. [4.331] and [4.342])

$$z = z_{10} \sin n_2 (t - t_2) ; \qquad Z = z_{10}\, n_2 \cos n_2 (t - t_2) , \tag{4.832}$$

where

$$n_2^2 = \left(\frac{\partial^2 \mathfrak{B}}{\partial z^2}\right)_0 = 4\pi G\bar{\rho} . \tag{4.833}$$

Hence

$$z^2 + \frac{Z^2}{n_2^2} = \text{constant} \tag{4.834}$$

represents the integral of the equations of motion. Consequently, in a steady state the distribution function can involve only the combination (4.834), as far as its dependence on z and Z is concerned (§ 3.3). Accordingly, equation (4.831) implies a complete distribution function of the form

$$N(\varpi, z, Z) = N(\varpi, 0) \frac{1}{(2\pi\overline{Z^2})^{1/2}}\, e^{-\frac{2\pi G\bar{\rho}}{\overline{Z^2}}\left(z^2 + \frac{Z^2}{4\pi G\bar{\rho}}\right)} , \tag{4.835}$$

an equation which appears to be in fair agreement with observations.

Finally, we may note that, according to equation (4.834) and the assumed independence of the z-motions from those in the galactic plane, *a Maxwellian distribution of the Z-velocities implies the law of density distribution* (4.831) *and conversely.*

BIBLIOGRAPHICAL NOTES

§§ 4.1 and 4.2.—The theory described in these sections is that due to Chandrasekhar:

1. S. CHANDRASEKHAR, *Ap. J.*, **92**, 441, 1941 (see particularly pp. 573–635).

§§ 4.3–4.6.—In these sections an attempt has been made to describe some of the methods and ideas which have been developed by Lindblad in recent years. While it has not been possible to do justice to all phases of Lindblad's researches, it is hoped that the more essential parts of his work have found adequate treatment.

The following references represent a more or less complete bibliography of Lindblad's writings on the problems of the spiral structure in nebulae and the evolution of rotating stellar systems:

2. *Arkiv f. mat., astr., och fysik*, **19A**, No. 21, 1925; **19B**, No. 7, 1926; **19A**, No. 35, 1926; **20A**, No. 10, 1927; **20A**, No. 17, 1927; **21A**, No. 3, 1928; **22A**, No. 11, 1930; **24A**, No. 21, 1934; **27A**, No. 2, 1939; and **27B**, No. 13, 1940.

3. *Kungl. svenska vetensk. handl.*, Tredje serien, **4**, No. 7, 1927 (*Uppsala Medd.*, No. 31).

4. *Stockholms obs. ann.*, **12**, No. 4, 1936; **13**, No. 5, 1940; **13**, No. 8, 1941; **13**, No. 10, 1941.

5. *M.N.*, **87**, 420, 553, 1927; **94**, 231, 1934; **95**, 12, 1934; **97**, 15, 1936; **98**, 576, 1938.

6. *Ap. J.*, **62**, 191, 1925; **92**, 1, 1940.

7. *Zs. f. Ap.*, **15**, 124, 1938.

8. *A.N.*, **264**, 304, 1937.

9. *Ann. d'ap.*, **1**, 173, 1938.

10. *Bergstrand Festschrift*, p. 30, Uppsala, 1938. Also—

11. *Astronomical Papers Dedicated to E. Strömgren*, p. 137, Copenhagen, 1940. See also—

12. S. CHANDRASEKHAR, *M.N.*, **98**, 710, 1938. A reference of importance for Lindblad's work is—

13. G. H. BRYAN, *Phil. Trans. R. Soc.*, London, A, **180**, 187, 1889.

In view of the importance which the stability of the circular orbits plays in the discussion in §§ 4.3–4.6 we may remark that the criterion for the stability of the circular orbits in a *central field of force* has been known in dynamics for a long time. For example, the matter is considered at length in—

14. L. Boltzmann, *Prinzipe der Mechanik*, **1**, 73–87, Leipzig, 1897, and—

15. H. Lamb, *Dynamics*, pp. 256–271, Cambridge, England, 1914.

The general problem of the stability of an orbit adjacent to a given one is considered in—

16. E. T. Whittaker, *Analytical Dynamics*, 2d ed., pp. 395–399, Cambridge, England, 1917 (we may note that the matter in this form is not discussed in the more recent editions of this book [see Appen. II]).

§ 4.7.—The discussion in this section is in part based on the remarks contained in—

17. G. Randers, *Ap. J.*, **92**, 235, 1940, and—

18. E. Hubble, *Sci. Monthly*, p. 391, November, 1940.

§ 4.8.—The equation of stellar hydrodynamics were first written down by Jeans—

19. J. H. Jeans, *M.N.*, **76**, 70, 1915 (see particularly pp. 81–82); *ibid.*, **82**, 122, 1922. See also—

20. J. H. Jeans, *Problems of Cosmogony and Stellar Dynamics*, pp. 230–236, Cambridge, England, 1919.

Equations (4.831) and (4.835) have been used by Oort to analyze the motions and the density distribution of the stars perpendicular to the galactic plane:

21. J. H. Oort, *B.A.N.*, **6**, 249, 1932. See also—

22. B. Bok, *The Distribution of Stars in Space*, chap. iii, pp. 88–95, Chicago, 1937.

CHAPTER V

THE DYNAMICS OF STAR CLUSTERS

The star clusters present dynamical problems which are of an entirely different nature from those we have considered in chapters iii and iv. The most striking aspect of this difference consists in the part played by stellar encounters in effectively controlling the behavior of these systems. Further, the galactic and the globular clusters themselves suggest different types of problems in the extent to which galactic rotation influences the evolution of these objects. In this chapter we shall survey some of the problems related to the dynamics of star clusters and indicate the essential factors which are involved.

5.1. *The equations of motion of an isolated star cluster. The Lagrangian identities.*—Fundamentally, the dynamics of an isolated cluster is the dynamics of n mutually attracting mass points. In other words, the problem is equivalent to the n-body problem of classical dynamics. We shall therefore begin our study of star clusters by writing down the general equations of motion and obtaining their first integrals.

i) *The general equations of motion. The energy and the angular-momentum integrals.*—Let $m_1, m_2, \ldots, m_n$ denote the masses of the different stars. Between any two stars m_i and m_j there exists a force Gm_im_j/r_{ij}^2, where r_{ij} is the distance between the two stars. The components of this force acting on the star m_i are

$$-Gm_im_j\frac{x_i-x_j}{r_{ij}^3}, \quad -Gm_im_j\frac{y_i-y_j}{r_{ij}^3}, \quad -Gm_im_j\frac{z_i-z_j}{r_{ij}^3}, \qquad (5.101)$$

or

$$-\frac{\partial\Omega_{ij}}{\partial x_i}, \quad -\frac{\partial\Omega_{ij}}{\partial y_i}, \quad -\frac{\partial\Omega_{ij}}{\partial z_i}, \qquad (5.102)$$

where

$$\Omega_{ij}=-\frac{Gm_im_j}{r_{ij}}. \qquad (5.103)$$

Consequently, the components of the force acting on the star i due to the gravitational attraction of all the other stars in the cluster can be written as

$$-\frac{\partial\Omega_i}{\partial x_i}, \qquad -\frac{\partial\Omega_i}{\partial y_i}, \qquad -\frac{\partial\Omega_i}{\partial z_i}, \tag{5.104}$$

where

$$\Omega_i = \Sigma_j\Omega_{ij} = -Gm_i\sum\frac{m_j}{r_{ij}} \tag{5.105}$$

and where the summations are extended over all j not equal to i. Ω_i is clearly the potential energy of the star under consideration due to its position relative to the attracting system.

According to equation (5.104), the components of the force acting on a star is given by the gradient of a function which is different for the different stars. But we can treat all the stars on the same footing by considering the function

$$\Omega = -G\sum_{i\neq j}\frac{m_i m_j}{r_{ij}}, \tag{5.106}$$

where the summation is extended over all the different pairs of stars. For, since the only terms in Ω which depend on the co-ordinates (x_i, y_i, z_i), are those included in Ω_i,

$$\frac{\partial\Omega}{\partial x_i} = \frac{\partial\Omega_i}{\partial x_i}; \qquad \frac{\partial\Omega}{\partial y_i} = \frac{\partial\Omega_i}{\partial y_i}; \qquad \frac{\partial\Omega}{\partial z_i} = \frac{\partial\Omega_i}{\partial z_i}. \tag{5.107}$$

The quantity Ω defined by equation (5.106) is seen to represent the potential energy of the cluster. For, by considering the sum on the right-hand side of equation (5.106) term by term, we successively obtain the potential energy of a second star in the presence of a first, of a third in the presence of the first two, and so on. And, since the sum contains just exactly as many terms as there are distinct pairs of stars $(=n[n-1]/2)$, we verify that Ω does, in fact, represent the total potential energy of the cluster.

We can now write down the equations of motion for the stars in the cluster. We have

$$\left.\begin{aligned} m_i\ddot{x}_i = -\frac{\partial\Omega}{\partial x_i}; \qquad m_i\ddot{y}_i = -\frac{\partial\Omega}{\partial y_i}; \qquad m_i\ddot{z}_i = -\frac{\partial\Omega}{\partial z_i} \\ (i = 1, 2, \ldots, n)\,. \end{aligned}\right\} \tag{5.108}$$

Now

$$\sum_i \frac{\partial \Omega}{\partial x_i} = \sum_i \sum_j m_i m_j \frac{x_i - x_j}{r_{ij}^3} = 0 \quad (i \neq j) . \quad (5.109)$$

Hence

$$\sum_i m_i \ddot{x}_i = \sum_i m_i \ddot{y}_i = \sum_i m_i \ddot{z}_i = 0 . \quad (5.110)$$

These equations can be integrated to give

$$\sum_i m_i \dot{x}_i = a_1 ; \qquad \sum_i m_i \dot{y}_i = a_2 ; \qquad \sum_i m_i \dot{z}_i = a_3 , \quad (5.111)$$

and

$$\left.\begin{aligned} \sum_i m_i x_i &= \bar{x} \sum_i m_i = a_1 t + b_1 , \\ \sum_i m_i y_i &= \bar{y} \sum_i m_i = a_2 t + b_2 , \\ \sum_i m_i z_i &= \bar{z} \sum_i m_i = a_3 t + b_3 . \end{aligned}\right\} \quad (5.112)$$

In equations (5.111) and (5.112) a_1, a_2, a_3, b_1, b_2, and b_3 are constants of integration. Further, in equations (5.112) we have used $\bar{x}$, $\bar{y}$, and $\bar{z}$ to denote the co-ordinates of the center of gravity of the cluster. We have thus obtained the six integrals corresponding to the fact that the center of gravity of the cluster moves with a uniform velocity in a certain definite direction.

Again, we have

$$\left.\begin{aligned} &\sum_i \left(y_i \frac{\partial \Omega}{\partial z_i} - z_i \frac{\partial \Omega}{\partial y_i} \right) \\ &\quad = \sum_i \sum_j m_i m_j \left(y_i \frac{z_i - z_j}{r_{ij}^3} - z_i \frac{y_i - y_j}{r_{ij}^3} \right) \\ &\quad = \sum_i \sum_j \frac{m_i m_j}{r_{ij}^3} (-y_i z_j + y_j z_i) = 0 , \quad (i \neq j) . \end{aligned}\right\} \quad (5.113)$$

Hence,

$$\sum_i m_i (y_i \ddot{z}_i - z_i \ddot{y}_i) = 0 , \quad (5.114)$$

or

$$\sum_i m_i (y_i \dot{z}_i - z_i \dot{y}_i) = c_1 , \quad (5.115)$$

where c_1 is a constant of integration. Similarly,

$$\left.\begin{aligned}\sum_i m_i(z_i\dot{x}_i - x_i\dot{z}_i) &= c_2\,,\\ \sum_i m_i(x_i\dot{y}_i - y_i\dot{x}_i) &= c_3\,,\end{aligned}\right\} \tag{5.116}$$

where c_2 and c_3 are further constants. These are the three angular-momentum integrals.

Finally, we have

$$\left.\begin{aligned}\sum m_i(\dot{x}_i\ddot{x}_i + \dot{y}_i\ddot{y}_i + \dot{z}_i\ddot{z}_i)\\ &= -\sum_i\left(\dot{x}_i\frac{\partial\Omega}{\partial x_i} + \dot{y}_i\frac{\partial\Omega}{\partial y_i} + \dot{z}_i\frac{\partial\Omega}{\partial z_i}\right)\\ &= -\frac{d\Omega}{dt}\,,\end{aligned}\right\} \tag{5.117}$$

or, after integration,

$$\frac{1}{2}\sum_i m_i(\dot{x}_i^2 + \dot{y}_i^2 + \dot{z}_i^2) + \Omega = h\,, \tag{5.118}$$

where h is a constant. This is the energy integral.

Equations (5.111), (5.112), (5.115), (5.116), and (5.118) represent, in fact, the ten general integrals for the motion of a system of particles moving under their mutual attractions.

ii) *The equations of motion relative to the center of gravity of the cluster.*—We shall now choose a frame of reference in which the center of gravity is at rest. Let (ξ_i, η_i, ζ_i) be the co-ordinates of m_i in this new frame of reference. Then

$$\xi_i = x_i - \bar{x}\,; \qquad \eta_i = y_i - \bar{y}\,; \qquad \zeta_i = z_i - \bar{z}\,. \tag{5.119}$$

In equation (5.119), $\bar{x}$, $\bar{y}$, and $\bar{z}$ are defined as in equations (5.112). Accordingly,

$$\sum_i m_i\xi_i = \sum_i m_i\eta_i = \sum_i m_i\zeta_i = 0\,. \tag{5.120}$$

In this frame of reference the equations of motion become

$$\left.\begin{aligned}m_i\ddot{\xi}_i = -\frac{\partial\Omega}{\partial\xi_i}\,; \qquad m_i\ddot{\eta}_i = -\frac{\partial\Omega}{\partial\eta_i}\,; \qquad m_i\ddot{\zeta}_i = -\frac{\partial\Omega}{\partial\zeta_i}\\ (i = 1, \ldots, n)\,,\end{aligned}\right\} \tag{5.121}$$

where Ω is the same as before. But r_{ij} is now given by

$$r_{ij}^2 = (\xi_i - \xi_j)^2 + (\eta_i - \eta_j)^2 + (\zeta_i - \zeta_j)^2 . \qquad (5.122)$$

We shall now transform the angular momentum and the energy integrals to this new frame of reference.

According to equations (5.115) and (5.119),

$$\left.\begin{aligned} c_1 &= \sum_i m_i (y_i \dot{z}_i - z_i \dot{y}_i) \\ &= \sum_i m_i \{ (\bar{y} + \eta_i)(\dot{\bar{z}} + \dot{\zeta}_i) - (\bar{z} + \zeta_i)(\dot{\bar{y}} + \dot{\eta}_i) \} \\ &= \sum_i m_i (\eta_i \dot{\zeta}_i - \zeta_i \dot{\eta}_i) + (\bar{y}\dot{\bar{z}} - \bar{z}\dot{\bar{y}}) \sum_i m_i , \end{aligned}\right\} \qquad (5.123)$$

since (cf. eq. [5.120])

$$\sum_i m_i \eta_i = \sum_i m_i \zeta_i = \sum_i m_i \dot{\eta}_i = \sum_i m_i \dot{\zeta}_i = 0 . \qquad (5.124)$$

Using the explicit forms for $\bar{y}$ and $\bar{z}$ (eq. [5.112]) in equation (5.123), we obtain

$$\sum_i m_i (\eta_i \dot{\zeta}_i - \zeta_i \dot{\eta}_i) = c_1 + (a_2 b_3 - a_3 b_2) / \Sigma m_i = c_1' . \qquad (5.125)$$

Similarly,

$$\left.\begin{aligned} \Sigma m_i (\zeta_i \dot{\xi}_i - \xi_i \dot{\zeta}_i) &= c_2 + (a_3 b_1 - a_1 b_3) / \Sigma m_i = c_2' , \\ \Sigma m_i (\xi_i \dot{\eta}_i - \eta_i \dot{\xi}_i) &= c_3 + (a_1 b_2 - a_2 b_1) / \Sigma m_i = c_3' . \end{aligned}\right\} \qquad (5.126)$$

The energy integral (5.118) becomes

$$\left.\begin{aligned} h - \Omega &= \frac{1}{2} \sum_i m_i \{ (\dot{\bar{x}} + \dot{\xi}_i)^2 + (\dot{\bar{y}} + \dot{\eta}_i)^2 + (\dot{\bar{z}} + \dot{\zeta}_i)^2 \} \\ &= \frac{1}{2} \sum_i m_i (\dot{\xi}_i^2 + \dot{\eta}_i^2 + \dot{\zeta}_i^2) + \tfrac{1}{2} (a_1^2 + a_2^2 + a_3^2) / \Sigma m_i . \end{aligned}\right\} \qquad (5.127)$$

Hence,

$$\frac{1}{2} \sum_i m_i (\dot{\xi}_i^2 + \dot{\eta}_i^2 + \dot{\zeta}_i^2) + \Omega = h' \qquad (5.128)$$

where

$$h' = h - \tfrac{1}{2} (a_1^2 + a_2^2 + a_3^2) \Big/ \sum_i m_i . \qquad (5.129)$$

Let T denote the total kinetic energy of the "residual motions" in the cluster. Then

$$\mathrm{T}=\frac{1}{2}\sum_i m_i(\dot{\xi}_i^2+\dot{\eta}_i^2+\dot{\zeta}_i^2)\ . \tag{5.130}$$

Equation (5.128) can now be written in the form

$$\mathrm{T}+\Omega=\mathrm{E}=\text{constant}\ . \tag{5.131}$$

iii) *Lagrange's identities.*—We shall now derive an important relation involving the mutual distances of the masses.[1] We have

$$\left.\begin{aligned}2\sum_{i,\,j} m_i m_j(\xi_i-\xi_j)^2 & \\ &=\sum_i\sum_j m_i m_j(\xi_i^2+\xi_j^2-2\xi_i\xi_j)\\ &=\sum_i m_i\xi_i^2\cdot\sum_j m_j+\sum_i m_i\cdot\sum_j m_j\xi_j^2\\ &\qquad -2\sum_i m_i\xi_i\cdot\sum_j m_j\xi_j\\ &=2\sum_i m_i\cdot\sum_i m_i\xi_i^2\,,\end{aligned}\right\} \tag{5.132}$$

with similar equations for other co-ordinates. Hence

$$\sum_{i,\,j} m_i m_j r_{ij}^2=\sum_i m_i\cdot\sum_i m_i(\xi_i^2+\eta_i^2+\zeta_i^2)\ . \tag{5.133}$$

Accordingly,

$$\left.\begin{aligned}\frac{1}{\Sigma m_i}\frac{d^2}{dt^2}(\Sigma m_i m_j r_{ij}^2) & \\ &=2\frac{d}{dt}\{\Sigma m_i(\xi_i\dot{\xi}_i+\eta_i\dot{\eta}_i+\zeta_i\dot{\zeta}_i)\}\\ &=2\Sigma m_i(\dot{\xi}_i^2+\dot{\eta}_i^2+\dot{\zeta}_i^2)+2\Sigma m_i(\xi_i\ddot{\xi}_i+\eta_i\ddot{\eta}_i+\zeta_i\ddot{\zeta}_i)\\ &=2\Sigma m_i(\dot{\xi}_i^2+\dot{\eta}_i^2+\dot{\zeta}_i^2)-2\sum\Big(\xi_i\frac{\partial\Omega}{\partial\xi_i}+\eta_i\frac{\partial\Omega}{\partial\eta_i}\\ &\qquad\qquad +\zeta_i\frac{\partial\Omega}{\partial\zeta_i}\Big).\end{aligned}\right\} \tag{5.134}$$

[1] J. L. Lagrange, *Œuvres*, IX, 836; also *ibid.*, VI, 240. See also C. G. Jacobi, *Vorlesungen über Dynamik* (vierte Vorlesung), pp. 19–30, Berlin, 1866.

On the other hand, since Ω is a homogeneous function of the coordinates of degree -1, by Euler's theorem

$$\sum\left(\xi_i \frac{\partial\Omega}{\partial\xi_i} + \eta_i \frac{\partial\Omega}{\partial\eta_i} + \zeta_i \frac{\partial\Omega}{\partial\zeta_i}\right) = -\Omega\,. \qquad (5.135)$$

Equation (5.134) therefore reduces to (cf. eq. [5.130])

$$\frac{1}{2\Sigma m_i} \frac{d^2}{dt^2} (\Sigma m_i m_j r_{ij}^2) = 2\mathrm{T} + \Omega\,, \qquad (5.136)$$

or alternatively, using equation (5.131),

$$\frac{1}{\Sigma m_i} \frac{d^2}{dt^2} (\Sigma m_i m_j r_{ij}^2) = 2\mathrm{E} - \Omega\,. \qquad (5.137)$$

The relations (5.136) and (5.137) are due to Lagrange and Jacobi.[2]

Equation (5.137) enables us to derive an important condition for the stability of a cluster. Now Ω is essentially negative (cf. eq. [5.106]). Consequently, if E is positive, the second derivative of $\Sigma m_i m_j r_{ij}^2$ will always be positive, and the first derivative will increase indefinitely with the time. Thus the first derivative, even if negative initially, will become positive after a certain time and therefore $\Sigma m_i m_j r_{ij}^2$ will increase without limit. This implies that at least one of the distances must tend to become infinite. We have thus shown that *a necessary (but not sufficient) condition for the stability of the cluster is that* E *must be negative.*

Further applications of Lagrange's identities to the dynamics of the clusters will be found in the following sections.

5.2. *The dispersion of the velocities in a cluster. The time of relaxation and the mean free path.*—As we have already remarked in § 5.1, the dynamics of an isolated cluster is strictly equivalent to the classical n-body problem. If we refer the motions to a frame of reference in which the center of gravity of the cluster is at rest, then, quite generally, we can infer the existence of only the energy and the angular-momentum integrals; in addition to these integrals we also have Lagrange's identities. It does not appear that we can go very

[2] These relations for the special case of the three-body problem were first obtained by Lagrange (*op. cit.*, IX, 836, and VI, 260). However, in their most general forms they are really due to Jacobi, who derived them in his Königsberg lectures during the winter of 1842–1843. They were later published by Clebsch in 1866 in his very well-known edition of Jacobi's *Vorlesungen*.

much beyond this from a strictly dynamical point of view. However, physical considerations would rather suggest that we seek a *statistical description* of the star clusters. It is on these lines that we shall try to analyze the general aspects of the problem.

We shall begin our discussion by assuming that the cluster is in a *statistically steady state*. We should then conclude that

$$\Sigma m_i m_j r_{ij}^2 = \text{constant} . \tag{5.201}$$

According to Lagrange's identities (eqs. [5.136]) and [5.137]) we now have

$$2T + \Omega = 0 ; \qquad 2E - \Omega = 0 , \tag{5.202}$$

or

$$2T = -\Omega = -2E . \tag{5.203}$$

It will be remembered that T represents the total kinetic energy of the *residual motions* (i.e., the motions relative to the center of gravity of the cluster). Thus

$$2T = \Sigma m_i (u_i^2 + v_i^2 + w_i^2) . \tag{5.204}$$

Further,

$$\Omega = -G\Sigma \frac{m_i m_j}{r_{ij}} . \tag{5.205}$$

For the sake of simplicity, we shall first consider the case when all the cluster members have the same mass, m. We can then write

$$2T = n m \overline{v^2} = M \overline{v^2} , \tag{5.206}$$

where $\sqrt{\overline{v^2}}$ denotes the root mean square velocity of the cluster stars, and M is the total mass of the cluster. We can obtain a similar expression for Ω. Since the summation on the right-hand side of equation (5.205) contains $n(n-1)/2$ terms, we can write

$$\Omega = -\frac{1}{2} \frac{Gm^2 n(n-1)}{\bar{R}} , \tag{5.207}$$

where $\bar{R}$ denotes the "average" radius of the cluster. For practical purposes it would clearly be sufficient to write

$$\Omega = -\frac{1}{2} \frac{Gm^2 n^2}{\bar{R}} = -\frac{1}{2} \frac{GM^2}{\bar{R}} . \tag{5.208}$$

From equations (5.203), (5.206), and (5.208) we obtain

$$\overline{v^2} = \frac{1}{2} \frac{Gnm}{\bar{R}} = \frac{1}{2} \frac{GM}{R} , \tag{5.209}$$

or, expressing the mass and the radius in units of solar mass and parsec, respectively, we find

$$\sqrt{\overline{v^2}} = 4.63 \times 10^{-2} \sqrt{\frac{M}{R}} \text{ km/sec.} \qquad (5.209')$$

If we apply this formula to the Pleiades ($M = 300\odot$, $R = 3.5$ parsecs) we find

$$\sqrt{\overline{v^2}} = 0.43 \text{ km/sec} \qquad (5.210)$$

which is in fair agreement with the observed dispersion of the velocities (§ 1.8, eq. [1.81]).

More generally, the magnitude of the mean residual motions predicted by the formula (5.209′) can be seen by an inspection of Table 8 where we have tabulated $(\overline{v^2})^{1/2}$ as a function of M and R for a few typical values.

TABLE 8*

THE PREDICTED DISPERSION OF THE VELOCITIES IN CLUSTERS

M \ $\bar{R}$	1	2	4	10	50	100
100	0.46	0.33	0.23	0.15	0.07	0.05
400	0.93	0.66	0.46	0.29	0.13	0.09
10^3	1.47	1.04	0.73	0.46	0.21	0.14
10^4	4.63	3.28	2.31	1.47	0.65	0.46
10^6	.....	.....	23.1	14.7	6.55	4.6
10^8	.....	.....	.....	.....	66	46

* M in solar masses; $\bar{R}$ in parsecs; $\sqrt{\overline{v^2}}$ in km/sec.

We shall now consider some further applications of the formula (5.209) for the dispersion of the velocities in isolated clusters.

i) *The time of relaxation of a cluster.*—In § 2.3 we found for the mean time of relaxation, $\bar{T}_E$, the expression (eq. [2.379])

$$\bar{T}_E = \frac{1}{16}\left(\frac{3}{\pi}\right)^{1/2} \frac{[\,\overline{v^2}\,]^{3/2}}{NG^2m^2 \log_e [\,D_0 \overline{v^2}/2Gm\,]}, \qquad (5.211)$$

where N is the number of stars per unit volume and D_0 is taken to be the order of the average distance between the stars. With $\overline{v^2}$ given by equation (5.209), we have

$$\frac{D_0 \overline{v^2}}{2Gm} = \tfrac{1}{4} n \frac{D_0}{\bar{R}}. \qquad (5.212)$$

But D_0 is related to n and $\bar{R}$ by the equation

$$\tfrac{4}{3}\pi\left(\frac{D_0}{2}\right)^3 n = \tfrac{4}{3}\pi\bar{R}^3 \tag{5.213}$$

or

$$\frac{D_0}{\bar{R}} = \frac{2}{n^{1/3}}. \tag{5.214}$$

Hence,

$$\frac{D_0\overline{v^2}}{2Gm} = \tfrac{1}{2}n^{2/3}. \tag{5.215}$$

Also, the number of stars per unit volume is given by

$$N = \frac{n}{\tfrac{4}{3}\pi\bar{R}^3}. \tag{5.216}$$

Again, substituting for $\overline{v^2}$ from equation (5.209) in the expression for $\bar{T}_E$ and using equations (5.215) and (5.216), we obtain

$$\bar{T}_E = \frac{1}{16}\left(\frac{3\pi}{2}\right)^{1/2}\left(\frac{n\bar{R}^3}{Gm}\right)^{1/2}\frac{1}{\log_e\,(n/2^{3/2})}, \tag{5.217}$$

or, expressing m and $\bar{R}$ in the units solar mass and parsec, respectively, we find

$$\bar{T}_E = 8.8\times 10^5\sqrt{\frac{n\bar{R}^3}{m}}\,\frac{1}{\log_{10} n - 0.45}\text{ years}. \tag{5.218}$$

Applying this formula for the conditions in the Pleiades, we find

$$\bar{T}_E = 2.9\times 10^7\text{ years}. \tag{5.219}$$

Comparing this with the probable time scale of the order of 3×10^9 years, we at once realize the importance of stellar encounters for setting up a *statistical equilibrium* in clusters. Table 9, showing more extensively the times of relaxation and computed for different values of n and $\bar{R}$, confirms this conclusion for clusters in general. We should therefore expect that the distribution of the velocities in clusters is Maxwellian:

$$dN = N\frac{j^3}{\pi^{3/2}}e^{-j^2|v|^2}du\,dv\,dw \tag{5.220}$$

where

$$\frac{1}{j^2} = \tfrac{2}{3}\overline{v^2} = \frac{4}{3}\frac{T}{M} = -\frac{2}{3}\frac{\Omega}{M}. \tag{5.221}$$

ii) *The mean free path.*—Having found that the time of relaxation of a cluster is short compared to its probable age, it is of interest to

TABLE 9*

THE TIME OF RELAXATION OF CLUSTERS

n \ $\overline{R}$	1	2	4	6	8	10	20	30	40	50	100
50	5.0×10^{6}	1.4×10^{7}	4.0×10^{7}	7.3×10^{7}	1.1×10^{8}	1.6×10^{8}	4.5×10^{8}	8.2×10^{8}	1.3×10^{9}	1.8×10^{9}	5.0×10^{9}
100	5.7×10^{6}	1.6×10^{7}	4.5×10^{7}	8.3×10^{7}	1.3×10^{8}	1.8×10^{8}	5.1×10^{8}	9.3×10^{8}	1.4×10^{9}	2.0×10^{9}	5.7×10^{9}
150	6.2×10^{6}	1.8×10^{7}	5.0×10^{7}	9.2×10^{7}	1.4×10^{8}	2.0×10^{8}	5.6×10^{8}	1.0×10^{8}	1.6×10^{9}	2.2×10^{9}	6.2×10^{9}
200	6.7×10^{6}	1.9×10^{7}	5.4×10^{7}	9.9×10^{7}	1.5×10^{8}	2.1×10^{8}	6.0×10^{8}	1.1×10^{9}	1.7×10^{9}	2.4×10^{9}	6.7×10^{9}
250	7.1×10^{6}	2.0×10^{7}	5.7×10^{7}	1.0×10^{8}	1.6×10^{8}	2.3×10^{8}	6.4×10^{8}	1.2×10^{9}	1.8×10^{9}	2.5×10^{9}	7.1×10^{9}
300	7.5×10^{6}	2.1×10^{7}	6.0×10^{7}	1.1×10^{8}	1.7×10^{8}	2.4×10^{8}	6.7×10^{8}	1.2×10^{9}	1.9×10^{9}	2.7×10^{9}	7.5×10^{9}
400	8.2×10^{6}	2.3×10^{7}	6.5×10^{7}	1.2×10^{8}	1.8×10^{8}	2.6×10^{8}	7.3×10^{8}	1.3×10^{9}	2.1×10^{9}	2.9×10^{9}	8.2×10^{9}
500	8.7×10^{6}	2.5×10^{7}	7.0×10^{7}	1.3×10^{8}	2.0×10^{8}	2.8×10^{8}	7.8×10^{8}	1.4×10^{9}	2.2×10^{9}	3.1×10^{9}	8.7×10^{9}
10^{3}	1.1×10^{7}	3.1×10^{7}	8.7×10^{7}	1.6×10^{8}	2.5×10^{8}	3.4×10^{8}	9.7×10^{8}	1.8×10^{9}	2.8×10^{9}	3.9×10^{9}	1.1×10^{10}
10^{4}	....	....	2.0×10^{8}	3.6×10^{8}	5.6×10^{8}	7.8×10^{8}	2.2×10^{9}	4.1×10^{9}	6.3×10^{9}	8.8×10^{9}	2.5×10^{10}
10^{5}	....	....	4.9×10^{8}	9.0×10^{8}	1.4×10^{9}	1.9×10^{9}	5.5×10^{9}	1.0×10^{10}	1.5×10^{10}	2.2×10^{10}	6.1×10^{10}
10^{6}	....	....	1.3×10^{9}	2.3×10^{9}	3.6×10^{9}	5.0×10^{9}	1.4×10^{10}	2.6×10^{10}	4.0×10^{10}	5.6×10^{10}	1.6×10^{11}
10^{8}	....	....	9.3×10^{9}	1.7×10^{10}	2.6×10^{10}	3.7×10^{10}	1.0×10^{11}	1.9×10^{11}	2.9×10^{11}	4.1×10^{11}	1.2×10^{12}

* $\overline{R}$ in parsecs, $\overline{T}_E$ in years.

estimate the mean free path of the cluster members. For this purpose we shall again use the results of chapter ii.

If we define the mean free path $\lambda(v)$ to be such that the probability of a star's moving with the velocity v and traversing a length l *without* suffering the expected change of energy of amount $\sqrt{\Sigma\Delta E^2}$ is

$$e^{-l/\lambda(v)}\,, \tag{5.222}$$

then (eq. [2.504])

$$\lambda(v)=\frac{v^4}{32\pi N G^2 m^2 G(x_0)\,\log_e\,[D_0 v^2/2Gm]}\,, \tag{5.223}$$

where $x_0 = jv$ and $G(x_0)$ is the function tabulated in Table 6.

For stars moving with average speed $\bar{v}$, we have (eq. [2.510])

$$\lambda(\bar{v})=0.0204\,\frac{\bar{v}^4}{NG^2m^2\log_{10}\,[D_0\bar{v}^2/2Gm]}\,. \tag{5.224}$$

For a Maxwellian distribution of the velocities the relation between $\bar{v}^2$ and $\overline{v^2}$ is

$$\bar{v}^2=\frac{8}{3\pi}\,\overline{v^2}=0.8488\,\overline{v^2}\,. \tag{5.225}$$

Hence, according to equations (5.209) and (5.215),

$$\bar{v}^2=0.4244\,\frac{Gnm}{\bar{R}}\,;\qquad \frac{D_0\bar{v}^2}{2Gm}=0.4244\,n^{2/3}\,. \tag{5.226}$$

Substituting the foregoing relations in equation (5.224) and after some further reductions, we find that

$$\frac{\lambda(\bar{v})}{\bar{R}}=0.023\,\frac{n}{\log_{10} n-0.56}\,. \tag{5.227}$$

It is remarkable that the quantity $\lambda(\bar{v})/\bar{R}$ depends only on the number of stars in the cluster.

In Table 10 we have tabulated the ratio $\lambda(\bar{v})/\bar{R}$ as a function of n. An inspection of this table shows that except in the richest of the galactic clusters the mean free path is of the same order as the dimensions of the cluster.

In regarding $\lambda(\bar{v})$ as defining the average mean free path for the stars in the cluster, it should be noted that in general the stars would suffer quite appreciable changes in their energies and directions of motion even before traversing this length, λ. For, from the manner in which we have defined λ, it follows that during the time taken for a star to describe the mean free path λ, the probability that $\sqrt{\Sigma\Delta E^2}$ becomes equal to $\bar{E}$ is $(1 - e^{-1}) = 0.63$. Consequently, the probability that the star suffers appreciable changes in its energy and direction of motion is quite considerable even for smaller distances. Thus, after traversing a length of only a *sixteenth* of λ, the probability that a star suffers a change of energy of amount $\sqrt{\Sigma\Delta E^2} = 0.25\bar{E}$ is seen to be 0.63.

We can therefore conclude that the cluster members continue to wander among themselves. This is certainly true of clusters with less than 250 stars.

TABLE 10

THE MEAN FREE PATH IN GALACTIC CLUSTERS

n	1000	500	400	300	200	100	75	50	25
$\frac{\lambda(\bar{v})}{\bar{R}}$	9.5	5.4	4.5	3.6	2.7	1.6	1.3	1.0	0.7

5.3. *The rate of disintegration of clusters by the escape of stars.*—As we have already shown in § 5.2, the time of relaxation of a galactic cluster is very short compared to the general time scale. Thus, while the time of relaxation is of the order of 3×10^7 years, the accepted time scale is more nearly 3×10^9 years. This short time scale raises some quite serious questions concerning the degree of permanence of these objects. The manner in which such considerations arise may be seen as follows:

We recall that, according to the general ideas outlined in chapter ii, the time of relaxation is essentially the time required for the setting-up of a Maxwellian distribution of the velocities in a system. Alternatively, if the statistical equilibrium of the system is disturbed at any time, it will take a time of the order of $\bar{T}_E$ to recover its original equilibrium. On the other hand, the existence of a Maxwellian distribution implies that a small, but finite, fraction of the total number of stars in the system will have velocities sufficient for their escape from the gravitational attraction of all the other stars. If and when these stars escape, the statistical equilibrium will be disturbed. But after a time $\bar{T}_E$, new stars with the necessary velocities for escape will again come into existence. On the escape of these new stars with the requisite velocities, the sequence of events will be repeated. In this manner there will result a continuous loss of stars from the system, leading to a gradual disintegration of the system. While we cannot assume that this process will continue indefinitely, it is clear that the problem we are here encountering is, in its broad aspects, analogous to the problem of the escape of molecules from the planetary atmospheres.

According to equation (5.105), the potential energy of a star is given by

$$\Omega_i = -Gm_i \sum \frac{m_j}{r_{ij}} . \tag{5.301}$$

The kinetic energy necessary for this star to escape from the system is therefore $-\Omega_i$. The average value of this quantity is readily obtained. For, by comparing Ω_i with the expression (5.106) for the total potential energy of the system, we obtain

$$\sum_i \Omega_i = 2\Omega . \tag{5.302}$$

Hence,

$$\bar{E}_\infty = -\frac{2}{n}\Omega , \tag{5.303}$$

where we have used $\bar{E}_\infty$ to denote the average kinetic energy required for escape.

Using equation (5.208) for Ω, we find

$$\bar{E}_\infty = \frac{Gm^2n}{\bar{R}} \tag{5.304}$$

or

$$\overline{v_\infty^2} = 2\frac{Gmn}{\bar{R}} , \tag{5.305}$$

where $(\overline{v_\infty^2})^{1/2}$ represents the root mean square velocity of escape. Comparing equation (5.305) with the formula (5.209) for $\overline{v^2}$, we obtain

$$\overline{v_\infty^2} = 4\,\overline{v^2} . \tag{5.306}$$

In other words, the root mean square velocity of escape is twice the root mean square velocity.

In statistical equilibrium, the fraction Q of the total number of stars with velocities greater than $(\overline{v_\infty^2})^{1/2}$ is given by (cf. eq. [5.220])

$$Q=\frac{4\,j^3}{\pi^{1/2}}\int_{\sqrt{\overline{v_\infty^2}}}^{\infty} e^{-j^2v^2}v^2 d\,v\,. \tag{5.307}$$

But, according to equations (5.221) and (5.306),

$$\overline{v_\infty^2}=\frac{6}{j^2}\,. \tag{5.308}$$

Hence,

$$Q=\frac{4}{\pi^{1/2}}\int_{\sqrt{6}}^{\infty} e^{-x^2}x^2 d x\,, \tag{5.309}$$

or, as may be readily verified,

$$Q=2\left(\frac{6}{\pi}\right)^{1/2}e^{-6}+1-\frac{2}{\sqrt{\pi}}\int_0^{\sqrt{6}} e^{-x^2}d x\,. \tag{5.310}$$

Numerically, it is found that

$$Q=0.0074\,; \tag{5.311}$$

this, then, is the fraction of the total number of stars in the cluster which have velocities greater than the average velocity of escape. But we cannot therefore conclude that all these stars will necessarily escape from the cluster. For, if these stars suffer even a few encounters before they finally "emerge" from the cluster, they may lose a sufficient fraction of their energies to prevent them from escaping. Disregarding this contingency for the present, we may say that the rate of escape of stars from the cluster is given by

$$\frac{\Delta n}{n}\simeq -0.0074\,\frac{\Delta t}{\bar{T}_E}\,. \tag{5.312}$$

Since the time of relaxation of the galactic clusters is of the order of 3×10^7 years, it follows that equation (5.312) implies a relatively rapid rate of disintegration of these clusters. This important aspect in the evolution of the galactic clusters was first fully recognized by Ambarzumian and Spitzer.[3]

Finally, substituting for $\bar{T}_E$ according to equation (5.217),

$$\frac{dn}{dt}=-16\left(\frac{2}{3\pi}\right)^{1/2}Q\left(\frac{Gmn}{\bar{R}^3}\right)^{1/2}\log_e\frac{n}{2^{3/2}}\,, \tag{5.313}$$

[3] *Ann. Leningrad State University*, No. 22 (Astronomical Ser., Issue 4), p. 19, 1938; L. Spitzer, *M.N.*, **100**, 396, 1940.

or, expressing length, mass, and time in units of parsec, solar mass, and year, respectively, we find

$$\frac{dn}{dt} = -8.4 \times 10^{-9} \left(\frac{mn}{\bar{R}^3}\right)^{1/2} (\log_{10} n - 0.45) . \tag{5.314}$$

In the form (5.314) we readily see the importance of this phenomenon for the evolution of clusters.

We shall now return to the matter to which we have already drawn attention, namely, the question of the mean free path of these "high-velocity" stars. According to equation (5.223),

$$\lambda(\sqrt{\overline{\overline{v^2_\infty}}}) = \frac{[\overline{v^2_\infty}]^2}{32\pi N G^2 m^2 G(x_0) \log_e \left[\frac{D_0 \overline{\overline{v^2_\infty}}}{2Gm}\right]} , \tag{5.315}$$

where $x_0 = j\sqrt{\overline{\overline{v^2_\infty}}}$. Substituting from equations (5.306) and (5.308) in equation (5.315), we have

$$\lambda(\sqrt{\overline{\overline{v^2_\infty}}}) = \frac{[\overline{v^2}]^2}{2\pi N G^2 m^2 G(\sqrt{6}) \log_e \left[\frac{4 D_0 \overline{\overline{v^2}}}{2Gm}\right]} . \tag{5.316}$$

From the definition of $G(x_0)$ (eq. [2.356]) we find that to a sufficient accuracy

$$G(\sqrt{6}) = \tfrac{1}{12} . \tag{5.317}$$

Finally, substituting from equations (5.209), (5.215), and (5.317) in equation (5.316), we obtain

$$\frac{\lambda(\sqrt{\overline{\overline{v^2_\infty}}})}{\bar{R}} = \frac{3n}{\log_e (2^{3/2} n)} \tag{5.318}$$

or, somewhat differently,

$$\frac{\lambda(\sqrt{\overline{\overline{v^2_\infty}}})}{\bar{R}} = 1.30 \frac{n}{\log_{10} n + 0.45} . \tag{5.319}$$

From this formula we find that

$$\frac{\lambda(\sqrt{\overline{\overline{v^2_\infty}}})}{\bar{R}} = \begin{cases} 95 & (n = 200) , \\ 53 & (n = 100) , \\ 30 & (n = 50) . \end{cases} \tag{5.320}$$

On the strength of this evidence it might appear that every star in the cluster which has acquired a sufficient amount of energy will escape without interference from the other stars. But this is not necessarily true. For, in spite of these apparently long mean free paths, the stars will suffer quite appreciable changes in their energies and directions of motions over considerably smaller distances. Thus, after traversing a length of only *one-hundredth* of λ, the probability that the star suffers a change in its energy by *one-tenth* of its initial energy is 0.63. Consequently, the influence of the other stars in preventing some of the stars with the requisite energies from escaping cannot be entirely neglected. This is particularly true of the smaller clusters. But it is clear that the order of magnitude of the rate of disintegration of a cluster predicted by equation (5.314) is not likely to be seriously affected by a more detailed consideration of the mechanism of escape.

5.4. *The escape of stars of different masses from a cluster.*—In § 5.3 we consider the gradual impoverishment of a cluster arising from the loss of stars by escape. But, in estimating the rate of loss, it was assumed that the members of the cluster are all of the same mass. We shall now consider the case when there is a small dispersion of the masses among the cluster members.

First of all, it is clear that the results of § 5.4 will be valid for the general case, if m is taken to refer to an average mass, $\bar{m}$, of the stars in the cluster. In other words, we may use equation (5.312) to give the rate of escape of the average stars. Thus (cf. eqs. [5.307] and [5.312]),

$$\frac{1}{n(\bar{m})}\frac{dn(\bar{m})}{dt} = -\frac{Q(\bar{m})}{\bar{T}_E(\bar{m})}, \tag{5.401}$$

where, according to equation (5.307),

$$Q(\bar{m}) = \frac{4\bar{j}^3}{\pi^{1/2}}\int_{\sqrt{\overline{v^2_\infty}}}^{\infty} e^{-\bar{j}^2v^2}v^2 dv\,. \tag{5.402}$$

In equation (5.402), we have used $\bar{j}$ to indicate that reference is now being made to an average modulus.

We shall now suppose that the cluster contains a few stars which have a mass, m_2, different from $\bar{m}$. If the total number of these stars is small compared to $n(\bar{m})$, we can ignore the encounters among themselves and take into account only their interaction with the other stars. We can therefore regard these stars as a *group* moving through the field of the average stars. The situation is thus the same as that contemplated in subsections (ix) and (x) of § 2.3. Accordingly, the mean time of relaxation of these stars is given by (eq. [2.377])

$$\bar{T}_E(m_2) = \frac{9(\bar{j}^2 + j_2^2)^{3/2}}{128\pi^{1/2} N G^2 \bar{m}^2 \bar{j}\, j_2^5 \log q \overline{\overline{v^2}}}. \tag{5.403}$$

Hence,

$$\frac{\bar{T}_E(m_2)}{\bar{T}_E(\bar{m})} = \frac{1}{2^{3/2}}(\bar{j}^2 + j_2^2)^{3/2}\frac{\bar{j}^2}{j_2^5}, \tag{5.404}$$

or, somewhat differently,

$$\frac{\bar{T}_E(m_2)}{T_E(\bar{m})} = \left\{\frac{1}{2}\left(1 + \frac{\bar{j}^2}{j_2^2}\right)\right\}^{3/2}\frac{\bar{j}^2}{j_2^2}. \tag{5.405}$$

There is an approximate relation between the ratio of the j's and the corresponding ratio of the masses, which we can write down. For under the conditions of strict statistical equilibrium we must require that

$$\bar{m}\,\overline{v^2} = m_2 \overline{v_2^2}, \tag{5.406}$$

or, since the root mean square velocities are inversely as the j's,

$$\frac{\bar{m}}{m_2} = \frac{\bar{j}^2}{j_2^2}; \tag{5.407}$$

and we can expect this relation to be approximately valid in clusters. Equation (5.405) therefore becomes

$$\frac{\bar{T}_E(m_2)}{\bar{T}_E(\bar{m})} = \left\{\frac{1}{2}\left(1 + \frac{\bar{m}}{m_2}\right)\right\}^{3/2}\frac{\bar{m}}{m_2}. \tag{5.408}$$

According to this equation, the time of relaxation for stars of masses which are small compared to that of the average stars is longer. Thus, for $m_2 = \bar{m}/4$, the time of relaxation is about sixteen times longer.

The *increase* in the time of relaxation predicted by equation (5.408) for the smaller masses would tend to *reduce* the rate of loss by escape of these stars. But there is another important factor, which works in the opposite direction. For, according to equation (5.406), the smaller masses have larger mean velocities, and consequently a higher proportion of them would have the necessary velocities for escape. More explicitly, the fraction of the total number of these stars which have velocities greater than the velocity of escape is

$$Q(m_2) = \frac{4\, j_2^3}{\pi^{1/2}} \int_{\sqrt{\overline{v_\infty^2}}}^{\infty} e^{-j_2^2 v_2^2} v_2^2 d\, v_2 \,. \tag{5.409}$$

Since (cf. eqs. [5.306] and [5.406])

$$\overline{v_\infty^2} = 4\,\overline{v^2} = 4\,\frac{m_2}{\bar{m}}\,\overline{v_2^2} = 6\,\frac{m_2}{\bar{m}}\,\frac{1}{j_2^2}\,, \tag{5.410}$$

we have

$$Q(m_2) = \frac{4}{\pi^{1/2}} \int_{\sqrt{6 m_2/\bar{m}}}^{\infty} e^{-x^2} x^2 dx \,. \tag{5.411}$$

Hence (cf. eq. [5.410]),

$$Q(m_2) = 2\left(\frac{6\,m_2}{\pi\,\bar{m}}\right)^{1/2} e^{-6 m_2/\bar{m}} + 1 - \Phi\left(\sqrt{\frac{6\,m_2}{\bar{m}}}\right), \tag{5.412}$$

where Φ stands for the error function.

For $m_2/\bar{m} < 1$, $Q(m_2)$ is considerably larger than equation (5.311) and therefore corresponds to a *larger* rate of loss by escape. But this is largely compensated by the increased time of relaxation, according to equation (5.408). Thus the fraction of the number of stars of mass, m_2, which escape in the time, $\bar{T}_E(\bar{m})$, is given by

$$Q(m_2)\,\frac{\bar{T}_E(\bar{m})}{\bar{T}_E(m_2)} = \frac{2\left(\frac{6\,m_2}{\pi\,\bar{m}}\right)^{1/2} e^{-6 m_2/\bar{m}} + 1 - \Phi\left(\sqrt{\frac{6\,m_2}{\bar{m}}}\right)}{\left\{\frac{1}{2}\left(1+\frac{\bar{m}}{m_2}\right)\right\}^{3/2} \frac{\bar{m}}{m_2}} \,. \tag{5.413}$$

The factor (5.413) is tabulated in Table 11. An inspection of this table reveals the interesting fact that stars of about four-tenths the average mass are characterized by the maximum rate of loss by escape. But even at the maximum the rate is only four times greater than the average. Stars of about one-quarter the average mass escape only at three times the average rate, and the stars with somewhat smaller $m_2/\bar{m}$ values do not escape very much more rapidly than the average stars. Again, stars even appreciably more massive than the average stars are characterized by such small rates of escape that even after 3×10^9 years the clusters are likely to have lost none of their original massive members.

As a result of the differential rate of escape of stars of different masses from clusters, we may conclude that (i) they retain practically all the stars more massive than the average; (ii) they have lost a

TABLE 11

THE ESCAPE OF STARS OF DIFFERENT MASSES FROM A CLUSTER

$\frac{m_2}{\bar{m}}$	$\frac{\bar{T}_E(m_2)}{\bar{T}_E(\bar{m})}$	Q	$Q\frac{\bar{T}_E(m_2)}{T_E(\bar{m})}$
0.00	∞	1.000	0.00
0.05	680	0.896	.0013
0.075	256	0.825	.0032
0.10	129	0.753	.0058
0.125	76	0.682	.0089
0.15	50	0.615	.0123
0.20	26	0.494	.0190
0.25	15.8	0.392	.0248
0.30	10.6	0.308	.0290
0.35	7.65	0.241	.0315
0.40	5.79	0.187	.0323
0.45	4.54	0.145	.0318
0.50	3.67	0.112	.0304
0.55	3.04	0.0858	.0282
0.60	2.57	0.0658	.0256
0.70	1.91	0.0384	.0201
0.80	1.49	0.0222	.0149
0.90	1.21	0.0129	.0107
1.0	1.00	0.00738	.0074
1.1	0.848	0.00422	.0050
1.2	0.731	0.00241	.0033
1.3	0.640	0.00137	.0021
1.4	0.567	0.00078	.0014
1.5	0.507	0.00044	0.0009

somewhat higher proportion of the stars of about four-tenths the average mass than either the more or the less massive stars; and (iii) they probably retain all their least massive members which are likely to be still far from a state of complete statistical equilibrium.

Finally, it should be remarked that even the differential rates of escape indicated in Table 11 are likely to be overestimates, for the less massive stars will have a tendency to be in the less dense regions of the cluster. This will therefore increase the time of relaxation of these stars more than by the factor (5.408); and this, in turn, will tend to reduce the rate of loss still further. But, broadly, we may summarize the results of this discussion by saying that, while we should expect differential rates of escape for stars of different masses, it is unlikely that factors larger than 3 or 4 are involved.

5.5. *The effect of galactic rotation on the dynamics of clusters.*— In the preceding sections we have restricted ourselves to the dynamics of isolated clusters. The special simplifying feature of this case is that the motions can be analyzed into two distinct parts: the part referring to the motions of the individual cluster members with respect to their common center of gravity and the part referring to the motion of the center of gravity. And, since the latter is a uniform motion in a straight line, the only significant aspect of the dynamics is that relating to the residual motions. But, in practice, the galactic clusters share in the differential rotation of the Galaxy, and under these more general conditions we cannot expect that the motions can still be analyzed into the same two parts in any simple manner. Physical considerations would, however, suggest that, to the extent that the notion of a cluster is definable, to that same extent we should be able to analyze the motions simply into the two parts referring, respectively, to the motion of the center of gravity and the motions with respect to it. In a first approximation we can therefore suppose that the center of gravity of the cluster describes an orbit in the external field of force represented by the gravitational potential $\mathfrak{B}$ and that the cluster members have additional residual motions with respect to the center of gravity. On this scheme, the force acting on a star in the cluster can be expressed as the sum of two terms: the first representing the interaction of the star under consideration with the other cluster stars and the second arising from the general gravitational field.

Now the variation of $\mathfrak{B}$ over the spatial extent of the cluster will give rise to what is essentially a *tidal field*. The question naturally suggests itself: Will the tidal field succeed in disrupting the cluster? In a general way it is clear that, if the density of the cluster is sufficiently high (cf. § 5.6), the disintegrating tendency of the tidal field can be neglected. But if the cluster is "loose," then the tidal effects will become very pronounced. In the former case the idealization of clusters as "isolated" is a satisfactory one; in the latter case this notion largely loses its meaning.

The simplest case of the problem we have outlined above is when the center of gravity of the cluster describes a circular orbit in the galactic plane—in other words, the case of a cluster sharing in the

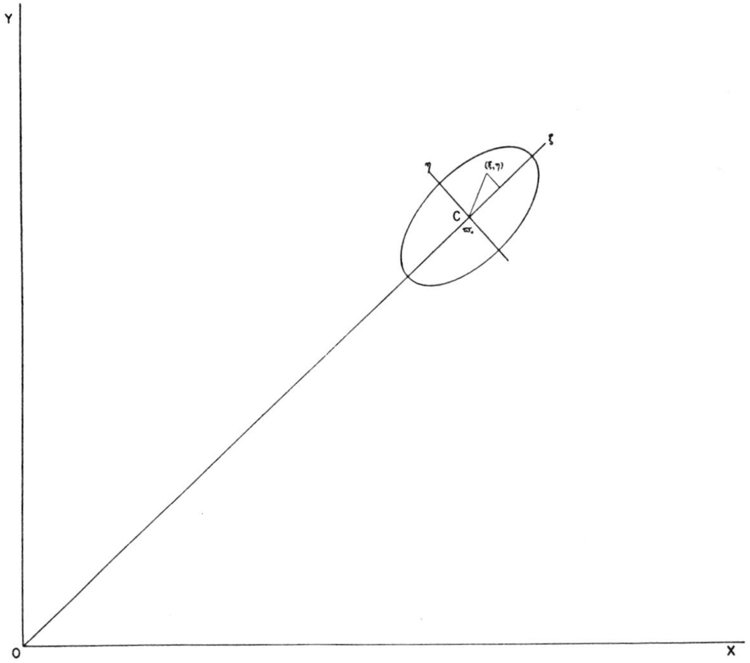

FIG. 24.—Illustrating the co-ordinate system appropriate for studying star clusters sharing in galactic rotation. O denotes the center of the Galaxy and C the center of gravity of the cluster (distant ϖ_0 from O). C is assumed to describe a circular orbit about O with a constant angular velocity ω_c. The ξ- and the η-axes are in the radial and the transverse directions, respectively, and the ζ-axis (not shown) is perpendicular to the plane of the paper.

galactic rotation. This problem was first considered by Bok and later in a more extensive study by Mineur.

We accordingly picture to ourselves a cluster moving in a field which is characterized by both an axis and a plane of symmetry. More particularly, the center of gravity of the cluster is assumed to describe a circular orbit in the galactic plane. If we denote by ϖ_0

the constant distance of the center of gravity of the cluster from the galactic center, then the rotational and the angular velocities are given by (eqs. [4.311] and [4.312])

$$\Theta_c^2 = \left(\varpi \frac{\partial \mathfrak{V}}{\partial \varpi} \right)_0 ; \qquad \omega_c^2 = \left(\frac{1}{\varpi} \frac{\partial \mathfrak{V}}{\partial \varpi} \right)_0 , \tag{5.501}$$

where the subscript 0 is to indicate that the quantity in parenthesis is to be evaluated at $\varpi = \varpi_0$ and $z = 0$.

The nature of our present problem suggests that we introduce a frame of reference rotating uniformly about the z-axis with the angular velocity ω_c. We shall choose the origin of this frame of reference to be at the center of gravity of the cluster and denote by ξ, η, and ζ the distances measured from this origin along the radial, the transverse, and the z-directions, respectively (see Fig. 24). The transformation from the stationary frame (x, y, z) to the rotating frame (ξ, η, ζ) is governed by the formulae

$$\varpi_0 + \xi = x \cos \theta + y \sin \theta ; \qquad \eta = -x \sin \theta + y \cos \theta \tag{5.502}$$

and

$$x = (\varpi_0 + \xi) \cos \theta - \eta \sin \theta ; \quad y = (\varpi_0 + \xi) \sin \theta + \eta \cos \theta , \tag{5.503}$$

where

$$\theta = \omega_c t . \tag{5.504}$$

i) *The equations of motion in the rotating frame of reference.*—The equations of motion of a star in the cluster are most conveniently expressed in terms of the Lagrangian function

$$L = T - m\mathfrak{V} - \Omega , \tag{5.505}$$

where T denotes the kinetic energy and $\mathfrak{V}$ the general gravitational potential which is a function of ϖ and z only; finally, Ω is the potential energy of the cluster

$$\Omega = -G \sum \frac{m_i m_j}{r_{ij}} \qquad (i \neq j) . \tag{5.506}$$

The explicit expression for T is readily obtained. According to equations (5.503) and (5.504),

$$\left. \begin{aligned} \dot{x} &= \dot{\xi} \cos \theta - \dot{\eta} \sin \theta - \dot{\theta} [(\varpi_0 + \xi) \sin \theta + \eta \cos \theta] , \\ &= \dot{\xi} \cos \theta - \dot{\eta} \sin \theta - \omega_c y . \end{aligned} \right\} \tag{5.507}$$

Similarly,

$$\dot{y} = \dot{\xi} \sin \theta + \dot{\eta} \cos \theta + \omega_c x \, . \tag{5.508}$$

From equations (5.507) and (5.508) we obtain

$$\left.\begin{aligned} \dot{x}^2 + \dot{y}^2 = \dot{\xi}^2 + \dot{\eta}^2 - 2\omega_c \dot{\xi}\eta + 2\omega_c \dot{\eta} (\varpi_0 + \xi) \\ + \omega_c^2 [(\varpi_0 + \xi)^2 + \eta^2] \, . \end{aligned}\right\} \tag{5.509}$$

Hence, the Lagrangian function takes the form

$$\left.\begin{aligned} L = m \{ \tfrac{1}{2} (\dot{\xi}^2 + \dot{\eta}^2 + \dot{\zeta}^2) - \omega_c \dot{\xi}\eta + \omega_c \dot{\eta} (\varpi_0 + \xi) \\ + \tfrac{1}{2} \omega_c^2 [(\varpi_0 + \xi)^2 + \eta^2] \} - m \mathfrak{V} ([\varpi_0 + \xi]^2 + \eta^2 ; \zeta) - \Omega \, . \end{aligned}\right\} \tag{5.510}$$

The corresponding Lagrangian equations of motion are

$$\left.\begin{aligned} \frac{d}{dt}\left(\frac{\partial L}{\partial \dot{\xi}}\right) &= m (\ddot{\xi} - \omega_c \dot{\eta}) = \frac{\partial L}{\partial \xi} = m \left(\omega_c \dot{\eta} + \omega_c^2 (\varpi_0 + \xi) - \frac{\partial \mathfrak{V}}{\partial \xi} \right) - \frac{\partial \Omega}{\partial \xi} \, , \\ \frac{d}{dt}\left(\frac{\partial L}{\partial \dot{\eta}}\right) &= m (\ddot{\eta} + \omega_c \dot{\xi}) = \frac{\partial L}{\partial \eta} = m \left(- \omega_c \dot{\xi} + \omega_c^2 \eta - \frac{\partial \mathfrak{V}}{\partial \eta} \right) - \frac{\partial \Omega}{\partial \eta} \, , \\ \frac{d}{dt}\left(\frac{\partial L}{\partial \dot{\zeta}}\right) &= m \ddot{\zeta} \qquad = \qquad - m \frac{\partial \mathfrak{V}}{\partial \zeta} - \frac{\partial \Omega}{\partial \zeta} \, , \end{aligned}\right\} \tag{5.511}$$

or, since

$$\frac{\partial \mathfrak{V}}{\partial \xi} = \frac{\varpi_0 + \xi}{\varpi} \frac{\partial \mathfrak{V}}{\partial \varpi} \, ; \qquad \frac{\partial \mathfrak{V}}{\partial \eta} = \frac{\eta}{\varpi} \frac{\partial \mathfrak{V}}{\partial \varpi} \, , \tag{5.512}$$

we have

$$\left.\begin{aligned} m (\ddot{\xi} - 2\omega_c \dot{\eta} - \omega_c^2 [\varpi_0 + \xi]) &= - m \frac{\varpi_0 + \xi}{\varpi} \frac{\partial \mathfrak{V}}{\partial \varpi} - \frac{\partial \Omega}{\partial \xi} \, , \\ m (\ddot{\eta} + 2\omega_c \dot{\xi} - \omega_c^2 \eta) &= - m \frac{\eta}{\varpi} \frac{\partial \mathfrak{V}}{\partial \varpi} - \frac{\partial \Omega}{\partial \eta} \, , \\ m \ddot{\zeta} &= - m \frac{\partial \mathfrak{V}}{\partial \zeta} - \frac{\partial \Omega}{\partial \zeta} \, . \end{aligned}\right\} \tag{5.513}$$

The foregoing equations are exact. We shall now suppose that the dimensions of the cluster are small compared to ϖ_0 and neglect all quantities of order higher than the first in ξ, η, and ζ.

From the relation

$$\varpi^2 = (\varpi_0 + \xi)^2 + \eta^2 \, , \tag{5.514}$$

we conclude, to the first order,

$$\varpi = \varpi_0 + \xi + \text{higher-order terms} \, . \tag{5.515}$$

Hence,

$$\left.\begin{aligned}\frac{\varpi_0+\xi}{\varpi}\frac{\partial\mathfrak{V}}{\partial\varpi}&=\left(\frac{\partial\mathfrak{V}}{\partial\varpi}\right)_0+\xi\left(\frac{\partial^2\mathfrak{V}}{\partial\varpi^2}\right)_0+\text{higher-order terms}\,,\\ \frac{\eta}{\varpi}\frac{\partial\mathfrak{V}}{\partial\varpi}&=\eta\left(\frac{1}{\varpi}\frac{\partial\mathfrak{V}}{\partial\varpi}\right)_0+\text{higher-order terms}\,,\\ \frac{\partial\mathfrak{V}}{\partial\zeta}&=\zeta\left(\frac{\partial^2\mathfrak{V}}{\partial z^2}\right)_0+\text{higher-order terms}\,.\end{aligned}\right\}\qquad(5.516)$$

In the last of these equations we have used the fact of the symmetry of $\mathfrak{V}$ about the galactic plane. Substituting from (5.516) in equations (5.513) and using the relation (5.501), we obtain

$$m_i(\ddot{\xi}_i-2\omega_c\dot{\eta}_i+a_1\xi_i)=-\frac{\partial\Omega}{\partial\xi_i}\,,\qquad(5.517)$$

$$m_i(\ddot{\eta}_i+2\omega_c\dot{\xi}_i)=-\frac{\partial\Omega}{\partial\eta_i}\,,\qquad(5.518)$$

and

$$m_i(\ddot{\zeta}_i+a_3\zeta_i)=-\frac{\partial\Omega}{\partial\zeta_i}\,,\qquad(5.519)$$

where we have written

$$a_1=\left(\frac{\partial^2\mathfrak{V}}{\partial\varpi^2}-\frac{1}{\varpi}\frac{\partial\mathfrak{V}}{\partial\varpi}\right)_0\,;\qquad a_3=\left(\frac{\partial^2\mathfrak{V}}{\partial z^2}\right)_0\,;\qquad(5.520)$$

further, in equations (5.517)–(5.519) we have introduced the subscript i explicitly to draw attention to the fact that these are the equations of motion of a particular star in the cluster and that there are similar equations for the other cluster members.

ii) *The energy integral.*—Multiplying equations (5.517), (5.518), and (5.519) by $\dot{\xi}_i$, $\dot{\eta}_i$, and $\dot{\zeta}_i$, respectively, and adding, we obtain

$$\left.\begin{aligned}&\Sigma m_i(\dot{\xi}_i\ddot{\xi}_i+\dot{\eta}_i\ddot{\eta}_i+\dot{\zeta}_i\ddot{\zeta}_i)+a_1\Sigma m_i\dot{\xi}_i\xi_i+a_3\Sigma m_i\dot{\zeta}_i\zeta_i\\ &\qquad=-\sum\left(\dot{\xi}_i\frac{\partial\Omega}{\partial\xi_i}+\dot{\eta}_i\frac{\partial\Omega}{\partial\eta_i}+\dot{\zeta}_i\frac{\partial\Omega}{\partial\zeta_i}\right)=-\frac{d\Omega}{dt}\,,\end{aligned}\right\}\qquad(5.521)$$

an equation which admits of immediate integration. We have

$$\left.\begin{aligned}&\tfrac{1}{2}\Sigma m_i(\dot{\xi}_i^2+\dot{\eta}_i^2+\dot{\zeta}_i^2)+\Omega+\tfrac{1}{2}a_1\Sigma m_i\xi_i^2\\ &\qquad\qquad+\tfrac{1}{2}a_3\Sigma m_i\zeta_i^2=\text{constant}\,.\end{aligned}\right\}\qquad(5.522)$$

Equation (5.522) represents the analogue of the energy integral (5.128).

iii) *The angular-momentum integrals.*—From the equations of motion (5.517)–(5.519) we readily obtain

$$\left.\begin{aligned}\Sigma m_i(\ddot{\eta}_i\xi_i-\ddot{\xi}_i\eta_i)+2\omega_c\Sigma m_i(\xi_i\dot{\xi}_i+\eta_i\dot{\eta}_i)-a_1\Sigma\xi_i\eta_i\\ =\sum\left(\eta_i\frac{\partial\Omega}{\partial\xi_i}-\xi_i\frac{\partial\Omega}{\partial\eta_i}\right),\end{aligned}\right\}\quad(5.523)$$

$$\left.\begin{aligned}\Sigma m_i(\ddot{\zeta}_i\eta_i-\ddot{\eta}_i\zeta_i)-2\omega_c\Sigma m_i\zeta_i\dot{\xi}_i+a_3\Sigma m_i\eta_i\zeta_i\\ =\sum\left(\zeta_i\frac{\partial\Omega}{\partial\eta_i}-\eta_i\frac{\partial\Omega}{\partial\zeta_i}\right),\end{aligned}\right\}\quad(5.524)$$

and

$$\left.\begin{aligned}\Sigma m_i(\ddot{\xi}_i\zeta_i-\ddot{\zeta}_i\xi_i)-2\omega_c\Sigma m_i\zeta_i\dot{\eta}_i+(a_1-a_3)\Sigma m_i\zeta_i\xi_i\\ =\sum\left(\xi_i\frac{\partial\Omega}{\partial\zeta_i}-\zeta_i\frac{\partial\Omega}{\partial\xi_i}\right).\end{aligned}\right\}\quad(5.525)$$

On the other hand, according to equation (5.113) the right-hand sides of the foregoing equations vanish identically. Hence,

$$\Sigma m_i\frac{d}{dt}(\dot{\eta}_i\xi_i-\dot{\xi}_i\eta_i)+\omega_c\Sigma m_i\frac{d}{dt}(\xi_i^2+\eta_i^2)-a_1\Sigma\xi_i\eta_i=0\,,\quad(5.526)$$

$$\Sigma m_i\frac{d}{dt}(\dot{\zeta}_i\eta_i-\dot{\eta}_i\zeta_i)-2\omega_c\Sigma m_i\zeta_i\dot{\xi}_i+a_3\Sigma m_i\eta_i\zeta_i=0\,,\quad(5.527)$$

and

$$\Sigma m_i\frac{d}{dt}(\dot{\xi}_i\zeta_i-\dot{\zeta}_i\xi_i)-2\omega_c\Sigma m_i\zeta_i\dot{\eta}_i+(a_1-a_3)\Sigma m_i\zeta_i\xi_i=0\,.\quad(5.528)$$

These equations do not lead to any immediate integrals of the equations of motion unless the cluster satisfies certain symmetries. Thus, if we suppose that the cluster is symmetrical with respect to the $\xi\zeta$- and/or $\eta\zeta$-plane, then

$$\Sigma m_i\xi_i\eta_i=0\,,\quad(5.529)$$

and equation (5.526) leads at once to the integral

$$\Sigma m_i(\xi_i\dot{\eta}_i-\eta_i\dot{\xi}_i)+\omega_c\Sigma m_i(\xi_i^2+\eta_i^2)=A_\zeta=\text{constant}\,.\quad(5.530)$$

If we further suppose that

$$\Sigma m_i\zeta_i\dot{\xi}_i=\Sigma m_i\zeta_i\dot{\eta}_i=\Sigma m_i\eta_i\zeta_i=\Sigma m_i\zeta_i\xi_i=0\,,\quad(5.531)$$

then equations (5.527) and (5.528) lead to the two further integrals

$$\left.\begin{aligned}\Sigma m_i(\eta_i\dot{\zeta}_i-\zeta_i\dot{\eta}_i)=A_\xi=\text{constant}\,,\\ \Sigma m_i(\zeta_i\dot{\xi}_i-\xi_i\dot{\zeta}_i)=A_\eta=\text{constant}\,.\end{aligned}\right\}\quad(5.532)$$

Equations (5.530) and (5.532) are our present analogues of the angular-momentum integrals which exist for an isolated cluster.

iv) *The generalized Lagrangian identities.*—According to equation (5.134) we have quite generally

$$\left.\begin{aligned}\frac{1}{2\Sigma m_i}\frac{d^2}{dt^2}(\Sigma m_i m_j r_{ij}^2) &= \Sigma m_i(\dot{\xi}_i^2+\dot{\eta}_i^2+\dot{\zeta}_i^2)\\ &\quad+\Sigma m_i(\xi_i\ddot{\xi}_i+\eta_i\ddot{\eta}_i+\zeta_i\ddot{\zeta}_i)\,,\end{aligned}\right\} \quad (5.533)$$

or, using the equations of motion (eqs. [5.517]–[5.519]),

$$\left.\begin{aligned}\frac{1}{2\Sigma m_i}\frac{d^2}{dt^2}(\Sigma m_i m_j r_{ij}^2) &= \Sigma m_i(\dot{\xi}_i^2+\dot{\eta}_i^2+\dot{\zeta}_i^2\\ &\quad+2\omega_c\Sigma m_i(\xi_i\dot{\eta}_i-\dot{\xi}_i\eta_i)-a_1\Sigma m_i\xi_i^2-a_3\Sigma m_i\zeta_i^2\\ &\quad-\sum\left(\xi_i\frac{\partial\Omega}{\partial\xi_i}+\eta_i\frac{\partial\Omega}{\partial\eta_i}+\zeta_i\frac{\partial\Omega}{\partial\zeta_i}\right).\end{aligned}\right\} \quad (5.534)$$

Since Ω is homogeneous and is of degree -1 in the co-ordinates, we have

$$\left.\begin{aligned}\frac{1}{2\Sigma m_i}\frac{d^2}{dt^2}(\Sigma m_i m_j r_{ij}^2) &= \Sigma m_i(\dot{\xi}_i^2+\dot{\eta}_i^2+\dot{\zeta}_i^2)+\Omega\\ &\quad+2\omega_c\Sigma m_i(\xi_i\dot{\eta}_i-\eta_i\dot{\xi}_i)-a_1\Sigma m_i\xi_i^2-a_3\Sigma m_i\zeta_i^2\,.\end{aligned}\right\} \quad (5.535)$$

If the cluster satisfies the symmetry condition (5.529) we can simplify equation (5.535) still further by using the angular-momentum integral (5.530). We thus obtain

$$\left.\begin{aligned}\frac{1}{2\Sigma m_i}\frac{d^2}{dt^2}(\Sigma m_i m_j r_{ij}^2) &= \Sigma m_i(\dot{\xi}_i^2+\dot{\eta}_i^2+\dot{\zeta}_i^2)+\Omega+2\omega_c A_\zeta\\ &\quad-2\omega_c^2\Sigma m_i(\xi_i^2+\eta_i^2)-a_1\Sigma m_i\xi_i^2-a_3\Sigma m_i\zeta_i^2\,.\end{aligned}\right\} \quad (5.536)$$

This is our present analogue of Lagrange's identity (5.136).

For a cluster in a statistically steady state equation (5.536) reduces to

$$2T+\Omega+2\omega_c A_\zeta = a_1\Sigma m_i\xi_i^2+a_3\Sigma m_i\zeta_i^2+2\omega_c^2\Sigma m_i(\xi_i^2+\eta_i^2)\,, \quad (5.537)$$

where, as in § 5.1, we have used T to denote the total kinetic energy of the residual motions in the cluster. In addition to equation (5.526), we also have the energy integral (eq. [5.522])

$$T+\Omega = -\tfrac{1}{2}\{a_1\Sigma m_i\xi_i^2+a_3\Sigma m_i\zeta_i^2\}+\text{constant}\,. \quad (5.538)$$

5.6. *The stability of a homogeneous ellipsoidal cluster.*—In § 5.5 we obtained the equations of motion for the stars in a cluster sharing in the galactic rotation. In continuing our discussion of the dynamics of such moving clusters, we can have recourse to one of two methods: *Either* to consider the clusters as being in statistically steady states and follow the general lines of §§ 5.2–5.4 but using the relations (5.537) and (5.538) appropriate to the case on hand *or* replace the cluster by a smoothed-out distribution and analyze the motions of the individual stars in terms of the explicit solutions of the equations of motion (eqs. [5.517]–[5.519]). As to which of these two methods we should adopt in practice will depend on the time of relaxation of the cluster under consideration. For the standard galactic clusters the statistical method should be preferred as physically the more appropriate of the two. However, the second method leads to an interesting criterion for the stability of a cluster against the shearing effect of differential galactic relation. Accordingly, we shall follow the second of the two methods in this section. On this scheme, Ω becomes a function of the co-ordinates of the star only and the equations of motion can be solved in principle.

For the sake of simplicity, we shall suppose that the smoothed-out distribution in the cluster can be approximated to a homogeneous ellipsoid. Then Ω will take the form[4]

$$\Omega_i = -\tfrac{1}{2} m_i \beta_0 + \tfrac{1}{2} m_i (\beta_1 \xi_i^2 + \beta_2 \eta_i^2 + \beta_3 \zeta_i^2) , \qquad (5.601)$$

where β_0, β_1, β_2, and β_3 are constants depending on the density and the geometry of the ellipsoid. More explicitly, we have

$$\left.\begin{aligned} \beta_1 &= \pi G \rho \beta_1' (a:b:c) ; \\ \beta_2 &= \pi G \rho \beta_2' (a:b:c) ; \\ \beta_3 &= \pi G \rho \beta_3' (a:b:c) , \end{aligned}\right\} \qquad (5.602)$$

where ρ is the density of the ellipsoid and β_1', β_2', and β_3' are pure numbers depending on the ratio of the axes a, b, and c of the ellipsoid only. Extensive tables of these functions have been published by Mineur.[5]

[4] Cf. eq. (4.501), which gives the potential of an oblate spheroid.

[5] *Ann. d'ap.*, **2**, No. 1, 1939; see particularly pp. 199–213.

For Ω of the form (5.601) the equations of motion (5.517)–(5.519) become

$$\left.\begin{aligned} \ddot{\xi} - 2\omega_c \dot{\eta} + (\alpha_1 + \beta_1)\, \xi &= 0 \,, \\ \ddot{\eta} + 2\omega_c \dot{\xi} + \beta_2 \eta &= 0 \,, \end{aligned}\right\} \tag{5.603}$$

and

$$\ddot{\zeta} + (\alpha_3 + \beta_3)\, \zeta = 0 \,. \tag{5.604}$$

Equation (5.604) admits of immediate integration. We have

$$\zeta = \zeta_0 \cos q_3 (t + t_3) \,, \tag{5.605}$$

where ζ_0 and t_3 are constants of integration and

$$q_3^2 = \alpha_3 + \beta_3 \,. \tag{5.606}$$

Equations (5.603) are two simultaneous linear second-order differential equations with constant coefficients for ξ and η and can be solved by standard methods. Substituting

$$\xi = \xi_0 e^{iqt} \,; \qquad \eta = \eta_0 e^{iqt} \tag{5.607}$$

(where ξ_0, η_0, and q are constants), in equations (5.603), we obtain

$$\left.\begin{aligned} (\alpha_1 + \beta_1 - q^2)\, \xi_0 - 2\omega_c i q \eta_0 &= 0 \,, \\ 2\omega_c i q\, \xi_0 + (\beta_2 - q^2)\, \eta_0 &= 0 \,; \end{aligned}\right\} \tag{5.608}$$

the compatibility of these two homogeneous linear equations requires that

$$\begin{vmatrix} (\alpha_1 + \beta_1) - q^2 & -2\omega_c i q \\ 2\omega_c i q & \beta_2 - q^2 \end{vmatrix} = 0 \,, \tag{5.609}$$

or, expanding the determinant,

$$q^4 - q^2 (\alpha_1 + \beta_1 + \beta_2 + 4\omega_c^2) + \beta_2 (\alpha_1 + \beta_1) = 0 \,. \tag{5.610}$$

Hence,

$$\left.\begin{aligned} q^2 = {} & \tfrac{1}{2} (\alpha_1 + \beta_1 + \beta_2 + 4\omega_c^2) \\ & \pm \tfrac{1}{2} \sqrt{(\alpha_1 + \beta_1 + \beta_2 + 4\omega_c)^2 - 4\beta_2 (\alpha_1 + \beta_1)} \,. \end{aligned}\right\} \tag{5.611}$$

Accordingly, there are two possible roots for q^2. Both these roots are positive if $\alpha_1 + \beta_1 > 0$; the corresponding roots for q are therefore all real. But if $\alpha_1 + \beta_1 < 0$, one of the two possible roots for q^2 becomes negative, and the corresponding roots for q are therefore imaginary. In the former case ($\alpha_1 + \beta_1 > 0$) the solutions will involve only the circular functions and the solutions correspond to stable oscillations. In the latter case ($\alpha_1 + \beta_1 < 0$), the solutions will involve the hyperbolic functions as well, and ξ and η will increase indefinitely. Thus *the condition for dynamical stability is*

$$\alpha_1 + \beta_1 > 0 \, . \tag{5.612}$$

According to equations (5.520) and (5.602), the foregoing condition takes explicitly the form

$$\left(\frac{\partial^2 \mathfrak{B}}{\partial \varpi^2} - \frac{1}{\varpi} \frac{\partial \mathfrak{B}}{\partial \varpi} \right)_0 + \pi G \rho \beta_1' > 0 \, . \tag{5.613}$$

The inequality (5.613) can be expressed more conveniently in terms of observable quantities as follows: From equation (5.501), we readily obtain the relation

$$\left(\frac{\partial^2 \mathfrak{B}}{\partial \varpi^2} - \frac{1}{\varpi} \frac{\partial \mathfrak{B}}{\partial \varpi} \right) = 2 \frac{\Theta_c}{\varpi_0} \left(\frac{d\Theta_c}{\partial \varpi} - \frac{\Theta_c}{\varpi} \right)_0 , \tag{5.614}$$

or, in terms of the Oort constants A and B (eqs. [1.428])

$$\alpha_1 = 4 A \, (B - A) \, . \tag{5.615}$$

Thus the inequality (5.613) is equivalent to

$$\rho > \rho^* , \tag{5.616}$$

where

$$\rho^* = \frac{4}{\pi G \beta_1'} A \, (A - B) \, . \tag{5.617}$$

In other words, the dynamical stability of a cluster requires that its density exceed a certain critical value ρ^*.

Expressing the density and the Oort constants in units of solar mass per cubic parsec and km per second per 1000 parsecs, we find that

$$\rho^* = 3.0 \times 10^{-4} \frac{A \, (A - B)}{\beta_1'} \, . \tag{5.618}$$

For the values of A and B given in chapter i (eq. [1.422]) (5.618) becomes

$$\rho^* = \frac{0.165}{\beta_1'} \, . \tag{5.619}$$

The critical densities required by the formula (5.619) for oblate spheroidal clusters for various values of the ratio of the axes c/a are given in Table 12. It is seen that these critical densities are considerably smaller than those which we ordinarily encounter in galactic clusters. Thus the average density of the Pleiades (~ 1.7) is about fifteen times the critical density; similarly for the Praesepe the corresponding factor is 20.

TABLE 12*

THE MINIMUM DENSITIES OF OBLATE SPHEROIDAL CLUSTERS FOR DYNAMICAL STABILITY

c/a	β_1'	ρ^*	c/a	β_1'	ρ^*
0.1	0.278	0.59	0.5	0.946	0.17
.2	.499	.33	0.6	1.048	.16
.3	.677	.24	0.8	1.211	.14
0.4	0.824	0.20	1.0	1.333	0.12

* The density is expressed in the unit of solar mass/(parsec)^3.

Returning to the solutions of the equations (5.603), we have, according to equations (5.607) and (5.608),

$$\left.\begin{aligned} \xi &= \xi_{01}\cos q_1(t+t_1) + \xi_{02}\cos q_2(t+t_2)\,,\\ \eta &= \frac{2\omega_c q_1}{\beta_2 - q_1^2}\,\xi_{01}\sin q_1(t+t_1) + \frac{2\omega_c q_2}{\beta_2 - q_2^2}\,\xi_{02}\sin q_2(t+t_2)\,,\end{aligned}\right\} \tag{5.620}$$

where ξ_{01}, ξ_{02}, t_1, and t_2 are constants of integration and q_1 and q_2 are the two positive roots derived from equation (5.611). The foregoing solution is valid only when $\alpha_1 + \beta_1 > 0$. But when $\alpha_1 + \beta_1$ is negative, one of the two (positive) roots becomes imaginary; and, if we denote this root by iq_2, the solution is seen to be

$$\left.\begin{aligned} \xi &= \xi_{01}\cos q_1(t+t_1) + \xi_{02}\cosh q_2(t+t_2)\,,\\ \eta &= \frac{2\omega_c q_1}{\beta_2 - q_1^2}\,\xi_{01}\sin q_1(t+t_1) - \frac{2\omega_c q_2}{\beta_2 + q_2^2}\,\xi_{02}\sinh q_2(t+t_2)\,.\end{aligned}\right\} \tag{5.621}$$

5.7. *The effect of stellar encounters on the dynamics of clusters.*— In our discussion in § 5.6 we replaced the cluster by a smoothed-out distribution and assumed further that the interaction of a star with the other cluster members can be derived from a potential function $\Omega(\xi, \eta, \zeta)$. The advantage of this procedure is that the equations of motion (eqs. [5.517]–[5.519]) then become separable in the co-ordinates of the different stars, and the motion of any one of them can be considered independently of the others. On the other hand, our study of isolated clusters (§§ 5.2–5.4) has shown the primary importance of stellar encounters in the dynamics of these objects. It would therefore appear that the procedure adopted in § 5.6 is not an entirely satisfactory one for the treatment of clusters. But we shall now show how the solution obtained in terms of a potential function Ω can be generalized to take into account the effect of stellar encounters in a higher approximation.

It appears that in a general way we can describe the interaction of a star with the rest of the system as follows: Each star describes an orbit in the gravitational field of the smoothed-out distribution of matter in the system unless otherwise involved in stellar encounters. In other words, we suppose that the motion of a star can be described in terms of Ω except when disturbed by the relatively near passages of stars. If we ignore ternary and higher-order encounters, we can idealize the passages of stars as a succession of binary encounters. Thus, when not involved in an encounter, the motion of a star will be governed by the general gravitational field. But during an encounter there will be an additional force acting on the star, the magnitude and the duration of which will depend on the initial parameters describing the encounter.

Quite generally, an encounter will define three functions

$$F_{\xi}(t) , \qquad F_{\eta}(t) , \qquad \text{and} \qquad F_{\zeta}(t) , \qquad (5.701)$$

which give the components of the force acting on a star (per unit mass) along the three directions indicated and for the duration of the encounter. A knowledge of these functions will enable us to determine the effect of the encounter on the orbit originally described under the influence of the field Ω. At the end of the encounter the star will again be left to pursue a new determinate orbit under the sole influence of the gravitational field. This will continue until the next encounter occurs. In this manner the effect of stellar encounters on the motions of stars can be followed.[6]

We shall illustrate the method outlined in the preceding para-

[6] The method which we have described was originally devised by Jeans.

graph by considering the motions of stars in a homogeneous ellipsoidal cluster.

The general solution of the equations of motion, outside of encounters, has already been obtained in § 5.6. We shall re-write the solutions (5.620) and (5.605) for ξ, η, and ζ in the forms

$$\left.\begin{aligned}\xi &= (\xi_{11}\cos q_1 t + \xi_{21}\sin q_1 t) + (\xi_{12}\cos q_2 t + \xi_{22}\sin q_2 t)\,,\\ \eta &= \lambda_1(\xi_{11}\sin q_1 t - \xi_{21}\cos q_1 t) + \lambda_2(\xi_{12}\sin q_2 t - \xi_{22}\cos q_2 t)\,,\end{aligned}\right\} \quad (5.702)$$

and

$$\zeta = \zeta_1 \sin q_3 t + \zeta_2 \cos q_3 t\,, \quad (5.703)$$

where $\xi_{11}, \xi_{21}, \ldots, \zeta_2$ are all constants and

$$\lambda_1 = \frac{2\omega_c q_1}{\beta_2 - q_1^2}\,; \qquad \lambda_2 = \frac{2\omega_c q_2}{\beta_2 - q_2^2}\,. \quad (5.704)$$

During an encounter the equations of motion (5.603) and (5.604) become

$$\left.\begin{aligned}\ddot{\xi} - 2\omega_c\dot{\eta} + (\alpha_1 + \beta_1)\,\xi &= F_\xi\,,\\ \ddot{\eta} + 2\omega_c\dot{\xi} + \beta_2\eta &= F_\eta\,,\end{aligned}\right\} \quad (5.705)$$

and

$$\ddot{\zeta} + (\alpha_3 + \beta_3)\,\zeta = F_\zeta\,. \quad (5.706)$$

Consider, first, the equations (5.705). The general solution of these equations can be derived from the solutions of the corresponding homogeneous system by the method of the variation of the parameters. We assume, therefore, that the solutions (5.705) are of the form (5.702); but $\xi_{11}, \ldots, \xi_{22}$ are now to be regarded as functions of time. However, we restrict $\xi_{11}, \ldots, \xi_{22}$ to satisfy the conditions

$$\left.\begin{aligned}(\dot{\xi}_{11}\cos q_1 t + \dot{\xi}_{21}\sin q_1 t) + (\dot{\xi}_{12}\cos q_2 t + \dot{\xi}_{22}\sin q_2 t) &= 0\,,\\ \lambda_1(\dot{\xi}_{11}\sin q_1 t - \dot{\xi}_{21}\cos q_1 t) + \lambda_2(\dot{\xi}_{12}\sin q_1 t - \dot{\xi}_{22}\cos q_2 t) &= 0\,.\end{aligned}\right\} \quad (5.707)$$

Substituting the formal solutions (5.702) in the equations (5.705) and making use of equation (5.707), we find that we are left with

$$\left.\begin{aligned}q_1(\dot{\xi}_{11}\sin q_1 t - \dot{\xi}_{21}\cos q_1 t) + q_2(\dot{\xi}_{12}\sin q_2 t &\\ - \dot{\xi}_{22}\cos q_2 t) &= -F_\xi\,,\\ \lambda_1 q_1(\dot{\xi}_{11}\cos q_1 t + \dot{\xi}_{21}\sin q_1 t) + \lambda_2 q_2(\dot{\xi}_{12}\cos q_2 t &\\ + \dot{\xi}_{22}\sin q_2 t) &= F_\eta\,.\end{aligned}\right\} \quad (5.707')$$

Equations (5.707) and (5.708) can be solved for $\dot{\xi}_{11}, \ldots, \dot{\xi}_{22}$. We find

$$\left.\begin{aligned}\dot{\xi}_{11} &= aF_\eta \cos q_1 t + \lambda_2 bF_\xi \sin q_1 t\,,\\ \dot{\xi}_{21} &= aF_\eta \sin q_1 t - \lambda_2 bF_\xi \cos q_1 t\,,\\ \dot{\xi}_{12} &= -aF_\eta \cos q_2 t - \lambda_1 bF_\xi \sin q_2 t\,,\\ \dot{\xi}_{22} &= -aF_\eta \sin q_2 t + \lambda_1 bF_\xi \cos q_2 t\,,\end{aligned}\right\} \tag{5.708}$$

where

$$a = \frac{1}{\lambda_1 q_1 - \lambda_2 q_2}\,; \qquad b = \frac{1}{\lambda_1 q_2 - \lambda_2 q_1}\,. \tag{5.709}$$

The solutions of equations (5.708) can be readily expressed in the form of integrals. Thus we have

$$\xi_{11} = \xi_{110} + a\int_{t_1}^{t} F_\eta \cos q_1\tau\, d\tau + \lambda_2 b \int_{t_1}^{t} F_\xi \sin q_1 \tau\, d\tau\,, \tag{5.710}$$

where ξ_{110} is a constant. There are, of course, similar expressions for ξ_{21}, ξ_{12}, and ξ_{22}. Substituting for the ξ_{ij}'s, accordingly, in equation (5.702), we find that the general solutions of the equations (5.705) take the forms

$$\left.\begin{aligned}\xi = \xi_0(t) &+ a\int_{t_1}^{t} F_\eta \cos q_1(t-\tau)\, d\tau\\ &- \lambda_2 b\int_{t_1}^{t} F_\xi \sin q_1(t-\tau)\, d\tau - a\int_{t_1}^{t} F_\eta \cos q_2(t-\tau)\, d\tau\\ &+ \lambda_1 b\int_{t_1}^{t} F_\xi \sin q_2(t-\tau)\, d\tau\,,\\ \eta = \eta_0(t) &+ \lambda_1 a\int_{t_1}^{t} F_\eta \sin q_1(t-\tau)\, d\tau\\ &+ \lambda_1\lambda_2 b\int_{t_1}^{t} F_\xi \cos q_1(t-\tau)\, d\tau\\ &- \lambda_2 a\int_{t_1}^{t} F_\eta \sin q_2(t-\tau)\, d\tau\\ &- \lambda_1\lambda_2 b\int_{t_1}^{t} F_\xi \cos q_2(t-\tau)\, d\tau\,,\end{aligned}\right\} \tag{5.711}$$

where we have written $\xi_0(t)$ and $\eta_0(t)$ for

$$\left.\begin{aligned}\xi_0(t) &= \xi_{110}\cos q_1 t + \xi_{210}\sin q_1 t + \xi_{120}\cos q_2 t + \xi_{220}\sin q_2 t\,,\\ \eta_0(t) &= \lambda_1(\xi_{110}\sin q_1 t - \xi_{210}\cos q_1 t)\\ &\quad + \lambda_2(\xi_{120}\sin q_2 t - \xi_{220}\cos q_2 t)\,,\end{aligned}\right\} \tag{5.712}$$

where $\xi_{110}, \ldots, \xi_{220}$ are all constants.

Equation (5.706) can be solved by similar methods. We find

$$\zeta = \zeta_0(t) + \frac{1}{q_3}\int_{t_1}^{t} F_\zeta \sin q_3(t-\tau)\,d\tau\,, \qquad (5.713)$$

where

$$\zeta_0(t) = \zeta_{10}\sin q_3 t + \zeta_{20}\cos q_3 t\,, \qquad (5.714)$$

and ζ_{10} and ζ_{20} are constants.

Now the periods of oscillation associated with the harmonic terms in the preceding equations are generally of the order of 10^8 years. On the other hand, the times during which stellar encounters effectively terminate are somewhat less and are of the order of 10^{6-7} years.[7] We can therefore interpret the solutions (5.711) and (5.713) in the following manner: The complementary functions $\xi_0(t)$, $\eta_0(t)$, and $\zeta_0(t)$ represent the orbits which the star would have described had there been no encounter, and the particular integrals refer to the changes in the co-ordinates induced by the encounter. We can thus re-write the solutions (5.711) and (5.713) in the forms

$$\xi = \xi_0(t) + \Delta\xi\,; \qquad \eta = \eta_0(t) + \Delta\eta\,; \qquad \zeta = \zeta_0(t) + \Delta\zeta\,, \qquad (5.715)$$

where

$$\left.\begin{aligned}
\Delta\xi &= a[\cos q_1(t-\tau_1) - \cos q_2(t-\tau_2)]\Delta Q_\eta \\
&\qquad - b[\lambda_2 \sin q_1(t-\tau_3) - \lambda_1 \sin q_2(t-\tau_4)]\Delta Q_\xi\,, \\
\Delta\eta &= a[\lambda_1 \sin q_1(t-\tau_5) - \lambda_2 \sin q_2(t-\tau_6)]\Delta Q_\eta \\
&\qquad + \lambda_1\lambda_2 b[\cos q_1(t-\tau_7) - \cos q_2(t-\tau_8)]\Delta Q_\xi\,, \\
\Delta\zeta &= \frac{1}{q_3}[\sin q_3(t-\tau_9)]\Delta Q_\zeta\,.
\end{aligned}\right\} \qquad (5.716)$$

In the foregoing equations $\tau_1, \ldots, \tau_9$ denote certain appropriately chosen values of t in the respective intervals of integration. Further,

$$\Delta Q_\xi = \int F_\xi dt\,; \qquad \Delta Q_\eta = \int F_\eta dt\,; \qquad \Delta Q_\zeta = \int F_\zeta dt\,, \qquad (5.717)$$

where the integrations are to be carried out for the duration of the encounter.

[7] E.g., in the field (5.601) the period of oscillation is $2\pi/\sqrt{\beta_i}$; or, according to equation (5.602), the order of magnitude of the periods involved is given by

$$\frac{2\pi}{\sqrt{\pi G\rho\beta_i'}} = \frac{5.3\times 10^7}{\sqrt{\beta_i\rho}}\ \text{years}\,,$$

where we have expressed the density in units of solar mass per cubic parsec.

Equations (5.716) give the changes in the co-ordinates resulting from a single encounter. A large number of such independent encounters may be expected to compound in the manner of accidental, uncorrelated errors. The *expectations* for $\overline{\Delta\xi^2}$, $\overline{\Delta\eta^2}$, and $\overline{\Delta\zeta^2}$ may therefore be expressed as

$$\left.\begin{aligned}\overline{\Delta\xi^2} &= a^2\overline{[\cos q_1(t-\tau_1)-\cos q_2(t-\tau_2)]^2}\Sigma\Delta Q_\eta^2\\ &\qquad + b^2\overline{[\lambda_2\sin q_1(t-\tau_3)-\lambda_1\sin q_2(t-\tau_4)]^2}\Sigma\Delta Q_\xi^2\,,\\ \overline{\Delta\eta^2} &= a^2\overline{[\lambda_1\sin q_1(t-\tau_5)-\lambda_2\sin q_2(t-\tau_6)]^2}\Sigma\Delta Q_\eta^2\\ &\qquad + \lambda_1^2\lambda_2^2 b^2\overline{[\cos q_1(t-\tau_7)-\cos q_2(t-\tau_8)]^2}\Sigma\Delta Q_\xi^2\,,\\ \overline{\Delta\zeta^2} &= \frac{1}{q_3^2}\overline{[\sin q_3(t-\tau_9)]^2}\Sigma\Delta Q_\zeta^2\,.\end{aligned}\right\}\quad(5.718)$$

The foregoing expressions give the expectations for one particular initial phase of the oscillation executed under the influence of the field Ω. A quantity of greater interest is, however, the *probable expectation*, i.e., the expectation averaged over all the possible initial phases of the oscillation. Without much loss of accuracy we can then replace the trigonometric terms in equation (5.718) by their mean values. Thus, for the probable expectations we have

$$\left.\begin{aligned}\overline{\overline{\Delta\xi^2}} &= a^2\Sigma\Delta Q_\eta^2+\tfrac{1}{2}b^2(\lambda_1^2+\lambda_2^2)\Sigma\Delta Q_\xi^2\,,\\ \overline{\overline{\Delta\eta^2}} &= \tfrac{1}{2}a^2(\lambda_1^2+\lambda_2^2)\Sigma\Delta Q_\eta^2+\lambda_1^2\lambda_2^2 b^2\Sigma\Delta Q_\xi^2\,,\\ \overline{\overline{\Delta\zeta^2}} &= \frac{1}{2q_3^2}\Sigma\Delta Q_\zeta^2\,.\end{aligned}\right\}\quad(5.719)$$

The quantities ΔQ_ξ, ΔQ_η, and ΔQ_ζ have simple physical meanings. According to equations (5.717), they represent the *impulses per unit mass* produced by a single encounter; or, alternatively, (ΔQ_ξ, ΔQ_η, ΔQ_ζ) denotes the net change in the velocity consequent to the encounter. An explicit expression for this change in the velocity can be obtained from our analysis of the deflections caused by stellar encounters in § 2.4. If $\Delta v_{||}$ and $\Delta v_\perp$ denote the changes in the velocity parallel to and perpendicular to the original direction of motion of the star, then

$$\Delta v_{||} = v_2'\cos(\pi-2\Psi)-v_2\,;\qquad \Delta v_\perp = v_2'\sin 2\Psi\,,\quad(5.720)$$

where $(\pi - 2\Psi)$ denotes the true deflection suffered by the star. From equations (2.415)–(2.418) we readily obtain for $v_{||}$ and $v_{\perp}$ the expressions

$$\left.\begin{aligned} \Delta v_{||} &= -\frac{2m_1}{m_1+m_2}\left[(v_2 - v_1\cos\theta)\cos\psi \right. \\ &\qquad\qquad \left. + v_1 \sin\theta \cos\Theta \sin\psi \right] \cos\psi , \\ \Delta v_{\perp} &= \frac{2m_1}{m_1+m_2}\left[v_1^2 + v_2^2 - 2v_1 v_2 \cos\theta \right. \\ &\quad \left. - \{ (v_2 - v_1\cos\theta)\cos\psi + v_1\sin\theta\cos\Theta\sin\psi \}^2 \right]^{1/2} \cos\psi . \end{aligned}\right\} \qquad (5.721)$$

We now require the sums

$$\Sigma\Delta v_{||}^2 \quad \text{and} \quad \Sigma\Delta v_{\perp}^2 . \qquad (5.722)$$

If we retain only the dominant terms in the evaluation of these sums, we verify that

$$\Sigma\Delta v_{||}^2 = \frac{1}{m_2^2 v_2^2}\Sigma\Delta E^2 ; \qquad \Sigma\Delta v_{\perp}^2 = v_2^2 \Sigma \sin^2 2\Psi . \qquad (5.723)$$

Accordingly, we have (cf. eqs. [2.355] and [2.430])

$$\left.\begin{aligned} \Sigma\Delta v_{||}^2 &= 8\pi N G^2 m_1^2 G(x_0) \frac{1}{v_2} \log q\, v_2^2 dt , \\ \Sigma\Delta v_{\perp}^2 &= 8\pi N G^2 m_1^2 H(x_0) \frac{1}{v_2} \log q\, v_2^2 dt , \end{aligned}\right\} \qquad (5.724)$$

where $x_0 = jv_2$. In equations (5.724), N and j both refer to the "field stars," i.e., the stars which cause the perturbations in the orbit described under the influence of Ω.

Equations (5.724) make it evident that the effect of encounters with the other members of the cluster is very much more important than the encounters with stars extraneous to the cluster. This arises as the result of two factors: First, the density of stars in the cluster is several times the density of the background stars, and, second, the factors $G(x_0)$ and $H(x_0)$, while they are of order 1 for the cluster members (cf. Tables 6 and 7), are very much smaller for the noncluster stars.[8] Assuming, then, that the main source of disturbance

[8] This becomes apparent when it is noted that x_0 is a measure of the velocity of the cluster stars in the units of an average velocity of the field stars (i.e., the disturbing stars) in a frame of reference in which the center of gravity of the cluster is at rest. It may be remarked in this connection that the point of view to which we are led by the equations (5.724) is contrary to the views which have been expressed by Bok and others.

are the cluster members themselves, we can re-write equations (5.724) in the forms (cf. eqs. [2.360] and [2.433])

$$\Sigma\Delta v_{||}^2 = \tfrac{1}{4} v_2^2 \frac{dt}{T_E}\,; \qquad \Sigma\Delta v_{\perp}^2 = v_2^2 \frac{dt}{T_D}\,, \tag{5.725}$$

where T_D and T_E now refer to the times of relaxation of the cluster.

Turning next to the sums $\Sigma\Delta Q_\xi^2$, etc., we can expect that on the average

$$\Sigma\Delta Q_\xi^2 = \Sigma\Delta Q_\eta^2 = \Sigma\Delta Q_\zeta^2 = \Sigma\Delta Q^2 \tag{5.726}$$

and that

$$\Sigma\Delta Q^2 = \tfrac{1}{2}\left(\Sigma\Delta v_{||}^2 + \Sigma\Delta v_{\perp}^2\right). \tag{5.727}$$

According to equations (5.725), we therefore have

$$\Sigma\Delta Q^2 = v_2^2\left(\frac{1}{8T_E} + \frac{1}{2T_D}\right) dt\,, \tag{5.728}$$

or, more conveniently,

$$\Sigma\Delta Q^2 = v_2^2 \frac{dt}{T_{v_2}}\,, \tag{5.729}$$

where

$$T_{v_2} = \frac{8T_E T_D}{T_D + 4T_E}\,. \tag{5.730}$$

Finally, substituting for $\Sigma\Delta Q^2$ according to equation (5.729) in the equations (5.719) and introducing also the expressions for a and b (eq. [5.709]), we obtain

$$\left.\begin{aligned}
\overline{\overline{\Delta\xi^2}} &= \left[\frac{1}{(\lambda_1 q_1 - \lambda_2 q_2)^2} + \frac{\lambda_1^2 + \lambda_2^2}{2(\lambda_2 q_1 - \lambda_1 q_2)^2}\right] v_2^2 \frac{dt}{T_{v_2}}\,,\\
\overline{\overline{\Delta\eta^2}} &= \left[\frac{\lambda_1^2 + \lambda_2^2}{2(\lambda_1 q_1 - \lambda_2 q_2)^2} + \frac{\lambda_1^2\lambda_2^2}{(\lambda_2 q_1 - \lambda_1 q_2)^2}\right] v_2^2 \frac{dt}{T_{v_2}}\,,\\
\overline{\overline{\Delta\zeta^2}} &= \frac{1}{2q_3^2}\, v_2^2 \frac{dt}{T_{v_2}}\,.
\end{aligned}\right\} \tag{5.731}$$

Equations (5.731) enable us to draw an important conclusion concerning the constitution of clusters whose densities are larger than the critical values required for dynamical stability, namely, that for such clusters the specific effects of galactic rotation are negligible. For under normal conditions the factors in the square brackets in the expressions for $\overline{\overline{\Delta\xi^2}}$ and $\overline{\overline{\Delta\eta^2}}$ are of the order 10^{28}. Hence, even for velocities of the order of 1 km/sec, the expectations $\sqrt{\overline{\overline{\Delta\xi^2}}}$ and $\sqrt{\overline{\overline{\Delta\eta^2}}}$ are already of the dimensions of the cluster after a time of the order of T_{v_2}. And, since the time of relaxation is of the order of 3×10^7 years, it follows that such clusters must be in statistical equilibrium. The dynamical considerations of § 5.6 are therefore valid only for clusters on the verge of stability. However, equations (5.731) introduce a new factor into our discussion. For according to these equations the clusters tend to be "loosened" with time, and this works in a direction opposite to what results from the loss of stars by escape (§ 5.3). A rigorous theory of galactic clusters must therefore take both these factors into account. But such a theory is not yet available.

5.8. *The dynamics of globular clusters.*—We shall now return to the consideration of isolated clusters, but this time specifically with reference to the dynamics of globular clusters.

After a re-examination of Table 9 (p. 203) we conclude that, with the possible exception of the richest clusters, these objects are likely to be well advanced in their evolution toward the state of complete statistical equilibrium. Even in the richest clusters it is possible that in the central regions statistical equilibrium obtains. Thus the analysis of the equilibrium of spherical distributions of stars in statistical equilibrium forms the natural starting-point for the study of globular clusters.

We begin our discussion, then, by assuming that at each point in the cluster we have a Maxwellian distribution of the velocities

$$dN = N(r)\,\frac{j^3}{\pi^{3/2}}\,e^{-j^2(u^2+v^2+w^2)}\,du\,dv\,dw\,dx\,dy\,dz\,, \qquad (5.801)$$

where $N(r)$ is a function of the distance r from the center of the cluster only. We shall further suppose that j is a constant and has the same value throughout the cluster. Under these circumstances the dependence of $N(r)$ on the gravitational potential $\mathfrak{B}(r)$ can be readily written down. We should, in fact, have

$$N(r) = N_0\,e^{-2j^2\mathfrak{B}(r)}\,, \qquad (5.802)$$

where N_0 is a constant. Equation (5.802) is simply the expression of

Boltzmann's principle for the case under consideration. For, according to equations (5.801) and (5.802),

$$dN = N_0 \frac{j^3}{\pi^{3/2}} e^{-2j^2 E} du\, dv\, dw\, dx\, dy\, dz \;, \tag{5.803}$$

where E denotes the energy (per unit mass) of the star. In the form (5.803) we also recognize that the distribution function on the right-hand side belongs to one of the types considered in § 3.3 (p. 87), since it depends only on the energy integral of the equations of motion.

Finally, we have Poisson's equation

$$\frac{1}{r^2}\frac{d}{dr}\left(r^2 \frac{d\mathfrak{B}}{dr}\right) = 4\pi G \rho \;. \tag{5.804}$$

For the sake of simplicity we shall suppose that all the stars in the cluster have the same mass, m. Accordingly, from equations (5.802) and (5.804) we now obtain

$$\frac{1}{r^2}\frac{d}{dr}\left(r^2 \frac{d\mathfrak{B}}{dr}\right) = 4\pi G N_0 m\, e^{-2j^2\mathfrak{B}} \;. \tag{5.805}$$

Introducing the new variables

$$2j^2\mathfrak{B} = \psi \;; \qquad r = \frac{1}{(8\pi G N_0 m j^2)^{1/2}}\, \xi \;, \tag{5.806}$$

equation (5.805) becomes

$$\frac{1}{\xi^2}\frac{d}{d\xi}\left(\xi^2 \frac{d\psi}{d\xi}\right) = e^{-\psi} \;. \tag{5.807}$$

Equation (5.807) is seen to be identical with the equation of equilibrium of an isothermal gas sphere.[9]

Again, if we consider N_0 in equation (5.802) as referring to the density of stars at the center of the cluster, then equation (5.807) has to be supplemented by the boundary conditions

$$\psi = 0 \;; \qquad \frac{d\psi}{d\xi} = 0 \qquad (\xi = 0) \;. \tag{5.808}$$

Hence the solution which is needed is also the same as the standard isothermal function in the theory of gas spheres. In terms of this

[9] See, e.g., S. Chandrasekhar, *An Introduction to the Study of Stellar Structure*, pp. 155–170, Chicago, 1939.

function the structure of the configuration is uniquely determined. Thus the variation of the density of stars through the cluster is given by

$$N = N_0 e^{-\psi} . \tag{5.809}$$

Similarly, the distribution of mass is given by

$$M(\xi) = 4\pi \frac{N_0 m}{(8\pi N_0 G m j^2)^{3/2}} \xi^2 \frac{d\psi}{d\xi} . \tag{5.810}$$

The predicted distributions of mass and density are given in Table 13 (see also Fig. 25).

A quantity of general interest is the variation of star density as counted on a direct photographic image of the cluster. If $\nu(x)$ denotes the observed number of stars (per unit area) at a distance x from the center of the cluster, then there is a simple integral relation between $\nu(x)$ and the true spatial variation of the density in the cluster as given by $N(r)$. For, since $\nu(x)$ represents the total number of stars (per unit area) in the line of sight, we clearly have

$$\nu(x) = \int_{-\infty}^{+\infty} N(s)\, ds , \tag{5.811}$$

where ds is an element of length measured along the line of sight. If we choose the origin of s at the point nearest to the center of the cluster, then

$$s^2 = r^2 - x^2 , \tag{5.812}$$

or

$$ds = \frac{r\, dr}{\sqrt{r^2 - x^2}} . \tag{5.813}$$

Hence equation (5.811) becomes

$$\nu(x) = 2\int_x^{\infty} \frac{r}{\sqrt{r^2 - x^2}} N(r)\, dr . \tag{5.814}$$

After an integration by parts, the foregoing equation reduces to

$$\nu(x) = -2\int_x^{\infty} \sqrt{r^2 - x^2} \frac{dN}{dr}\, dr . \tag{5.815}$$

Equations (5.814) and (5.815) are seen to be integral equations which relate the true space distributions of the stars in a globular cluster with the observed distributions on a photographic image of the cluster. These integral equations can be readily thrown into the

TABLE 13*

ISOTHERMAL DISTRIBUTION

ξ	$e^{-\psi}$	$\xi^2\psi'$	$\nu(\xi)/\nu_0$	ξ	$e^{-\psi}$	$\xi^2\psi'$	$\nu(\xi)/\nu_0$
0.0.....	1.0000	0.0000	1.000	6.0....	0.0848	14.35	0.0956
0.4.....	0.9739	0.0210	0.980	6.4....	.0726	15.55	....
0.8.....	0.9018	0.1604	0.922	6.6....	.0673	16.14	....
1.2.....	0.7992	0.5031	0.839	6.8....	.0626	16.73	....
1.6.....	0.6841	1.084	0.741	7.0....	.0583	17.30	.0525
2.0.....	0.5713	1.895	0.641	7.2....	.0543	17.87	....
2.4.....	0.4696	2.897	0.546	7.6....	.0475	18.98	....
2.8.....	0.3829	4.043	0.460	8.0....	.0418	20.06	.0246
3.2.....	0.3114	5.284	0.384	8.4....	.0370	21.12	....
3.6.....	0.2537	6.581	0.319	8.8....	.0329	22.15	....
4.0.....	0.2076	7.905	0.265	9.0....	.0311	22.66	.0076
4.4.....	0.1709	9.232	....	9.2....	.0294	23.16	....
4.8.....	0.1418	10.55	....	9.6....	.0264	24.14	....
5.0.....	0.1295	11.20	0.162	10.0....	.0238	25.11	0.0000
5.2.....	0.1185	11.84	....	12.5....	.0137	30.74	....
5.6.....	0.0999	13.11	....	20.0....	0.0045	45.25	....

* The solution of the isothermal equation given in this table is taken from an unpublished integration by Dr. Gordon W. Wares.

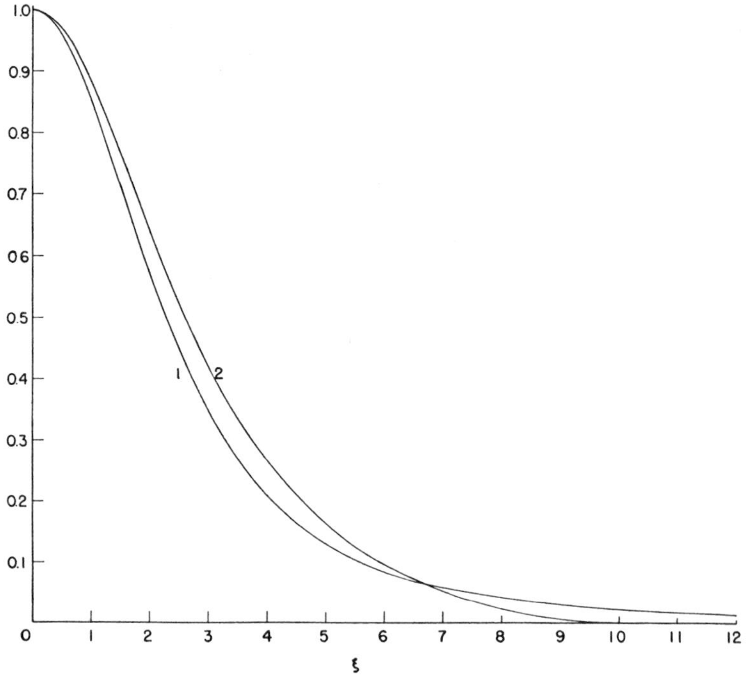

FIG. 25.—The isothermal distribution for globular clusters. Curve 1 illustrates the radial distribution $e^{-\psi}$ (cf. eq. [5.809]), and curve 2 the projected distribution $\nu(\xi)$, according to equation (5.820).

standard Abelian forms, and the formal solutions can therefore also be written down. But we shall not go into these matters here.

According to equations (5.815) and (5.809), the predicted form for $\nu(x)$ on the isothermal approximation is

$$\nu(x) = \frac{N_0^{1/2}}{(2\pi G m j^2)^{1/2}} \int_x^\infty \sqrt{\xi^2 - x^2}\, e^{-\psi} \frac{d\psi}{d\xi}\, d\xi\,, \qquad (5.816)$$

where x is now measured in the same units as ξ.

Unfortunately, we cannot use the isothermal approximation for a complete description of a globular cluster, for the distribution (5.809) predicts an infinite mass for the cluster. This arises in the following manner.

It is known that every solution of the isothermal equation (5.807) tends asymptotically to the special solution

$$e^{-\psi} = \frac{2}{\xi^2} \qquad (5.817)$$

of the differential equation,[10] and if we substitute this asymptotic form for ψ in equation (5.810) we find that

$$M(\xi) \to \text{constant} \cdot \xi \quad \text{as} \quad \xi \to \infty\,. \qquad (5.818)$$

Consequently, the isothermal approximation is seen to be inadequate for describing the outer regions at least, of a globular cluster. The reason for this failure must be attributed among other things to the deviations from strict statistical equilibrium which should be expected to become important in the outer regions. For, with decreasing density, the time of relaxation will increase, and we must eventually reach a point where the conditions for statistical equilibrium no longer obtain. Again, there must be a continual loss of stars by escape, and this phenomenon must begin to have an increasing importance for the equilibrium of the outer regions. It is probable that it is in terms of such considerations that we should look for an interpretation of the relatively sharp decrease that is observed in the density distributions of the globular clusters in the outer regions.

Anticipating the results of a more detailed investigation on the lines indicated in the preceding paragraph, we can tentatively assume that the statistical treatment (and the consequent use of the

[10] For a proof of this theorem see the reference given in n. 8.

isothermal distribution) will cease to be valid for $\xi > 10$, where the density is about a fortieth of the central density. Under these circumstances the number of stars per unit area (as registered on a photographic plate) will be given by (cf. eq. [5.816])

$$\nu(x) = \frac{N_0^{1/2}}{(2\pi G m j^2)^{1/2}} \int_x^{10} \sqrt{\xi^2 - x^2}\; e^{-\psi} \frac{d\psi}{d\xi}\, d\xi\,, \quad (5.819)$$

or, if ν_0 denotes the star density (per unit area) at the center, we have

$$\frac{\nu(x)}{\nu_0} = \frac{\int_x^{10} \sqrt{\xi^2 - x^2}\; e^{-\psi} \psi' d\xi}{\int_0^{10} \xi e^{-\psi} \psi' d\xi}\,. \quad (5.820)$$

The foregoing function is tabulated in Table 13 and further illustrated in Figure 25.

BIBLIOGRAPHICAL NOTES

§ 5.1.—As we have already stated in the text, the important relations (5.136) and (5.137) are due to Lagrange and Jacobi. Following the authorities on celestial mechanics, e.g.—

1. A. Wintner, *The Analytical Foundations of Celestial Mechanics*, pp. 235 and 426, Princeton, 1941, we have called these relations the "Lagrange's identities." In this connection we may draw attention to the fact that in current astronomical literature these identities have often been wrongly attributed to Poincaré (1911) and/or Eddington (1916).

§ 5.2.—The dispersion of the velocities in a cluster (based on Lagrange's identity) has been estimated by—

2. A. S. Eddington, *M.N.*, **76**, 525, 1916, and—
3. O. Heckmann and H. Sidentopf, *Zs. f. Ap.*, **1**, 67, 1930.

The time of relaxation of a cluster has been computed by Heckmann and Sidentopf (ref. 3) and also by—

4. H. Mineur, *Ann. d'ap.*, **2**, No. 1, 1939, and—
5. L. Spitzer, *M.N.*, **100**, 396, 1940.

But these authors based their estimates on formulae for the time of relaxation which are not entirely reliable. The analyses in the text are, however, based on the formulae derived in chapter ii.

The discussion of the mean free path in this section is believed to be new.

§ 5.3.—The fundamental physical ideas in this section are those of—

6. V. A. AMBARZUMIAN, *Ann. Leningrad State University*, No. 22 (Astronomical Ser., Issue 4), p. 19, 1938, and SPITZER (ref. 5). Again the analyses of these authors have been revised to be in conformity with our formulae of chapter ii.

§ 5.4.—See AMBARZUMIAN (ref. 6) and SPITZER (ref. 5). But these authors do not seem to have noticed that the very lightest stars (like the more massive stars) are characterized by slower rates of escape than the stars of normal mass.

§ 5.5.—The general equations of motion of a star in a cluster sharing in the galactic rotation were derived by—

7. B. BOK, *Harvard Circ.*, No. 384, 1934, and MINEUR (ref. 4). However, the generalized Lagrangian identity and the other integrals derived in this section appear to be new.

§ 5.6.—The analysis in this section is derived from BOK (ref. 7).

§ 5.7.—The method of analysis in this section goes back to Jeans—

8. J. H. JEANS, *M.N.*, **82**, 132, 1922, though Jeans was not himself considering clusters taking part in the differential rotation of a larger galactic system.

While following in part the ideas of Bok and Mineur, the actual conclusions reached in the text differ from those expressed by these authors.

§ 5.8.—The early investigations on the dynamics of a globular cluster are those of—

9. A. S. EDDINGTON, *M.N.*, **74**, 5, 1913; **75**, 366, 1915. But in these investigations the effect of stellar encounters is ignored, and the motions of the stars in the cluster are assumed to be governed by the general smoothed-out gravitational potential. However, according to our present ideas, this does not provide a satisfactory basis for the dynamics of globular clusters. Actually, it appears that the other limiting case of complete statistical equilibrium is likely to provide a closer approximation to the true state of affairs. See HECKMANN and SIDENTOPF (ref. 3). Also—

10. P. TEN BRUGGENCATE, *Sternhaufen*, pp. 90–113, Berlin, 1927.

APPENDIX I

DEFLECTION OF A STAR IN THE ORBITAL PLANE ACCORDING TO THE TWO-BODY PROBLEM

Let $\boldsymbol{r}_1$ and $\boldsymbol{r}_2$ denote the position vectors of two stars of masses m_1 and m_2 in a certain appropriately chosen fixed frame of reference. The Newtonian equations of motion are

$$\frac{d^2\boldsymbol{r}_1}{dt^2} = -Gm_2 \frac{\boldsymbol{r}_1 - \boldsymbol{r}_2}{|\boldsymbol{r}_1 - \boldsymbol{r}_2|^3}\,; \qquad \frac{d^2\boldsymbol{r}_2}{dt^2} = -Gm_1 \frac{\boldsymbol{r}_2 - \boldsymbol{r}_1}{|\boldsymbol{r}_2 - \boldsymbol{r}_1|^3}\,. \tag{1}$$

From these equations we readily obtain

$$m_1 \frac{d^2\boldsymbol{r}_1}{dt^2} + m_2 \frac{d^2\boldsymbol{r}_2}{dt^2} = 0 \tag{2}$$

and

$$\frac{d^2}{dt^2}(\boldsymbol{r}_1 - \boldsymbol{r}_2) = -G(m_1 + m_2) \frac{\boldsymbol{r}_1 - \boldsymbol{r}_2}{|\boldsymbol{r}_1 - \boldsymbol{r}_2|^3}\,. \tag{3}$$

Equation (2) clearly implies the uniform motion of the center of gravity, for, according to this equation,

$$m_1\boldsymbol{r}_1 + m_2\boldsymbol{r}_2 = \boldsymbol{R}_0 + (m_1 + m_2)\boldsymbol{V}_g t\,, \tag{4}$$

where $\boldsymbol{V}_g$ denotes the constant velocity of the center of gravity and $\boldsymbol{R}_0$ its position at time $t = 0$.

Equation (3), which determines the relative motion of the two stars, can be re-written in the form

$$\frac{d^2\boldsymbol{r}}{dt^2} = -\lambda \frac{\boldsymbol{r}}{|\boldsymbol{r}|^3} = \lambda \operatorname{grad} \frac{1}{r}\,, \tag{5}$$

where

$$\boldsymbol{r} = \boldsymbol{r}_1 - \boldsymbol{r}_2\,; \qquad \lambda = G(m_1 + m_2)\,. \tag{6}$$

Multiplying equation (5) vectorially by $\boldsymbol{r}$ we obtain

$$\boldsymbol{r} \times \frac{d^2\boldsymbol{r}}{dt^2} = 0\,. \tag{7}$$

This equation is clearly equivalent to

$$\frac{d}{dt}\left(\boldsymbol{r} \times \frac{d\boldsymbol{r}}{dt}\right) = 0\,. \tag{8}$$

Hence,

$$r \times \frac{dr}{dt} = h\,, \tag{9}$$

where h is a constant vector. Equation (9) represents the angular-momentum integral.

Again, multiplying equation (9) scalarly with r, we obtain

$$h \cdot r = 0\,; \tag{10}$$

in other words, the relative orbit is described in some fixed plane.

Returning to equation (5), we notice that the motion in the relative orbit is determined by the potential function

$$\mathfrak{B} = -\frac{\lambda}{r}. \tag{11}$$

Hence the relative orbit can be specified in terms of the Lagrangian function

$$L = T + \frac{\lambda}{r}\,, \tag{12}$$

where T is the kinetic energy (per unit mass) of the relative motion.

In addition to the integrals we have already derived, we also have the energy integral

$$T - \frac{\lambda}{r} = \tfrac{1}{2} V^2\,, \tag{13}$$

where V is the relative velocity at infinite separation.

If we now choose polar co-ordinates (r, θ) in the orbital plane, the Lagrangian function takes the form

$$L = \tfrac{1}{2}(\dot{r}^2 + r^2 \dot{\theta}^2) + \frac{\lambda}{r}\,, \tag{14}$$

and the corresponding Lagrangian equations are

$$\ddot{r} = r\dot{\theta}^2 - \frac{\lambda}{r^2} \tag{15}$$

and

$$\frac{d}{dt}(r^2 \dot{\theta}) = 0\,. \tag{16}$$

Equation (16), which is equivalent to equation (8), yields again the angular-momentum integral

$$r^2 \dot{\theta} = h = \text{constant}\,. \tag{17}$$

Equation (15) can now be re-written as

$$\ddot{r} = \frac{h^2}{r^3} - \frac{\lambda}{r^2}. \tag{18}$$

Introducing $u = r^{-1}$ as a new variable and using equation (17), we can reduce the foregoing equation to

$$\frac{d^2u}{d\,\theta^2} = -u + \frac{\lambda}{h^2}. \tag{19}$$

The solution of this equation can be expressed as

$$u = u_0 \cos(\theta + \theta_0) + \frac{\lambda}{h^2}, \tag{20}$$

where u_0 and θ_0 are constants of integration. Choosing the direction of maximum u (or minimum r) as the origin of θ, we can re-write equation (20) as

$$r = \frac{1}{u} = \frac{h^2}{\lambda}\frac{1}{1 + e\cos\theta}, \tag{21}$$

where e denotes the eccentricity of the orbit.

We shall now express e in terms of the other parameters describing the encounter. According to equation (21), the distance at closest approach is given by

$$r_0 = \frac{h^2}{\lambda}\frac{1}{1+e}. \tag{22}$$

At this distance $\dot{r}$ clearly vanishes. The energy integral (13), when written out explicitly for $r = r_0$, therefore becomes

$$\frac{1}{2}\frac{1}{r_0^2}(r_0^2\dot{\theta})^2 - \frac{\lambda}{r_0} = \tfrac{1}{2}V^2, \tag{23}$$

or, according to equations (17) and (22), we have

$$\frac{1}{2}\left[\frac{\lambda^2}{h^4}(1+e)^2\right]h^2 - \lambda\left[\frac{\lambda}{h^2}(1+e)\right] = \tfrac{1}{2}V^2. \tag{24}$$

After further reductions we obtain

$$e^2 = 1 + \frac{V^2h^2}{\lambda^2}. \tag{25}$$

On the other hand, we can write

$$h = DV, \tag{26}$$

where D stands for the impact parameter. Hence

$$e^2 = 1 + \frac{D^2V^4}{G^2(m_1+m_2)^2}, \tag{27}$$

where we have also substituted for λ according to equation (6).

Equation (27) enables us to derive an explicit expression for the angle

2ψ between the asymptotes of the relative orbit. For, according to equation (21), at

$$\theta = \cos^{-1} - \frac{1}{e}, \qquad r = \infty ; \tag{28}$$

and, since $\pi - \psi$ denotes this angle,

$$\cos \psi = \frac{1}{e} . \tag{29}$$

Hence,

$$\cos \psi = \frac{1}{\sqrt{1 + \frac{D^2 V^4}{G^2 (m_1 + m_2)^2}}}, \tag{30}$$

which is the required expression.

APPENDIX II

THE GENERAL THEORY OF THE STABILITY OF ORBITS

Suppose that a particular solution of the equations of motion derived from the Lagrangian function

$$L = \tfrac{1}{2}(\dot{x}^2 + \dot{y}^2) - \mathfrak{V}(x, y) \tag{1}$$

is known; and consider a solution which is immediately adjacent to the known solution and for which the constant of energy has the same value.

Let P and Q be the positions of the particle in the known and in the adjacent orbits, respectively, at time t. Draw QN perpendicular to the known orbit and let

$$\text{arc } PN = \xi\ ; \qquad QN = u\ . \tag{2}$$

Further, let s and σ be the lengths of the arcs measured along the solution from some fixed point on it to N and P, respectively. Then

$$\xi = s - \sigma\ . \tag{3}$$

Since the position on the adjacent solution is uniquely determined by u and s, we can use them as generalized co-ordinates. In these co-ordinates the Lagrangian function is clearly

$$L = \tfrac{1}{2}\dot{u}^2 + \frac{1}{2}\left(1 + \frac{u}{\rho}\right)^2 \dot{s}^2 - \mathfrak{V}(u, s)\ , \tag{4}$$

where ρ is the radius of curvature at N of the known orbit. The corresponding Lagrangian equations are seen to be

$$\ddot{u} - \left(1 + \frac{u}{\rho}\right)\frac{\dot{s}^2}{\rho} = -\frac{\partial \mathfrak{V}}{\partial u} \tag{5}$$

and

$$\frac{d}{dt}\left[\left(1 + \frac{u}{\rho}\right)^2 \dot{s}\right] + \left(1 + \frac{u}{\rho}\right)\frac{u\,\dot{s}^2}{\rho^2}\frac{d\rho}{ds} = -\frac{\partial \mathfrak{V}}{\partial s}\ . \tag{6}$$

These equations admit, of course, the energy integral

$$\tfrac{1}{2}\dot{u}^2 + \frac{1}{2}\left(1 + \frac{u}{\rho}\right)^2 \dot{s}^2 + \mathfrak{V} = E = \text{constant}\ . \tag{7}$$

We shall now expand the various quantities and neglect all terms of order higher than the first in u and ξ. Equations (5) and (7) then become

$$\left.\begin{aligned} &\ddot{u}-\frac{u\dot{\sigma}^2}{\rho_P^2}-\frac{\dot{\sigma}^2+2\dot{\sigma}\dot{\xi}}{\rho_P+\xi\left(\frac{d\rho}{d\sigma}\right)_P} \\ &\qquad = -\left\{\left(\frac{\partial\mathfrak{B}}{\partial u}\right)_P+\xi\left(\frac{\partial^2\mathfrak{B}}{\partial u\partial\sigma}\right)_P+u\left(\frac{\partial^2\mathfrak{B}}{\partial u^2}\right)_P\right\}\end{aligned}\right\} \tag{8}$$

and

$$\frac{1}{2}\left(1+\frac{2u}{\rho_P}\right)(\dot{\sigma}^2+2\dot{\sigma}\dot{\xi})+\mathfrak{B}_P+\xi\left(\frac{\partial\mathfrak{B}}{\partial\sigma}\right)_P+u\left(\frac{\partial\mathfrak{B}}{\partial u}\right)_P=E. \tag{9}$$

On the other hand, since σ and $\dot{\sigma}$ refer to the known solution,

$$\frac{\dot{\sigma}^2}{\rho_P}=\left(\frac{\partial\mathfrak{B}}{\partial u}\right)_P; \qquad \ddot{\sigma}=-\frac{\partial\mathfrak{B}}{\partial\sigma}, \tag{10}$$

and

$$\tfrac{1}{2}\dot{\sigma}^2+\mathfrak{B}_P=E. \tag{11}$$

Substituting the foregoing equations in (9), we obtain

$$\dot{\sigma}\dot{\xi}-\xi\ddot{\sigma}+\frac{2u\dot{\sigma}^2}{\rho_P}=0. \tag{12}$$

Similarly, equation (8) becomes

$$\left.\begin{aligned} &\ddot{u}-\frac{u\dot{\sigma}^2}{\rho_P^2}-\frac{\dot{\sigma}^2}{\rho_P}+\xi\frac{\dot{\sigma}^2}{\rho_P^2}\left(\frac{d\rho}{d\sigma}\right)_P-2\frac{\dot{\sigma}\dot{\xi}}{\rho_P} \\ &\qquad = -\left\{\frac{\dot{\sigma}^2}{\rho_P}+\xi\left(\frac{\partial^2\mathfrak{B}}{\partial u\partial\sigma}\right)_P+u\left(\frac{\partial^2\mathfrak{B}}{\partial u^2}\right)_P\right\}\end{aligned}\right\} \tag{13}$$

or, alternatively,

$$\ddot{u}-\frac{u\dot{\sigma}^2}{\rho_P^2}+\xi\left\{\frac{\dot{\sigma}^2}{\rho_P^2}\left(\frac{d\rho}{d\sigma}\right)_P+\left(\frac{\partial^2\mathfrak{B}}{\partial u\partial\sigma}\right)_P\right\}-2\frac{\dot{\sigma}\dot{\xi}}{\rho_P}=-u\left(\frac{\partial^2\mathfrak{B}}{\partial u^2}\right)_P. \tag{14}$$

But, according to the first of the equations (10),

$$\left.\begin{aligned}\left(\frac{\partial^2\mathfrak{B}}{\partial u\partial\sigma}\right)_P &= -\frac{\dot{\sigma}^2}{\rho_P^2}\left(\frac{d\rho}{d\sigma}\right)_P+2\frac{\dot{\sigma}}{\rho_P}\frac{d}{d\sigma}\left(\frac{d\sigma}{dt}\right) \\ &= -\frac{\dot{\sigma}^2}{\rho_P^2}\left(\frac{d\rho}{d\sigma}\right)_P+\frac{2}{\rho_P}\ddot{\sigma}.\end{aligned}\right\} \tag{15}$$

Equation (14) thus reduces to

$$\ddot{u}-\frac{u\dot{\sigma}^2}{\rho_P^2}-2\frac{\dot{\sigma}\dot{\xi}-\xi\ddot{\sigma}}{\rho_P}=-u\left(\frac{\partial^2\mathfrak{B}}{\partial u^2}\right)_P. \tag{16}$$

Eliminating $(\dot{\sigma}\xi - \xi\ddot{\sigma})$ from equations (12) and (16), we finally obtain

$$\ddot{u} + \left\{ \left(\frac{\partial^2 \mathfrak{V}}{\partial u^2} \right)_P + \frac{3\dot{\sigma}^2}{\rho_P^2} \right\} u = 0 \,, \tag{17}$$

or (taking s instead of t as the independent variable and writing v for $\dot{\sigma}$), we have

$$\frac{d^2 u}{d s^2} + \frac{1}{v}\frac{d v}{d s}\frac{d u}{d s} + \left\{ \frac{1}{v^2} \left(\frac{\partial^2 \mathfrak{V}}{\partial u^2} \right)_P + \frac{3}{\rho_P^2} \right\} u = 0 \,. \tag{18}$$

From equation (17) we can at once deduce consequences relating to the stability of the known orbit. According to the Sturmian theory,[1] if we have a differential equation of the form

$$\ddot{u} + G(t)\, u = 0 \,, \tag{19}$$

where for a certain range of t, $G(t)$ lies between two positive real quantities a^2 and b^2, then any solution u which is zero for $t = t_0$ within the range will have another zero for some other value of t in the range, where $t - t_0$ lies between π/a and π/b, provided the range is sufficiently large compared to this interval. Applying this result to equation (17), we conclude that, if

$$\left(\frac{\partial^2 \mathfrak{V}}{\partial u^2} \right)_P + \frac{3 v^2}{\rho_P^2} > 0 \tag{20}$$

for *all* points of the known orbit, this orbit will be *stable;* i.e., if an adjacent orbit intersects the known orbit once, it will not diverge greatly from it but intersect it again infinitely many times. The quantity on the left-hand side of the inequality (20) is therefore called the *coefficient of stability* of the orbit.

Our present condition for stability (which is only a *sufficient* one) is readily seen to include the result obtained in § 4.3 concerning the stability of the circular orbits in a central field of force.

For the case of *periodic orbits* we can obtain a necessary and sufficient condition for stability. Suppose, then, that the known orbit is periodic and has a perimeter S. If $u = \phi(s)$ is a solution of equation (18), then so are

$$u_n = \phi(s + nS) \qquad (n = 1, 2, \ldots) \,, \tag{21}$$

where n is an arbitrary integer.

[1] See, e.g., E. L. Ince, *Ordinary Differential Equations*, chap. x, London: Longmans, 1927.

Consider three such solutions, u_{n+2}, u_{n+1}, and u_n. Since the differential equation (18) for u is of the second order, there can be only two independent solutions. Since, further, the differential equation is linear, there must exist a relation of the form

$$u_{n+2} = k u_{n+1} + k_1 u_n \,, \tag{22}$$

where k and k_1 must be independent of s and n. On the other hand, we cannot suppose, without further justification, that k and k_1 are independent of the particular solution $u = \phi(s)$, from which the further solutions (21) have been derived. However, we shall show that this is actually the case. For, let

$$w_n = \psi(s + nS) \qquad (n = 1, 2, \dots), \tag{23}$$

be another set of solutions derived from a different basic solution $u = \psi(s)$. Since there must exist a relation of the form

$$w_n = c u_{n+1} + c' u_n \tag{24}$$

(where c and c' are constants), it is readily seen that the w's also satisfy relations of the form (22) with the same values for k and k_1.

We shall now find the value of the constant k_1. From the equations

$$\left.\begin{aligned} \frac{d^2 u_n}{d s^2} + \frac{1}{v}\frac{d v}{d s}\frac{d u_n}{d s} + \left\{\frac{1}{v^2}\left(\frac{\partial^2 \mathfrak{B}}{\partial u^2}\right)_P + \frac{3}{\rho_P^2}\right\} u_n = 0 \,, \\ \frac{d^2 u_{n+1}}{d s^2} + \frac{1}{v}\frac{d v}{d s}\frac{d u_{n+1}}{d s} + \left\{\frac{1}{v^2}\left(\frac{\partial^2 \mathfrak{B}}{\partial u^2}\right)_P + \frac{3}{\rho_P^2}\right\} u_{n+1} = 0 \,, \end{aligned}\right\} \tag{25}$$

we derive

$$u_{n+1}\frac{d^2 u_n}{d s^2} - u_n \frac{d^2 u_{n+1}}{d s^2} = -\frac{1}{v}\frac{d v}{d s}\left(u_{n+1}\frac{d u_n}{d s} - u_n \frac{d u_{n+1}}{d s}\right) \tag{26}$$

or

$$\frac{d}{d s}\left(u_{n+1}\frac{d u_n}{d s} - u_n \frac{d u_{n+1}}{d s}\right) = -\frac{1}{v}\frac{d v}{d s}\left(u_{n+1}\frac{d u_n}{d s} - u_n \frac{d u_{n+1}}{d s}\right). \tag{27}$$

Hence,

$$u_{n+1}\frac{d u_n}{d s} - u_n \frac{d u_{n+1}}{d s} = \frac{q}{v} \,, \tag{28}$$

where q is a constant. Writing $(n + 1)$ for n in the foregoing equation, we obtain

$$u_{n+2}\frac{d u_{n+1}}{d s} - u_{n+1}\frac{d u_{n+2}}{d s} = \frac{q}{v} \,. \tag{29}$$

Combining the two preceding equations and using equation (22), we have

$$\left.\begin{aligned} u_{n+1}\frac{du_n}{ds}-u_n\frac{du_{n+1}}{ds} &= (ku_{n+1}+k_1u_n)\frac{du_{n+1}}{ds}-u_{n+1}\frac{d}{ds}(ku_{n+1}+k_1u_n) \\ &= -k_1\left(u_{n+1}\frac{du_n}{ds}-u_n\frac{du_{n+1}}{ds}\right). \end{aligned}\right\} \quad (30)$$

Hence, $k_1 = -1$.

We have thus shown that the functions u_n derived from any basic solution of (18) satisfy the difference equation

$$u_{n+2}-ku_{n+1}+u_n=0\ , \quad (31)$$

where k is a constant which depends only on the original solution. We can also express the relation (31) differently as

$$\frac{u_{n+2}+u_n}{u_{n+1}} = \text{constant for all adjacent solutions}\ . \quad (32)$$

Now the general solution of the difference equation (31) must be of the form

$$u_n = A\,\alpha^n + B\beta^n\ , \quad (33)$$

where α and β are the roots of the equation

$$\lambda^2 - k\lambda + 1 = 0\ , \quad (34)$$

where A and B are arbitrary functions of period S.[2] (The arbitrary functions A and B introduced in the solution of the difference equation have to be so chosen that u satisfies equation [18].)

Now the roots of equation (34) are real or complex, according as $|k|$ is greater than or less than 2. From this it follows that *the necessary and sufficient condition for a given periodic orbit to be stable is that* $|k|<2$. Similarly, the orbit is unstable if $|k|\geqslant 2$.

[2] See S. Barnard and J. M. Child, *Higher Algebra*, p. 369, Macmillan, 1936. If the roots of equation (34) are equal (i.e., if $k = 2$), then the solution has the form $u = (A + nB)$.

APPENDIX III

ASTRONOMICAL CONSTANTS AND DATA

	Number	Logarithm
Astronomical unit (cm)	1.4945×10^{13}	13.1745
Parsec (cm)	3.0826×10^{18}	18.4889
Light year (cm)	9.4605×10^{17}	17.9759
Year (sec)	3.1558×10^{7}	7.4991
Solar mass (gm)	1.985×10^{33}	33.2978
Solar luminosity (erg/sec)	3.780×10^{33}	33.5775
Solar radius (cm)	6.951×10^{10}	10.8420
Solar mass per cubic parsec (gm/cm^3)	6.777×10^{-23}	$\overline{23}.8310$
Constant of gravitation, G (dynes cm^2/gm^2)	6.67×10^{-8}	$\overline{8}.8241$
Velocity of light (cm/sec)	2.9978×10^{10}	10.4768
Solar motion with respect to the local standard of rest (cm/sec)	1.96×10^{6}	6.2923
Co-ordinates of solar apex	$\alpha=18^h0^m$; $\delta=+30°$; $l=23°.5$; $b=21°.6$	
Co-ordinates of the vertex of star streaming	$\alpha=274°$; $\delta=-11°$; $l=347°$; $b=+0°$	
The maximum mean peculiar speed (km/sec)	24.5	
The minimum mean peculiar speed (km/sec)	$16_{(\Theta)}$, $12.4_{(Z)}$	
The ratio of the axes of the velocity spheroid	0.62	
Average distance between the stars in the neighborhood of the sun (parsec)	3	
Average local density (stars per cubic parsec)	0.1	
Co-ordinates of galactic pole	$\alpha=190°$; $\delta=+28°$	
Co-ordinates of galactic center	$\alpha=262°$; $\delta=-30°$; $l=325°$; $b=0$	
Sun's distance from the center of the Galaxy (parsec)	8000	
Oort's constants A (km/sec/1000 parsec)	18	
Oort's constants B (km/sec/1000 parsec)	−13	
Rotational velocity (Θ_0) (km/sec)	250	
Angular velocity (ω_0) (radian/sec)	1×10^{-15}	
Period of rotation (year)	2×10^{8}	
Mass of the Galaxy (solar mass)	2×10^{11}	

DYNAMICAL FRICTION

BY

S. CHANDRASEKHAR

Dynamical Friction was originally published in *The Astrophysical Journal.* Parts I and II appeared in Volume 97, No. 2 (March, 1943) and Part III appeared in Volume 98, No. 1 (July, 1943).

I. GENERAL CONSIDERATIONS: THE COEFFICIENT OF DYNAMICAL FRICTION

ABSTRACT

In this paper it is shown that a star must experience *dynamical friction*, i.e., it must suffer from a systematic tendency to be decelerated in the direction of its motion. This dynamical friction which stars experience is one of the direct consequences of the fluctuating force acting on a star due to the varying complexion of the near neighbors. From considerations of a very general nature it is concluded that the *coefficient of dynamical friction*, η, must be of the order of the reciprocal of the time of relaxation of the system. Further, an independent discussion based on the two-body approximation for stellar encounters leads to the following explicit formula for the coefficient of dynamical friction:

$$\eta = 4\pi m_1 \,(m_1 + m_2)\,\frac{G^2}{v^3}\log_e\left[\frac{D_0\overline{|u|^2}}{G(m_1+m_2)}\right]\int_0^v N(v_1)dv_1\,,$$

where m_1 and m_2 denote the masses of the field star and the star under consideration, respectively; G, the constant of gravitation; D_0, the average distance between the stars; $\overline{|u|^2}$, the mean square velocity of the stars; $N(v_1)\,dv_1$, the number of field stars with velocities between v_1 and $v_1 + dv_1$; and, finally, v, the velocity of the star under consideration. It is shown that the foregoing formula for η is in agreement with the conclusions reached on the basis of the general considerations. Finally, some remarks are made concerning the further development of these ideas on the basis of a proper statistical theory.

1. *General considerations.*—In a first approximative discussion[1] of the fluctuating part of the gravitational field acting on a star we may conveniently describe it in terms of two functions: a function $W(\boldsymbol{F})$, which governs the probability of occurrence of a force $\boldsymbol{F}$ per unit mass acting on a star, and a function $T(|\boldsymbol{F}|)$, which gives the average time during which such a force acts. On this assumption we can properly visualize the motion of the representative point in the velocity space as follows: The representative point suffers random displacements in a manner that can be described in terms of the theory of random flights.[2] More specifically, the star may be assumed to suffer a large number of discrete increments in velocity of amounts $|\boldsymbol{F}|T(|\boldsymbol{F}|)$ occurring in random directions. The mean square increase in velocity which the star may be expected to suffer in a time t (large compared to the mean periods of the elementary fluctuations in $\boldsymbol{F}$) is then given by

$$\overline{|\Delta \boldsymbol{u}|^2} = \overline{|\boldsymbol{F}|^2 T(|\boldsymbol{F}|)}\,t\,. \tag{1}$$

Equivalently, we may describe the same situation by asserting that the probability function $W(\boldsymbol{u}, t)$, governing the occurrence of the velocity $\boldsymbol{u}$ at time t, satisfies the *diffusion equation*

$$\frac{\partial W}{\partial t} = q\nabla_u^2 W\,, \tag{2}$$

[1] S. Chandrasekhar, *Ap. J.*, **94**, 511, 1941.

[2] For a general discussion of this and related theories see a forthcoming article by the writer in the *Reviews of Modern Physics.*

where the *diffusion coefficient* q has the value

$$q = \tfrac{1}{6}\,\overline{|F|^2 T}\,. \tag{3}$$

If the star has a velocity u_0 at time $t = 0$, then the solution of the diffusion equation (2) which will be appropriate for describing the distribution of u at later times is clearly

$$W(u,\, t;\, u_0) = \frac{1}{(4\pi q t)^{3/2}}\, e^{-|u-u_0|^2/4qt}\,. \tag{4}$$

It is now seen that formula (1) is an immediate consequence of the foregoing solution for W.

We shall now indicate why the considerations of the preceding paragraph can be valid only for times which are short compared to $\overline{|u|^2}/\overline{|F|^2 T}$, where $\overline{|u|^2}$ denotes the mean square velocity of the stars in an appropriately chosen local standard of rest. For, if $W(u,\, t;\, u_0)$ according to equation (4), described the stochastic variations of u for all times, then the probability for a star to suffer any assigned arbitrarily large acceleration can be made as close to unity as we may choose by allowing t to be sufficiently large. This conclusion is, however, contrary to what we should expect on quite general grounds, namely, that $W(u,\, t;\, u_0)$ tends to a Maxwellian distribution, independently of u_0 as $t \to \infty$. Expressed somewhat differently, we should strictly suppose that the stochastic variations in the velocity which a star suffers must be such as to leave an initial Maxwellian distribution of the velocities invariant. Defining, now, a stochastic process as *conservative* if it leaves a Maxwellian distribution unchanged, it is clear that the process described by equation (2) is *nonconservative*. Consequently, equation (2) is suitable for describing the underlying physical situation only for times t which satisfy the inequality

$$t \ll \frac{\overline{|u|^2}}{\overline{|F|^2 T}}\,. \tag{5}$$

The question now arises as to how our earlier approximate considerations can be modified so as to make the underlying stochastic process conservative. Now, as has been made familiar in the physical theories of Brownian motion by Ornstein, Uhlenbeck, and others,[3] this can be achieved by the introduction of *dynamical friction*. More particularly, we suppose that the acceleration, Δu, which a star suffers in a time Δt, which is short compared to the time intervals during which u may change appreciably but long compared to the periods of the elementary fluctuations in F, can be expressed as the sum of two terms in the form

$$\Delta u = \delta u\,(\Delta t) - \eta u \Delta t\,, \tag{6}$$

where the first term on the right-hand side is governed by the probability distribution (cf. eq. [4])

$$\psi(\delta u\,[\Delta t]) = \frac{1}{(4\pi q \Delta t)^{3/2}}\, e^{-|\delta u - \mathrm{grad}_u q\,\Delta t|^2/4q\Delta t} \tag{7}$$

and where the second term represents a *deceleration* of the star in the direction of its motion by an amount proportional to $|u|$. The constant of proportionality, η, can therefore be properly defined as the *coefficient of dynamical friction*.

With the underlying stochastic process defined as in equation (6) the distribution

[3] See the article quoted in n. 2 for further amplifications of what follows in the text.

function $W(\boldsymbol{u}, t + \Delta t)$ at time $t + \Delta t$ can be derived from the distribution $W(\boldsymbol{u}, t)$ at the earlier time t by means of the integral equation

$$W(\boldsymbol{u}, t+\Delta t) = \int_{-\infty}^{+\infty} W(\boldsymbol{u} - \Delta\boldsymbol{u}, t)\, \psi(\boldsymbol{u} - \Delta\boldsymbol{u}; \Delta\boldsymbol{u})\, d(\Delta\boldsymbol{u}) \;, \tag{8}$$

where $\psi(\boldsymbol{u}; \Delta\boldsymbol{u})$ denotes the *transition probability* (cf. eqs. [6] and [7])

$$\psi(\boldsymbol{u}; \Delta\boldsymbol{u}) = \frac{1}{(4\pi q \Delta t)^{3/2}}\, e^{-|\Delta\boldsymbol{u} - \text{grad}_{\boldsymbol{u}} q \Delta t + \eta \boldsymbol{u} \Delta t|^2 / 4q\Delta t} . \tag{9}$$

Expanding $W(\boldsymbol{u}, t + \Delta t)$, $W(\boldsymbol{u} - \Delta\boldsymbol{u}, t)$, and $\psi(\boldsymbol{u} - \Delta\boldsymbol{u}; \Delta\boldsymbol{u})$, which occur in equation (8) in the form of Taylor series, evaluating the various moments of $\Delta\boldsymbol{u}$ according to the distribution (9), and passing finally to the limit $\Delta t = 0$, we obtain the following equation, which is of the Fokker-Planck type:

$$\frac{\partial W}{\partial t} = \text{div}_{\boldsymbol{u}}\,(q\, \text{grad}_{\boldsymbol{u}} W) + \text{div}_{\boldsymbol{u}}\,(\eta W \boldsymbol{u}) \;. \tag{10}$$

At this point we may explicitly draw attention to the fact that the foregoing equation is valid also when q and η are functions of $\boldsymbol{u}$.

Finally, the condition that the Maxwellian distribution

$$\left(\frac{3}{2\pi\overline{|\boldsymbol{u}|^2}}\right)^{3/2} e^{-3|\boldsymbol{u}|^2/2\overline{|\boldsymbol{u}|^2}} \tag{11}$$

satisfy equation (10) *identically* requires that q and η be related according to

$$\frac{q}{\eta} = \tfrac{1}{3}\overline{|\boldsymbol{u}|^2} = \text{constant}. \tag{12}$$

Now the solution of equation (10) appropriate for describing the distribution of the velocities at time t, given that $\boldsymbol{u} = \boldsymbol{u}_0$ at time $t = 0$, is

$$W(\boldsymbol{u}, t; \boldsymbol{u}_0) = \left[\frac{3}{2\pi\overline{|\boldsymbol{u}|^2}(1 - e^{-2\eta t})}\right]^{3/2} e^{-3|\boldsymbol{u} - \boldsymbol{u}_0 e^{-\eta t}|^2 / 2\overline{|\boldsymbol{u}|^2}(1 - e^{-2\eta t})} . \tag{13}$$

In writing down the foregoing solution we have assumed that q and η are constants. We readily verify that $W(\boldsymbol{u}, t; \boldsymbol{u}_0)$, according to equation (13), tends to our earlier solution (4) for $t \ll \eta^{-1}$ in virtue of the relation (12); moreover, it tends to the Maxwellian distribution (11) as $t \to \infty$. Accordingly, η^{-1} can be taken as a measure of the *time of relaxation* of the system. Combining equations (3) and (12), we have

$$\frac{1}{\eta} = 2\,\frac{\overline{|\boldsymbol{u}|^2}}{|\boldsymbol{F}|^2 T}, \tag{14}$$

which agrees with the customary definition of the time of relaxation except for a factor 2.[4]

Summarizing the conclusions reached, we may say that *general considerations such as the invariance of the Maxwellian distribution to the underlying stochastic process require that stars experience dynamical friction during their motion and that the coefficient of dynamical friction be of the order of the reciprocal of the time of relaxation of the system.*

2. *An elementary derivation of the coefficient of dynamical friction on the two-body approximation for stellar encounters.*—In the preceding section we have seen how the exist-

[4] Cf. Chandrasekhar, *Ap. J.*, **94**, 511, 1941 (see particularly §§ 7, 8, and 9).

ence of dynamical friction can be inferred on quite general grounds. We shall now show how the operation of such a force can also be derived from a direct analysis of the fluctuating force acting on a star. It is perhaps simplest and most instructive to examine the problem on an approximation in which the fluctuations in $\boldsymbol{F}$ are analyzed in terms of single stellar encounters each idealized as a two-body problem. On this approximation the increments in velocity, $\Delta v_{||}$ and $\Delta v_{\perp}$, which a star with velocity $v_2 = |\boldsymbol{v}_2|$ and mass m_2 suffers as the result of an encounter in directions which are respectively parallel to and perpendicular to the direction of motion are[5]

$$\Delta v_{||} = -\frac{2m_1}{m_1+m_2}\left[(v_2 - v_1\cos\theta)\cos\psi + v_1\sin\theta\cos\Theta\sin\psi\right]\cos\psi \qquad (15)$$

and

$$\left.\begin{aligned}\Delta v_{\perp} = \pm\frac{2m_1}{m_1+m_2}\Big[v_1^2 + v_2^2 - 2v_1v_2\cos\theta - \{(v_2 - v_1\cos\theta)\cos\psi \\ + v_1\sin\theta\cos\Theta\sin\psi\}^2\Big]^{1/2}\cos\psi\,,\end{aligned}\right\} \qquad (16)$$

where m_1 and v_1 denote the mass and the velocity of a typical field star and the rest of the symbols have the same meanings as in *Stellar Dynamics*, chapter ii (see, particularly, pp. 51–64).

According to equation (16), and as can, indeed, be expected on general symmetry grounds, $\Delta v_{\perp}$, when summed over a large number of encounters, vanishes identically. But this is not the case with $\Delta v_{||}$, for the net increase in the velocity which the star suffers in the direction of its motion during a time Δt (long compared to the periods of the elementary fluctuations but short compared to the time intervals during which $\boldsymbol{v}_2$ may be expected to change appreciably) is given by

$$\Sigma\Delta v_{||} = \Delta t\int_0^\infty dv_1\int_0^\pi d\theta\int_0^{2\pi} d\varphi\int_0^{D_0} dD\int_0^{2\pi}\frac{d\Theta}{2\pi}\{2\pi N(v_1,\theta,\varphi)\,V\,D\Delta v_{||}\}\,, \qquad (17)$$

where the various integrations are, with respect to the different parameters, defining the single encounters. The integration over Θ, the inclination of the orbital plane to the fundamental plane containing the vectors $\boldsymbol{v}_1$ and $\boldsymbol{v}_2$, is readily effected, and we are left with

$$\left.\begin{aligned}\Sigma\Delta v_{||} = -4\pi\frac{m_1}{m_1+m_2}\Delta t\int_0^\infty dv_1\int_0^\pi d\theta\int_0^{2\pi} d\varphi\int_0^{D_0} dD\,N(v_1,\theta,\varphi) \\ \times V(v_2 - v_1\cos\theta)\frac{D}{1+\dfrac{D^2V^4}{G^2(m_1+m_2)^2}}\,,\end{aligned}\right\} \qquad (18)$$

where we have substituted for $\cos^2\psi$ from *Stellar Dynamics*, equation (2.301). The integral over the impact parameter D when extended from 0 to ∞ diverges; but for reasons explained in *Stellar Dynamics*, page 56, we allow for D only a finite range of integration, namely, from 0 to D_0, where D_0 is of the order of the average distance between the stars. Performing, now, the integration over D, we obtain

$$\left.\begin{aligned}\Sigma\Delta v_{||} = -2\pi m_1(m_1+m_2)G^2\Delta t\int_0^\infty dv_1\int_0^\pi d\theta\int_0^{2\pi} d\varphi N(v_1,\theta,\varphi)\frac{1}{V^3} \\ \times(v_2 - v_1\cos\theta)\log(1+\mathscr{Y}^2V^4)\,,\end{aligned}\right\} \qquad (19)$$

[5]Cf. S. Chandrasekhar, *Principles of Stellar Dynamics*, p. 229 (eq. [5.721]). This monograph will be referred to hereafter as *Stellar Dynamics*.

where we have written

$$\mathscr{D} = \frac{D_0}{G(m_1 + m_2)} . \tag{20}$$

If we now assume that the distribution of the velocities $\boldsymbol{v}_1$ is spherical, then $N(v_1, \theta, \varphi)$ has the form (cf. *Stellar Dynamics*, eq. [2.336])

$$N(v_1, \theta, \varphi) = N(v_1) \frac{1}{4\pi} \sin \theta . \tag{21}$$

Substituting the foregoing form for $N(v_1, \theta, \varphi)$ in equation (19) and performing the integration over φ, we obtain

$$\left.\begin{aligned} \Sigma \Delta v_{||} = -\pi m_1 (m_1 + m_2) G^2 \Delta t \int_0^\infty d v_1 N(v_1) \int_0^\pi d\theta \frac{\sin \theta}{V^3} \\ \times (v_2 - v_1 \cos \theta) \log (1 + \mathscr{D}^2 V^4) . \end{aligned}\right\} \tag{22}$$

To effect the integration over θ, we shall use the relative velocity V as the variable of integration instead of θ. Since

$$V^2 = v_1^2 + v_2^2 - 2 v_1 v_2 \cos \theta , \tag{23}$$

we have

$$\left.\begin{aligned} V dV &= v_1 v_2 \sin \theta d\theta , \\ v_2 - v_1 \cos \theta &= \frac{1}{2 v_2} (V^2 + v_2^2 - v_1^2) . \end{aligned}\right\} \tag{24}$$

Using relations (24), we find that equation (22) can be reduced to the form

$$\Sigma \Delta v_{||} = -\tfrac{1}{2} \pi m_1 (m_1 + m_2) \frac{G^2}{v_2^2} \Delta t \int_0^\infty \frac{1}{v_1} N(v_1) J d v_1 , \tag{25}$$

where we have used J to denote

$$J = \int_{|v_1 - v_2|}^{(v_1 + v_2)} \left(1 + \frac{v_2^2 - v_1^2}{V^2}\right) \log (1 + \mathscr{D}^2 V^4) \, dV . \tag{26}$$

After an integration by parts the expression for J becomes

$$\left.\begin{aligned} J = \left(V - \frac{v_2^2 - v_1^2}{V}\right) \log (1 + \mathscr{D}^2 V^4) \Bigg|_{|v_1 - v_2|}^{(v_1 + v_2)} \\ - 4 \int_{|v_1 - v_2|}^{(v_1 + v_2)} \left(1 - \frac{v_2^2 - v_1^2}{V^2}\right) \frac{\mathscr{D}^2 V^4}{1 + \mathscr{D}^2 V^4} dV . \end{aligned}\right\} \tag{27}$$

Now, under most conditions of practical interest $\mathscr{D}^2 V^4$ is generally very large compared to unity (cf. *Stellar Dynamics*, eqs. [2.323] and [2.347]; also eq. [5.215]). Hence, to a sufficient accuracy we have

$$J = \left[\left(V - \frac{v_2^2 - v_1^2}{V}\right) \log (1 + \mathscr{D}^2 V^4) - 4 \left(V + \frac{v_2^2 - v_1^2}{V}\right)\right]_{|v_1 - v_2|}^{(v_1 + v_2)} . \tag{28}$$

After some further reductions we find that the foregoing equation becomes

$$J = \begin{cases} 2\,v_1 \log\,(1+\mathscr{C}^2[v_1+v_2]^4)\,(1+\mathscr{C}^2[v_1-v_2]^4) & (v_1 < v_2)\,, \\ 2\,v_1 \log\,(1+16\mathscr{C}^2 v_1^4) - 8\,v_1 & (v_1 = v_2)\,, \\ 2\,v_1 \log \dfrac{1+\mathscr{C}^2(v_1+v_2)^4}{1+\mathscr{C}^2(v_1-v_2)^4} - 16\,v_2 & (v_1 > v_2)\,. \end{cases} \tag{29}$$

Again, since $\mathscr{C}^2(v_1 + v_2)^4$ and $\mathscr{C}^2(v_1 - v_2)^4$ are also generally very large compared to unity, we can further simplify equation (29) to

$$J = \begin{cases} 8\,v_1 \log \mathscr{C}\,(v_2^2 - v_1^2) & (v_1 < v_2)\,, \\ 4\,v_1 \log 4\mathscr{C}\,v_1^2 - 8\,v_1 & (v_1 = v_2)\,, \\ 8\,v_1 \log \dfrac{v_1+v_2}{v_1-v_2} - 16\,v_2 & (v_1 > v_2)\,. \end{cases} \tag{30}$$

The foregoing formula for J shows that in an approximation in which we retain only the "dominant term" (cf. *Stellar Dynamics*, pp. 62–64) we have

$$J = \begin{cases} 8\,v_1 \log \mathscr{C}\,\overline{|\boldsymbol{u}|^2} & (v_1 < v_2)\,, \\ 0 & (v_1 > v_2)\,, \end{cases} \tag{31}$$

where $\overline{|\boldsymbol{u}|^2}$ may be taken to denote the mean square velocity of the stars in the system. According to equations (30) and (31), we have the remarkable result that *to a sufficient accuracy only stars with velocities less than the one under consideration contribute to* $\Sigma\Delta v_{||}$. As we shall see presently, it is precisely on this account that dynamical friction appears on our present analysis.

Combining equations (25) and (31), we have

$$\Sigma\Delta\,v_{||} = -4\pi m_1(m_1+m_2)\frac{G^2}{v_2^2}\log\,(\mathscr{C}\,\overline{|\boldsymbol{u}|^2})\,\Delta t\int_0^{v_2} N\,(v_1)\,d\,v_1\,. \tag{32}$$

Finally, if we assume that the velocities $\boldsymbol{v}_1$ are distributed according to Maxwell's law, then

$$\int_0^{v_2} N\,(v_1)\,d\,v_1 = \frac{4\,j^3}{\pi^{1/2}}\,N\int_0^{v_2} e^{-j^2 v_1^2} v_1^2 d\,v_1\,, \tag{33}$$

where N denotes the number of stars per unit volume and j is a parameter which measures the dispersion of the velocities in the system. Expressing the integral on the right-hand side of equation (33) in terms of the error integral

$$\Phi\,(x) = \frac{2}{\pi^{1/2}}\int_0^x e^{-x^2} d\,x\,, \tag{34}$$

and substituting the result in equation (32), we find that

$$\Sigma\Delta\,v_{||} = -4\pi N\,m_1(m_1+m_2)\frac{G^2}{v_2^2}\log\,(\mathscr{C}\,\overline{|\boldsymbol{u}|^2})\,\Delta t\,[\Phi\,(x_0) - x_0\Phi'(x_0)]\,, \tag{35}$$

where we have written $x_0 = jv_2$.

Equation (35) shows that the star does, in fact, experience dynamical friction and that the coefficient of dynamical friction has the value

$$\eta = 4\pi N m_1 (m_1 + m_2) \frac{G^2}{v_2^3} \log (\mathscr{V} \overline{|u|^2}) [\Phi(x_0) - x_0 \Phi'(x_0)] . \qquad (36)$$

It is now of interest to see that with the coefficient of dynamical friction defined as in equation (36) we can directly verify the existence of a relation of the form (12). For, according to equations (2.356) and (5.724) in *Stellar Dynamics*, we have

$$\Sigma \Delta v_{||}^2 = \tfrac{8}{3}\pi N m_1^2 \frac{G^2}{v_2^3} \overline{|u|^2} \log (\mathscr{V} \overline{|u|^2}) \Delta t [\Phi(x_0) - x_0 \Phi'(x_0)] . \qquad (37)$$

Hence,

$$\frac{\Sigma \Delta v_{||}^2}{\eta \Delta t} = \frac{2}{3} \frac{m_1}{m_1 + m_2} \overline{|u|^2} , \qquad (38)$$

which is to be compared with equation (12). It is thus seen that a detailed analysis of the fluctuating field of the near-by stars in terms of individual stellar encounters idealized as two-body problems fully confirms the conclusions reached in § 1 on the basis of certain general principles.

3. *Dynamical friction as a consequence of the statistical properties of the fluctuating gravitational field of a random distribution of stars.*—The discussion of dynamical friction in § 1, while sufficiently general for a first orientation in the subject, suffers, nevertheless, from certain drawbacks. For example, in writing down the probability distribution for $\delta u (\Delta t)$ (eq. [7]) we have assumed that it has spherical symmetry. However, to be entirely general we should rather suppose that $\psi(\delta u[\Delta t])$ has the form

$$\psi(\delta u [\Delta t]) = \frac{1}{\pi^{3/2}} \begin{vmatrix} a_{11} & a_{12} & a_{13} \\ a_{21} & a_{22} & a_{23} \\ a_{31} & a_{32} & a_{33} \end{vmatrix} e^{-(a_{11}\delta u_1^2 + a_{22}\delta u_2^2 + a_{33}\delta u_3^2 + 2a_{12}\delta u_1 \delta u_2 + 2a_{23}\delta u_2 \delta u_3 + 2a_{31}\delta u_3 \delta u_1)/\Delta t} , \qquad (39)$$

where $\delta u = (\delta u_1, \delta u_2, \delta u_3)$ and $(a_{\mu\nu})$ is a symmetric tensor of the second rank. The components of $(a_{\mu\nu})$ can very well depend on u. While it would not be difficult to write down for the correspondingly more general form of the transition probability the appropriate generalization of equation (10), we should not be able to make much practical use of such an equation without some direct knowledge concerning $(a_{\mu\nu})$. In other words, a detailed statistical analysis of the fluctuating part of the gravitational field acting on a star must precede a discussion of the necessary generalization of equation (10). A start in this direction has recently been made by Chandrasekhar and von Neumann in two papers.[6] Particularly in their second paper, where all the first and the second moments of $\dot{F}$ for given F and v have been evaluated, a direct indication for the existence of dynamical friction on the statistical theory has indeed been found. However, a complete solution of the problem will require a more far reaching discussion than has yet been undertaken. But the general outlines of such a theory are not difficult to foresee. For, the essential information which is needed is, of course, the average force, $\overline{F_t}$, per unit mass acting on a star at time t when a force F_0 acted at time $t = 0$. The statistical problem is thus merely one of finding the joint distribution $W(F_0, F_t)$ of F_0 and F_t, where

$$F_0 = G \sum_i M_i \frac{r_i}{|r_i|^3} \qquad (40)$$

[6] *Ap. J.*, **95**, 489, 1942, and **97**, 1, 1943.

and

$$F_t = G\sum_i M_i \frac{r_i + V_i t}{|r_i + V_i t|^3}. \tag{41}$$

In equations (40) and (41) r_i and V_i denote, respectively, the position and the velocity of a typical field star *relative* to the one under consideration. By an application of Markoff's method (cf. the papers of Chandrasekhar and von Neumann) we readily find that the required distribution is formally given by

$$W(F_0, F_t) = \frac{1}{64\pi^6}\int_{-\infty}^{+\infty}\int_{-\infty}^{+\infty} e^{-i(\rho\cdot F_0 + \sigma\cdot F_t)} A(\rho, \sigma)\, d\rho d\sigma, \tag{42}$$

where ρ and σ are two auxiliary vectors and

$$A(\rho, \sigma) = e^{-NC(\rho,\sigma)} \tag{43}$$

and where

$$C(\rho, \sigma) = \int_{-\infty}^{\infty}\int_{-\infty}^{\infty}\int_{0}^{\infty}\left[1 - e^{iGM\left\{\frac{r\cdot\rho}{|r|^3} + \frac{(r+Vt)}{|r+Vt|^3}\cdot\sigma\right\}}\right]\tau(V, M)\, dM dr dV. \tag{44}$$

In equation (44) $\tau(V, M)$ governs the probability of occurrence of a star with a relative velocity V and with a mass M.

For our purposes it would, however, be sufficient to know the first moment of F_t for given F and v, in which case we shall need only the behavior of $C(\rho, \sigma)$ for $|\sigma| \to 0$. It is not difficult to push the formal theory a little further, but without going into these developments here it is clear that in terms of $\overline{F_t}(F_0, v)$ we shall be able to solve the entire problem of the stochastic variation of F acting on a star. More particularly the consideration of the integral

$$\int_0^{\infty} \overline{F_t}(F_0, v)\, dt \tag{45}$$

will not only provide us with the means of giving a precise meaning to the notion of the mean life of F but will also disclose in a direct manner the existence of dynamical friction on the statistical theory. We shall return to the development of the theory along these lines on a later occasion.

4. *General remarks.*—To avoid misunderstandings we shall make some remarks (which are otherwise obvious) concerning the reasons for introducing the new notion of dynamical friction and avoiding the usage of the term "viscosity." First, the physical ideas underlying the concepts of dynamical friction and viscosity are quite distinct: thus, while the "coefficient of dynamical friction" refers to the systematic deceleration which *individual* stars experience during their motion, "viscosity," as commonly understood, refers to the sheering force exerted by one *element of gas* on another. Second, dynamical friction is an exact notion expressing the systematic decelerating effect of the fluctuating field of force acting on a star *in motion*, in contrast to viscosity, which, as a concept, is valid only when averaged over times which are long compared to the time of relaxation of the system and over spatial dimensions which are large compared to the mean free paths of the individual molecules. Thus, while the introduction of dynamical friction in stellar dynamics presents no difficulty, the circumstances are very different for a rational introduction of "viscosity" in the subject (cf. *Stellar Dynamics*, pp. 76–78 and 184).

II. THE RATE OF ESCAPE OF STARS FROM CLUSTERS AND THE EVIDENCE FOR THE OPERATION OF DYNAMICAL FRICTION

ABSTRACT

In this paper a general method is described for determining the rate of escape of stars from galactic and globular clusters which is based on certain general statistical principles. Essentially the method consists in reducing the problem to a boundary-value problem in partial differential equations and in making use of the interpretation of the stochastic process in the velocity space as a diffusion process of a rather general type.

The rate of escape has been evaluated, first, ignoring dynamical friction, and, second, making due allowance for it. It appears that the rate of escape of stars predicted on the first basis is too rapid to be compatible with a life for galactic clusters even of the order of 5×10^8 years. However, the rates of escape are drastically reduced when dynamical friction is allowed for and permits a time scale of the order of 3×10^9 years. It is concluded that in the very existence of galactic clusters like the Pleiades we can look for direct evidence for the operation of dynamical friction which was predicted on theoretical grounds in the preceding paper.

1. *Introduction.*—In the preceding paper[1] we have shown that stars must experience dynamical friction during their motion. This conclusion, first reached on the basis of certain very general considerations, was later confirmed by a more direct analysis of the fluctuating force acting on a star in terms of the two-body approximation for stellar encounters. In this paper we propose to draw attention to certain facts of stellar dynamics which provide direct evidence for the operation of dynamical friction.

Since the coefficient of dynamical friction is of the order of the reciprocal of the time of relaxation of the system (cf. I, eq. [14]), it is evident that it is only during times of the order of the time of relaxation itself that dynamical friction will have a chance to become an effective agent. Consequently, the effects of dynamical friction will be apparent only in stellar systems with relatively short times of relaxation. Such systems are provided by galactic clusters like the Pleiades, which are characterized by times of relaxation of the order of 6×10^7 years.[2] Since the times of relaxation of the galactic clusters are of this order of magnitude, it is clear that an important factor in their evolution must be the escape of stars from them.[3] For, in times of the order of the time of relaxation, the probability that a star will, on account of accidental fluctuations, acquire a velocity equal to or greater than the velocity of escape must be appreciable. And, if this should happen, we can reasonably expect the star to escape from the cluster. The question now arises as to the rate at which stars will thus leave the cluster. In this paper we shall show how this rate can be evaluated on the basis of certain general statistical principles and how

[1] Referred to hereafter as "I."

[2] Cf. S. Chandrasekhar, *Principles of Stellar Dynamics*, chap. v. This monograph will be referred to hereafter as *Stellar Dynamics*.

In *Stellar Dynamics* (p. 202) the time of relaxation of the Pleiades is given as 2.9×10^7 years. However, in view of the fact that in a sufficient approximation η^{-1} is equal to *twice* the time of relaxation as defined in *Stellar Dynamics* (cf. the remarks in I following eq. [14]), and since for our present purposes η^{-1} provides a better unit for measuring time, we have quoted in the text a value which is twice that given in *Stellar Dynamics*.

[3] This fact was first clearly recognized by Ambarzumian and Spitzer. For references to these papers and for a general discussion of the related ideas see *Stellar Dynamics*, chap v, §§ 5.2–5.4.

precisely in this rate of escape we can look for evidence for the operation of dynamical friction.

2. *A general method for estimating the rate of escape of stars from galactic and globular clusters.*—In the preceding paper we have shown that, when the diffusion coefficient, q, and the coefficient of dynamical friction, η, are functions of $\boldsymbol{u}$, the equation which governs the distribution $W(\boldsymbol{u}, t)$ of $\boldsymbol{u}$ at time t is

$$\frac{\partial W}{\partial t} = \text{div}_{\boldsymbol{u}} \left(q \, \text{grad}_{\boldsymbol{u}} W + \eta W \boldsymbol{u} \right) , \tag{1}$$

where q and η are further related according to

$$\frac{q}{\eta} = \tfrac{1}{3} \overline{| \boldsymbol{u} |^2} = \text{constant} . \tag{2}$$

This differential equation for W leads to an important interpretation of the stochastic process which takes place in the velocity space. For, according to equation (1), we can visualize the motion of the representative points in the velocity space as a *process of diffusion* in which the rate of flow across an element of surface $d\sigma$ is given by

$$- \left(q \, \text{grad}_{\boldsymbol{u}} W + \eta W \boldsymbol{u} \right) \cdot \mathbf{1}_{d\sigma} d\sigma , \tag{3}$$

where $\mathbf{1}_{d\sigma}$ is a unit vector which is normal to the element of surface considered. With this interpretation of the stochastic process in mind, the following method for finding the rate at which a star may be expected to acquire a given velocity naturally suggests itself.

First, we find the probability, $p(v_0, t)\, dt$, that a star with an initial velocity $|\boldsymbol{u}| = v_0$ will acquire for the *first time* a certain preassigned velocity, $|\boldsymbol{u}| = v_\infty$, say, between t and $t + dt$. We then integrate $p(v_0, t)$ over t from 0 to t, to obtain the total probability, $Q(v_0, t)$, that the star will have acquired the velocity v_∞ during the entire interval from 0 to t. Finally, we average $Q(v_0, t)$ over the relevant range of the initial velocities v_0, to obtain the *expectation*, $Q(t)$, that a star will have acquired the velocity v_∞ during a time t.

The advantage of formulating the problem in the manner described is that the function $p(v_0, t)$ can be determined in terms of a spherically symmetric solution of equation (1) which satisfies the boundary conditions

$$W (| \boldsymbol{u} | , t) = 0 \qquad \text{for} \qquad | \boldsymbol{u} | = v_\infty \text{ for all } t > 0 \tag{4}$$

and

$$W (| \boldsymbol{u} | , t) \to \frac{1}{4 \pi v_0^2} \, \delta (| \boldsymbol{u} | - v_0) \text{ as } t \to 0 , \tag{5}$$

where δ stands for Dirac's δ-function. If W is such a solution, the required probability function $p(v_0, t)$ is given by (cf. the interpretation of eq. [1] in an earlier paragraph)

$$p (v_0, t) = - \left(4 \pi q | \boldsymbol{u} |^2 \frac{\partial W (| \boldsymbol{u} | , t)}{\partial | \boldsymbol{u} |} \right)_{| \boldsymbol{u} | = v_\infty} \tag{6}$$

The probability $Q(v_0, t)$ that a star having an initial velocity v_0 will have acquired the velocity v_∞ during a time t is then given by

$$Q (v_0, t) = \int_0^t p (v_0, t) \, dt . \tag{7}$$

And, finally, the expectation $Q(t)$ that a star will have acquired the velocity v_∞ during a time t is given by

$$Q(t) = \int_0^{v_\infty} Q(v_0, t)\, f(v_0)\, dv_0\,, \tag{8}$$

where $f(v_0)$ governs the frequency of occurrence of an initial velocity v_0.

Now the coefficient of dynamical friction η, as derived on the basis of the two-body approximation for stellar encounters, is (cf. I, eq. [32] for the case $m_1 = m_2 = m$)

$$\eta = 8\pi N m^2 G^2 \log\left[\frac{D_0 \overline{|u|^2}}{2Gm}\right] \frac{1}{|u|^3} \int_0^{|u|} f(v)\, dv\,. \tag{9}$$

According to this formula, η tends to a constant limiting value as $|u| \to 0$. But, as $|u| \to \infty$, $\eta \to 0$; however, according to the relation (2), q also tends to zero simultaneously with η. Consequently, by allowing q and η to be constants and equal to their respective average values, we shall be compensating for the overestimation of η for large values of $|u|$ by a corresponding overestimation in the diffusion coefficient q. In this paper we shall accordingly restrict ourselves, for the sake of simplicity, to the case where q and η are constants. In a later paper we shall present the results of a similar calculation in which due allowance will be made for the dependence of q and η on $|u|$.

3. *The rate of escape of stars from galactic clusters.*—For the reasons explained toward the end of the last section we shall suppose in this investigation that q and η are both constants and independent of $|u|$. Equation (1) can then be re-written as (cf. eq. [2])

$$\frac{\partial W}{\partial t} = \tfrac{1}{3}\overline{|u|^2}\eta \nabla_u^2 W + \eta\, \mathrm{div}_u (W u)\,. \tag{10}$$

Let

$$\eta t = \tau\,; \qquad u = (\tfrac{2}{3}\overline{|u|^2})^{1/2} \boldsymbol{\rho}\,; \tag{11}$$

or, in words, τ measures the time in units of the time of relaxation; and, if a Gaussian distribution of the velocities

$$\frac{j^3}{\pi^{3/2}} e^{-j^2|u|^2} du \tag{12}$$

be assumed, $\boldsymbol{\rho}$ measures the velocity u in units of j^{-1}. With the transformation of the variables (11) equation (10) becomes

$$\frac{\partial W}{\partial \tau} = \tfrac{1}{2}\nabla_{\boldsymbol{\rho}}^2 W + \mathrm{div}_{\boldsymbol{\rho}} (W \boldsymbol{\rho})\,. \tag{13}$$

It should be noted that in our present choice of the units the diffusion coefficient has the value $\frac{1}{2}$.

For a spherically symmetric solution, equation (12) reduces to

$$\frac{\partial W}{\partial \tau} = \frac{1}{2\rho^2}\frac{\partial}{\partial \rho}\left(\rho^2 \frac{\partial W}{\partial \rho}\right) + \left(3W + \rho \frac{\partial W}{\partial \rho}\right), \tag{14}$$

where we have used ρ to denote $|\boldsymbol{\rho}|$. And, according to our remarks in § 2, we have to seek a solution of equation (14) which satisfies the boundary conditions

$$W(\rho, \tau) = 0 \quad \text{for} \quad \rho_0 = \rho_\infty \text{ (say) for } \tau > 0 \tag{15}$$

and

$$W(\rho, \tau) \to \frac{1}{4\pi\rho_0^2}\, \delta(\rho - \rho_0) \text{ as } \tau \to 0\,. \tag{16}$$

i) *The rate of escape of stars from clusters when dynamical friction is ignored.*—When dynamical friction is ignored, equation (14) further simplifies to

$$\frac{\partial W}{\partial \tau}=\frac{1}{2\rho^2}\frac{\partial}{\partial \rho}\left(\rho^2\frac{\partial W}{\partial \rho}\right), \tag{17}$$

and the solution of this equation satisfying the boundary conditions (15) and (16) is[4]

$$W=\frac{1}{2\pi\rho\rho_\infty\rho_0}\sum_{n=1}^{\infty}e^{-n^2\pi^2\tau/2\rho_\infty^2}\sin\left(\frac{n\pi}{\rho_\infty}\rho\right)\sin\left(\frac{n\pi}{\rho_\infty}\rho_0\right). \tag{18}$$

In terms of the foregoing solution we can determine the probability $p(\rho_0, \tau)\,d\tau$ that a star with an initial velocity corresponding to ρ_0 will acquire for the first time a velocity corresponding to ρ_∞ during τ and $\tau+d\tau$. Remembering that in our present units the coefficient of diffusion has the value $\frac{1}{2}$, we have (cf. eq. [6])

$$p(\rho_0, \tau)=-2\pi\rho_\infty^2\left(\frac{\partial W}{\partial \rho}\right)_{\rho=\rho_\infty}; \tag{19}$$

or, using the solution (18), we have

$$p(\rho_0, \tau)=\frac{\pi}{\rho_0\rho_\infty}\sum_{n=1}^{\infty}n(-1)^{n+1}e^{-n^2\pi^2\tau/2\rho_\infty^2}\sin\left(\frac{n\pi}{\rho_\infty}\rho_0\right). \tag{20}$$

The total probability $Q(\rho_0, \tau)$ that the star would have acquired the velocity ρ_∞ during the interval $(0, \tau)$ is therefore given by

$$Q(\rho_0, \tau)=\int_0^\tau p(\rho_0,\tau)\,d\tau=\frac{2\rho_\infty}{\pi\rho_0}\sum_{n=1}^{\infty}\frac{(-1)^{n+1}}{n}\left(1-e^{-n^2\pi^2\tau/2\rho_\infty^2}\right)\sin\left(\frac{n\pi}{\rho_\infty}\rho_0\right). \tag{21}$$

Finally, to obtain the expectation that an "average" star will have acquired the velocity ρ_∞ in a time τ, we must average the foregoing expression over all ρ_0. For this purpose we shall use for the distribution over ρ_0 the radial Gaussian function

$$\frac{4}{\pi^{1/2}}e^{-\rho_0^2}\rho_0^2 \tag{22}$$ [5]

and extend the range of integration from 0 to ∞. Strictly speaking, this is not a valid procedure, particularly the extending of the range of integration beyond ρ_∞. However, for the values of ρ_∞ we shall be normally interested in (cf. eqs. [25] and [26], below), the number of stars with $\rho>\rho_\infty$ forms a negligible fraction of the total number (see, e.g., *Stellar Dynamics*, p. 207, eq. [5.311]). With this understanding, the averaging of $Q(\rho_0, \tau)$ over ρ_0 leads to the formula

$$Q(\tau)=2\sum_{n=1}^{\infty}(-1)^{n+1}\left(1-e^{-n^2\pi^2\tau/2\rho_\infty^2}\right)e^{-n^2\pi^2/4\rho_\infty^2}. \tag{23}$$

[4] See, e.g., H. S. Carslaw and J. C. Jaeger, *Operational Methods in Applied Mathematics*, p. 235 (Ex. 16), Oxford, England, 1941.

[5] Remembering that in our present choice of the units $j=1$.

Now, in a star cluster we have the following relation between the mean square velocity of escape and the mean square velocity of the stars in the system (cf. *ibid.*, pp. 206–207, eqs. [5.306] and [5.311])

$$\overline{v_\infty^2} = 4\overline{|\boldsymbol{u}|^2}\,; \tag{24}$$

or, in our present choice of the units (cf. eq. [11]), we have

$$\overline{\rho_\infty^2} = 6\,. \tag{25}$$

However, in view of the circumstance that a star acquiring a velocity $2(\overline{|\boldsymbol{u}|^2})^{1/2}$ does not necessarily imply its leaving the cluster unless it acquires a somewhat higher velocity (cf. *ibid.*, pp. 208–209), we shall suppose that

$$\rho_\infty^2 = 8\,, \tag{26}$$

to allow a reasonable margin. Table 1 gives the values of $Q(\tau)$ both for $\rho_\infty = \sqrt{6}$ and for $\rho_\infty = \sqrt{8}$.

TABLE 1

THE EXPECTATION $Q(\tau)$ FOR A STAR TO ESCAPE FROM A CLUSTER DURING A TIME τ (MEASURED IN UNITS OF THE TIME OF RELAXATION) WHEN DYNAMICAL FRICTION IS IGNORED

τ	$Q(\tau)$		τ	$Q(\tau)$	
	$\rho_\infty^2=6$	$\rho_\infty^2=8$		$\rho_\infty^2=6$	$\rho_\infty^2=8$
0.25	0.069	0.023	2.5	0.82	0.68
0.5	.19	.081	3.0	.87	.77
1.0	.42	.25	4.0	.94	.87
1.5	.60	.43	5.0	0.97	0.93
2.0	0.73	0.57			

Remembering that the time of relaxation of galactic clusters is of the order of 6×10^7 years, an examination of Table 1 reveals that the rates of escape predicted (when dynamical friction is ignored) are far too rapid to be compatible even with lives for these clusters of the order of 3×10^8 years. This can also be seen directly from equation (23). For, according to this equation,

$$Q(\tau) \sim 2e^{-\pi^2/4\rho_\infty^2}\,(1-e^{-\pi^2\tau/2\rho_\infty^2}) \qquad (\tau \gtrsim 1)\,; \tag{27}$$

or, for $\rho_\infty^2 = 6$, respectively 8, we have the approximate formulae

$$\left.\begin{aligned} Q(\tau) &\sim 1.3\,(1-e^{-0.82\tau}) \qquad (\rho_\infty^2=6)\,,\\ Q(\tau) &\sim 1.5\,(1-e^{-0.62\tau}) \qquad (\rho_\infty^2=8)\,.\end{aligned}\right\} \tag{28}$$

However, as we shall presently see, the rates of escape are drastically reduced from what we have just now found when proper allowance is made for dynamical friction.

ii) *The rate of escape of stars from clusters when allowance is made for dynamical friction.*—Passing now to the case when dynamical friction is not ignored, we have to solve equation (14), together with the boundary conditions (15) and (16). Introducing the variable

$$w = W\rho\,, \tag{29}$$

equation (14) simplifies to

$$\frac{\partial w}{\partial \tau}=\frac{1}{2}\frac{\partial^2 w}{\partial \rho^2}+2w+\rho\frac{\partial w}{\partial \rho}. \tag{30}$$

The boundary conditions (15) and (16) now become

$$w(\rho, \tau)=0 \text{ for both } \rho=\rho_\infty \quad \textit{and} \quad \rho=0 \text{ for all } \tau>0 \tag{31}$$

and

$$w(\rho, \tau)\to\frac{1}{4\pi\rho_0}\,\delta(\rho-\rho_0) \text{ as } \tau\to 0. \tag{32}$$

We shall now show how the solution of equation (30), together with the boundary conditions (31), can be reduced to a problem in characteristic values.

First we notice that a separation of the variables can be effected by the substitution

$$w=e^{-\lambda\tau}\phi(\rho), \tag{33}$$

where λ is, for the present, an unspecified constant. Equation (30) now leads to the differential equation

$$\frac{d^2\phi}{d\rho^2}+2\rho\frac{d\phi}{d\rho}+(2\lambda+4)\phi=0. \tag{34}$$

Again, writing

$$\phi=e^{-\rho^2/2}\psi, \tag{35}$$

we have for ψ the differential equation

$$\frac{d^2\psi}{d\rho^2}+(2\lambda+3-\rho^2)\psi=0; \tag{36}$$

or, putting

$$\lambda=\mu-1, \tag{37}$$

we have

$$\frac{d^2\psi}{d\rho^2}+(2\mu+1-\rho^2)\psi=0. \tag{38}$$

It is seen that the differential equation (38) for ψ is the same as the familiar wave equation for a simple harmonic oscillator. However, the boundary conditions with which we have now to solve equation (38) are different from those customary in solving the problem of the simple harmonic oscillator in the quantum theory, for the solution we are now looking for must satisfy the boundary conditions

$$\psi=0 \quad \text{for} \quad \rho=0 \quad \text{and also for} \quad \rho=\rho_\infty. \tag{39}$$

In other words, the ψ's of our problem are the characteristic functions of a simple harmonic oscillator bounded at the origin and at $\rho=\rho_\infty$, i.e., an oscillator in a "box." It is, therefore, clear that the ψ's which satisfy the boundary conditions (39) form a complete set of orthogonal functions which can be further normalized.

Let

$$\psi_1, \psi_2, \ldots, \psi_n, \ldots \tag{40}$$

represent the normalized characteristic functions of our problem belonging respectively to the characteristic values

$$\mu_1, \mu_2, \ldots, \mu_n, \ldots. \tag{41}$$

The general solution of equation (30) satisfying the boundary conditions (31) can therefore be expressed in the form

$$w = \sum_{n=1}^{\infty} A_n e^{-(\mu_n - 1)\tau} e^{-\rho^2/2} \psi_n(\rho) , \tag{42}$$

where the A_n's are certain constants which should be so chosen that the boundary condition for $\tau = 0$ is satisfied.

Now, since a δ-function can always be built up from any complete set of normalized orthogonal functions according to

$$\delta(\rho - \rho_0) = \sum_{n=1}^{\infty} \psi_n(\rho) \psi_n(\rho_0) , \tag{43}$$

it follows that the solution which satisfies the boundary conditions (31) *and* (32) is

$$w = \frac{e^{-(\rho^2 - \rho_0^2)/2}}{4\pi \rho_0} \sum_{n=1}^{\infty} e^{-(\mu_n - 1)\tau} \psi_n(\rho) \psi_n(\rho_0) . \tag{44}$$

Thus our solution for W takes the form

$$W = \frac{e^{-(\rho^2 - \rho_0^2)/2}}{4\pi \rho \rho_0} \sum_{n=1}^{\infty} e^{-(\mu_n - 1)\tau} \psi_n(\rho) \psi_n(\rho_0) . \tag{45}$$

Using the foregoing solution for W, we find that (cf. eq. [67])

$$p(\rho_0, \tau) = \frac{\rho_\infty}{2\rho_0} e^{-(\rho_\infty^2 - \rho_0^2)/2} \sum_{n=1}^{\infty} e^{-(\mu_n - 1)\tau} \left(-\frac{d\psi_n}{d\rho} \right)_{\rho=\rho_\infty} \psi_n(\rho_0) ; \tag{46}$$

or, for the probability $Q(\rho_0, \tau)$, we have

$$Q(\rho_0, \tau) = \frac{\rho_\infty}{2\rho_0} e^{-(\rho_\infty^2 - \rho_0^2)/2} \sum_{n=1}^{\infty} \frac{1}{\mu_n - 1} [1 - e^{-(\mu_n - 1)\tau}] \left(-\frac{d\psi_n}{d\rho} \right)_{\rho=\rho_\infty} \psi_n(\rho_0) . \tag{47}$$

Finally, to obtain $Q(\tau)$ we must further average the foregoing expression over the relevant range of ρ_0. With this we have formally solved the problem. To make the solution explicit, it remains only to specify the characteristic functions ψ_n and the corresponding characteristic values μ_n.

The nature of the dependence of the characteristic values μ_n on the length of the "box" ρ_∞ can be obtained by following a procedure developed by Sommerfeld in his studies of the Kepler problem and the problem of the rotator in the quantum theory with "artificial" boundary conditions.[6]

First, it is clear that when

$$\rho_\infty \to \infty , \qquad \mu_n \to n \qquad (n = 1, 3, 5, \ldots) . \tag{48}$$

(Only the odd integral values of n need concern us here, since the wave function has to vanish at the origin.) It is further evident that the functions

$$\Psi_n = e^{-\rho^2/2} H_n(\rho) , \tag{49}$$

where the H_n's are the various Hermite polynomials, formally solve equation (38) with $\mu_n = n$; and, if n is an odd integer, these functions Ψ_n satisfy also the boundary condition

[6] A. Sommerfeld and H. Welker, *Ann. d. Phys.*, **32**, 56, 1938, and A. Sommerfeld and H. Hartmann, *Ann. d. Phys.*, **37**, 333, 1940.

at the origin. If it should now happen that ρ_∞ coincides with a zero of one of the odd Hermite polynomials, then the corresponding wave function ψ_n will satisfy the boundary condition at ρ_∞ as well. Thus,

$$H_3 = 8\rho^3 - 12\rho \tag{50}$$

has a zero at $\rho = (1.5)^{1/2}$. Accordingly, if $\rho_\infty = (1.5)^{1/2}$, $\mu = 3$ is a characteristic value of our problem, and Ψ_3 for $\rho \leqslant (1.5)^{1/2}$ is the characteristic function which belongs to it. This represents, then, a special solution to our problem. Similarly, the higher-order Hermite polynomials will further provide such special solutions. The advantage in obtaining these special solutions is that by plotting the zeros of the various Hermite polynomials in a (μ, ρ_∞) diagram (as in Fig. 1) we obtain at once a general indication of how the various characteristic values are modified by the "artificial" boundary condition at $\rho = \rho_\infty$.

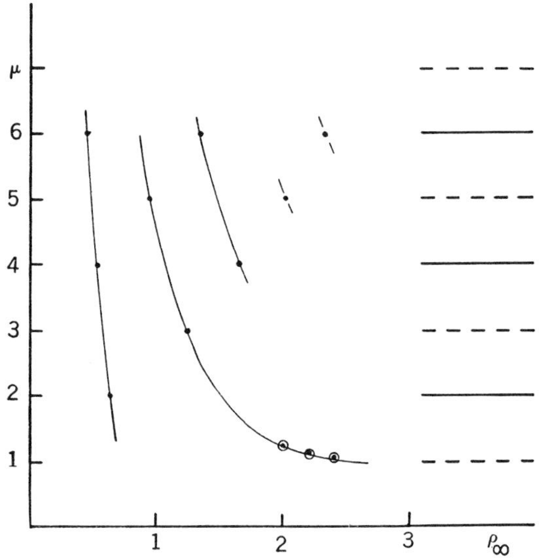

FIG. 1

Now an examination of Figure 1 shows that for $\rho_\infty > 2$ the first characteristic value of our problem must be extremely close to unity, so that $\mu_1 - 1$ must be a very small quantity. On the other hand, the higher characteristic values will lead to values of $(\mu_n - 1) \sim (n - 1)$ $(n > 1$, but an odd integer). Accordingly, for values of τ of the order of unity and greater, the first term in the series on the right-hand side of equation (47) will provide ample accuracy. Thus,

$$\left.\begin{aligned} &Q(\rho_0, \tau) \\ &\simeq \frac{\rho_\infty}{2\rho_0(\mu_1 - 1)} e^{-(\rho_\infty^2 - \rho_0^2)/2}\left[1 - e^{-(\mu_1 - 1)\tau}\right]\left(-\frac{d\psi_1}{d\rho}\right)_{\rho=\rho_\infty} \psi_1(\rho_0) \quad (\tau \gtrsim 1) \,. \end{aligned}\right\} \tag{51}$$

Finally, to determine $(\mu_1 - 1)$ corresponding to the "lowest state" of our artificially limited simple harmonic oscillator, we proceed as follows:

Writing

$$\psi = e^{-\rho^2/2} f \tag{52}$$

in equation (38), we obtain the differential equation

$$\frac{d^2 f}{d\rho^2} - 2\rho \frac{df}{d\rho} + 2\mu f = 0 . \tag{53}$$

Substituting for f the series

$$f = \Sigma c_s \rho^s , \tag{54}$$

where s runs through all the odd integers, we obtain the recursion formula

$$c_{s+2} = -\frac{2(\mu - s)}{(s+2)(s+1)} . \tag{55}$$

We already know that the particular characteristic value we are interested in must be very close to unity. Accordingly, writing

$$\mu_1 = 1 + \epsilon \tag{56}$$

and treating ϵ as a small quantity, we find that all the coefficients $c_3, c_5, \ldots$, contain ϵ as a factor. Retaining only the first-order terms in ϵ and letting $c_1 = 1$, we readily find that we can write f in the form

$$f = \rho(1 - \epsilon\chi) , \tag{57}$$

where

$$\chi = \tfrac{1}{3}\rho^2 + \tfrac{1}{15}\rho^4 + \tfrac{4}{315}\rho^6 + \tfrac{2}{945}\rho^8 + \ldots . \tag{58}$$

The condition that f has to vanish at some specified ρ_∞ will determine ϵ. Thus it was found that

$$\left.\begin{aligned} \epsilon &= 0.059 \qquad (\rho_\infty^2 = 6) , \\ \epsilon &= 0.013 \qquad (\rho_\infty^2 = 8) ; \end{aligned}\right\} \tag{59}$$

and, as was expected, ϵ is in fact a very small quantity.

In a first approximation ψ_1 can therefore be written as

$$\psi_1 = a e^{-\rho^2/2} \rho (1 - \epsilon\chi) , \tag{60}$$

where a denotes the normalizing factor, which can be determined numerically in any given case.

Substituting for ψ_1 from equation (60) in equation (51), we obtain

$$\left.\begin{aligned} &Q(\rho_0, \tau) \\ &\simeq \frac{a^2 \rho_\infty e^{-\rho_\infty^2}}{2\epsilon} \left[-\frac{d}{d\rho}(\rho - \epsilon\rho\chi) \right]_{\rho=\rho_\infty} [1 - \epsilon\chi(\rho_0)] (1 - e^{-\epsilon\tau}) \qquad (\tau \gtrsim 1) . \end{aligned}\right\} \tag{61}$$

It is found that for the cases $\rho_\infty^2 = 6$, respectively 8, the foregoing equation (after averaging over ρ_0) takes the simple numerical forms

$$\left.\begin{aligned} Q(\tau) &\simeq (1 - e^{-0.059\tau}) \qquad (\rho_\infty^2 = 6;\ \tau \gtrsim 1) , \\ Q(\tau) &\simeq (1 - e^{-0.013\tau}) \qquad (\rho_\infty^2 = 8;\ \tau \gtrsim 1) . \end{aligned}\right\} \tag{62}$$

Comparing the formulae (28) and (62), we see that when allowance is made for dynamical friction the mean life of a cluster is increased by factors ranging from 15 ($\rho_\infty \sim 2.5$) to 50 ($\rho_\infty \sim 2.8$). More particularly, the rates of escape given in Table 2 should be compared with those of Table 1.

It is seen that the rates of escape are sufficiently reduced to be compatible with a time scale of the order of 3×10^9 years. Physically, this drastic reduction in the rates of escape when dynamical friction is allowed for is readily understood, for dynamical friction operates essentially in the direction of preventing a star from being accelerated by too large amounts with any appreciable probability (cf. the remarks in I, § 1), and it is clearly on this account that the probability that a star will acquire the necessary high velocities for escape is so small. Further, it is to be noticed that in the mathematical analysis this reduction is brought about by the small numerical values of $(\mu_1 - 1)$, where μ_1 corresponds to the lowest quantum state of an artificially restricted simple harmonic oscillator; and, as we have seen (cf. Fig. 1) for the values of ρ_∞ which come under discussion, $(\mu_1 - 1)$ is not only a small quantity but it also depends very sensitively on the precise value of ρ_∞ (cf. the values of $[\mu_1 - 1]$ for the cases $\rho_\infty^2 = 6$ and $\rho_\infty^2 = 8$ given in eq. [62]). We may

TABLE 2

THE EXPECTATION $Q(\tau)$ FOR A STAR TO ESCAPE FROM A CLUSTER DURING A TIME τ (MEASURED IN UNITS OF THE TIME OF RELAXATION) WHEN ALLOWANCE IS MADE FOR DYNAMICAL FRICTION

τ	$Q(\tau)$		τ	$Q(\tau)$	
	$\rho_\infty^2=6$	$\rho_\infty^2=8$		$\rho_\infty^2=6$	$\rho_\infty^2=8$
5.	0.26	0.064	20.	0.95	0.23
10.	0.44	0.12	100.	. . . .	0.73

therefore conclude that dynamical friction provides exactly the right kind of agency for preventing too rapid a disintegration of an isolated cluster; and thus, in the very existence of galactic clusters like the Pleiades, we can look for evidence not only for the operation of dynamical friction but also for the now generally adopted time scale of the order of 3×10^9 years.

4. *Remarks on further developments.*—Our discussion of the rate of escape of stars from clusters has shown that dynamical friction must be a dominating factor in the dynamics of these systems. The question now arises as to how we can incorporate in a rational system of dynamics the stochastic variations in the velocity which a star suffers on account of the fluctuating force acting on it. It is evident that to build such a system of dynamics what we need is essentially a differential equation which will be appropriate for discussing the probability distribution in *phase space* in contrast to equations of the Fokker-Planck type, which describe the situation only in the velocity space. In other words, we need a proper generalization of Liouville's equation of classical dynamics to include terms corresponding to the stochastic variations in $\boldsymbol{u}$. Such a generalized Liouville equation can be readily found.

Quite generally we may write (cf. I, eq. [6])

$$\left.\begin{aligned} \Delta \boldsymbol{u} &= \boldsymbol{K}\Delta t + \delta \boldsymbol{u}\,(\Delta t) - \eta \boldsymbol{u}\Delta t\,, \\ \Delta \boldsymbol{r} &= \boldsymbol{u}\Delta t\,, \end{aligned}\right\} \tag{63}$$

where $\boldsymbol{K}$ denotes the external force per unit mass acting on a star and the rest of the symbols have the same meanings as in I, § 1. Also, analogous to the integral equation in the velocity space (I, eq. [8]), we now have

$$\left.\begin{aligned} &W(\boldsymbol{r}, \boldsymbol{u}, t+\Delta t) \\ &= \int_{-\infty}^{+\infty}\int_{-\infty}^{+\infty} W(\boldsymbol{r}-\Delta\boldsymbol{r}, \boldsymbol{u}-\Delta\boldsymbol{u}, t)\Psi(\boldsymbol{r}-\Delta\boldsymbol{r}, \boldsymbol{u}-\Delta\boldsymbol{u}; \Delta\boldsymbol{r}, \Delta\boldsymbol{u})\,d(\Delta\boldsymbol{r})\,d(\Delta\boldsymbol{u})\,, \end{aligned}\right\} \tag{64}$$

where $\Psi(\boldsymbol{r}, \boldsymbol{u}; \Delta\boldsymbol{r}, \Delta\boldsymbol{u})$ denotes the transition probability in the phase space. We have (cf. I, eq. [9])

$$\left.\begin{aligned}\Psi(\boldsymbol{r}, \boldsymbol{u}; \Delta\boldsymbol{r}, \Delta\boldsymbol{u}) = \frac{1}{(4\pi q\Delta t)^{3/2}}\, e^{-|\Delta\boldsymbol{u}-\mathrm{grad}_{\boldsymbol{u}} q\,\Delta t+\eta\boldsymbol{u}\,\Delta t-\boldsymbol{K}\,\Delta t|^2/4q\,\Delta t} \\ \times\,\delta(\Delta x - u_x\Delta t)\,\delta(\Delta y - u_y\Delta t)\,\delta(\Delta z - u_z\Delta t)\,.\end{aligned}\right\} \qquad (65)$$

Expanding the various terms in equation (64) in the form of Taylor series and proceeding as in usual deviation of the Fokker-Planck equation, we obtain[7]

$$\frac{\partial W}{\partial t} + \boldsymbol{u}\cdot\mathrm{grad}_{\boldsymbol{r}}\, W + \boldsymbol{K}\cdot\mathrm{grad}_{\boldsymbol{u}}\, W = \mathrm{div}_{\boldsymbol{u}}\,(q\,\mathrm{grad}_{\boldsymbol{u}}\, W + \eta W\boldsymbol{u})\,. \qquad (66)$$

In the foregoing equation q and η can be functions of $\boldsymbol{r}$ and $\boldsymbol{u}$; they should, however, be related according to

$$\frac{q}{\eta} = \tfrac{1}{3}\overline{|\boldsymbol{u}|^2} \qquad (67)$$

at all points of the phase space.

Equation (66) is the required generalization of Liouville's equation of classical dynamics, and it is on the basis of this equation that the dynamics of the galactic and the globular clusters should be developed. We shall return to these further developments on a future occasion.

[7] For details of the derivation see a forthcoming article by the writer in the *Reviews of Modern Physics*.

III. A MORE EXACT THEORY OF THE RATE OF ESCAPE OF STARS FROM CLUSTERS

ABSTRACT

A more exact estimate of the rate of escape of stars from clusters is made than in an earlier paper by properly allowing for the dependence of the coefficient of dynamical friction on the velocity. It is found that the probability that a star will have acquired the necessary velocity of escape (assumed to be equal to twice the root mean square velocity of the stars in the system) in a time τ (measured in units of the time of relaxation of the system) is given by

$$Q(\tau) = (1 - e^{-0.0075\tau}) .$$

On this basis, half-lives for galactic clusters of the order of 3×10^9 years are provided for, and it is further concluded that dynamical friction provides the principal mechanism for the continued existence of galactic clusters like the Pleiades for times of the order of 3×10^9 years.

1. *Introduction.*—In the two earlier papers of this series on "Dynamical Friction"[1] we have shown how stars must experience dynamical friction during their motion and how in the rate of escape of stars from clusters we can look for direct evidence for the operation of this force. However, in estimating this rate of escape of stars from clusters in II we assumed (for the sake of simplicity) that the coefficient of dynamical friction, η, and the diffusion coefficient, q (in the *velocity space*), were both constants. On the other hand, an explicit evaluation of the coefficient of dynamical friction on the two-body approximation for stellar encounters gave

$$\eta = 8\pi m^2 G^2 \left(\log_e \left[\frac{D_0 \overline{|\boldsymbol{u}|^2}}{2Gm}\right]\right) \frac{1}{|\boldsymbol{u}|^3} \int_0^{|\boldsymbol{u}|} N(v)\, dv . \tag{1}$$

According to this formula,

$$\eta \to \eta_0 = \text{constant as } |\boldsymbol{u}| \to 0 \tag{2}$$

and

$$\eta \to \text{constant } |\boldsymbol{u}|^{-3} \text{ as } |\boldsymbol{u}| \to \infty . \tag{3}$$

In view particularly of (3) it does not appear entirely satisfactory that we ignore the dependence of η on $|\boldsymbol{u}|$. It is therefore a matter of some importance that we make proper allowance for the variation of η with $|\boldsymbol{u}|$ according to equation (1) in estimating the rate of escape of stars from clusters. This is the main purpose of this paper.

2. *The general theory of the rate of escape of stars from clusters allowing for the variation of η with $|\boldsymbol{u}|$.*—As in II, we shall suppose that, in order that a star may escape from a cluster, it is only necessary that it acquire a velocity greater than (or equal to) a certain critical velocity, v_∞, which we may call the "velocity of escape." On this assumption the probability that a star will have acquired the necessary velocity for escape during a certain time can be determined very simply in terms of the probability, $p(v_0, t)\, dt$, that a star having initially a velocity $|\boldsymbol{u}| = v_0$ at time $t = 0$ will acquire for the *first time* the velocity $|\boldsymbol{u}| = v_\infty$ between t and $t + dt$. And as we have already explained in

[1] These two papers will be referred to as "I" and "II," respectively.

II, § 2, this probability function $p(v_0, t)$ can be derived in turn from the spherically symmetric solution of the equation

$$\frac{\partial W}{\partial t} = \operatorname{div}_{\boldsymbol{u}} \left(q \operatorname{grad}_{\boldsymbol{u}} W + \eta W \boldsymbol{u} \right) , \tag{4}$$

which satisfies the boundary conditions

$$W(|\boldsymbol{u}|, t) = 0 \quad \text{for} \quad |\boldsymbol{u}| = v_\infty \quad \text{for all } t > 0 \tag{5}$$

and

$$W(|\boldsymbol{u}|, t) \to \frac{1}{4\pi v_0^2} \delta(|\boldsymbol{u}| - v_0) \text{ as } t \to 0 , \tag{6}$$

where δ stands for the usual δ-function of Dirac.

For the case under discussion we have (I, eq. [36])

$$\eta = 8\pi N m^2 G^2 \left(\log_e \left[\frac{D_0 \overline{|\boldsymbol{u}|^2}}{2Gm} \right] \right) \frac{1}{|\boldsymbol{u}|^3} \left[\Phi(j|\boldsymbol{u}|) - j|\boldsymbol{u}|\Phi'(j|\boldsymbol{u}|) \right] , \tag{7}$$

where Φ and Φ' denote, respectively, the error function and its derivative. Further, in equation (7), j is the parameter which occurs in the assumed Maxwellian distribution of velocities:

$$\frac{j^3}{\pi^{3/2}} e^{-j^2|\boldsymbol{u}|^2} d\boldsymbol{u} ; \qquad j = \left(\frac{3}{2\overline{|\boldsymbol{u}|^2}} \right)^{1/2} . \tag{8}$$

The formula (7) for η can be written more conveniently as

$$\eta = \eta_0 \nu(j|\boldsymbol{u}|) , \tag{9}$$

where

$$\eta_0 = 8\pi N m^2 G^2 \left(\log_e \left[\frac{D_0 \overline{|\boldsymbol{u}|^2}}{2Gm} \right] \right) \left(\frac{3}{2\overline{|\boldsymbol{u}|^2}} \right)^{3/2} \frac{4}{3\pi^{1/2}} \tag{10}$$

and

$$\nu(\rho) = \frac{3\pi^{1/2}}{4} \rho^{-3} \left[\Phi(\rho) - \rho\Phi'(\rho) \right] . \tag{11}$$

With $\nu(\rho)$ defined in this manner,

$$\nu(\rho) \to 1 \quad \text{as} \quad \rho \to 0 \tag{12}$$

and

$$\nu(\rho) \sim \frac{3\pi^{1/2}}{4} \rho^{-3} \quad \text{as} \quad \rho \to \infty . \tag{13}$$

Again, since q and η are quite generally related according to

$$q = \tfrac{1}{3} \overline{|\boldsymbol{u}|^2} \eta , \tag{14}$$

we have

$$q = \tfrac{1}{3} \overline{|\boldsymbol{u}|^2} \eta_0 \nu(j|\boldsymbol{u}|) . \tag{15}$$

The function $\nu(\rho)$ is tabulated in Table 1.

Returning to equation (4), we now introduce a change of the independent variables $\boldsymbol{u}$ and t. Let

$$\tau = \eta_0 t ; \qquad \boldsymbol{u} = \left(\tfrac{2}{3} \overline{|\boldsymbol{u}|^2} \right)^{1/2} \boldsymbol{\rho} . \tag{16}$$

Equation (4) now takes the dimensionless form

$$\frac{\partial W}{\partial \tau} = \mathrm{div}_{\boldsymbol{\rho}} \left[\tfrac{1}{2}\nu(|\boldsymbol{\rho}|) \,\mathrm{grad}_{\boldsymbol{\rho}} W + \nu(|\boldsymbol{\rho}|) W \boldsymbol{\rho} \right] . \tag{17}$$

For a spherically symmetric solution $W(|\boldsymbol{\rho}|, \tau)$ equation (17) reduces to

$$\rho \frac{\partial w}{\partial \tau} = \frac{\partial}{\partial \rho} \left[\nu(\rho) \left\{ \tfrac{1}{2} \rho \frac{\partial w}{\partial \rho} + (\rho^2 - \tfrac{1}{2}) w \right\} \right] , \tag{18}$$

TABLE 1

THE FUNCTIONS $\nu(\rho)$ AND $-d \log \nu / d\rho$

ρ	$\nu(\rho)$	$-\frac{d \log \nu}{d\rho}$	ρ	$\nu(\rho)$	$-\frac{d \log \nu}{d\rho}$
0.00	1.00000	0.0000	1.45	0.33133	1.3062
0.05	0.99850	0.0600	1.50	.31026	1.3206
0.10	0.99402	0.1199	1.55	.29035	1.3323
0.15	0.98661	0.1795	1.60	.27157	1.3413
0.20	0.97634	0.2389	1.65	.25392	1.3477
0.25	0.96332	0.2979	1.70	.23734	1.3515
0.30	0.94770	0.3563	1.75	.22183	1.3528
0.35	0.92962	0.4141	1.80	.20732	1.3518
0.40	0.90927	0.4712	1.85	.19379	1.3486
0.45	0.88684	0.5274	1.90	.18117	1.3432
0.50	0.86257	0.5827	1.95	.16943	1.3358
0.55	0.83666	0.6369	2.00	.15852	1.3267
0.60	0.80936	0.6899	2.05	.14839	1.3159
0.65	0.78090	0.7417	2.10	.13898	1.3036
0.70	0.75152	0.7921	2.15	.13025	1.2901
0.75	0.72145	0.8409	2.20	.12216	1.2754
0.80	0.69093	0.8881	2.25	.11466	1.2597
0.85	0.66016	0.9336	2.30	.10770	1.2433
0.90	0.62936	0.9772	2.35	.10126	1.2262
0.95	0.59872	1.0188	2.40	.09528	1.2087
1.00	0.56842	1.0584	2.45	.08973	1.1907
1.05	0.53861	1.0958	2.50	.08458	1.1726
1.10	0.50944	1.1309	2.55	.07980	1.1544
1.15	0.48104	1.1636	2.60	.07536	1.1361
1.20	0.45350	1.1939	2.65	.07123	1.1179
1.25	0.42692	1.2216	2.70	.06739	1.0999
1.30	0.40137	1.2468	2.75	.06381	1.0820
1.35	0.37689	1.2693	2.80	.06048	1.0645
1.40	0.35354	1.2891	2.85	0.05737	1.0472

where we have written

$$\rho = |\boldsymbol{\rho}| \qquad \text{and} \qquad w = W \rho \, . \tag{19}$$

According to equations (5) and (6), we require a solution of equation (18) which satisfies the boundary conditions

$$w(\rho, \tau) = 0 \ \text{ for both } \ \rho = 0 \ \text{ and } \ \rho = \rho_\infty \ \text{ for all } \ \tau > 0 \tag{20}$$

and

$$w(\rho, \tau) \to \frac{1}{4\pi \rho_0} \delta(\rho - \rho_0) \ \text{ as } \ \tau \to 0 \, . \tag{21}$$

Now, equation (18) is separable in the variables ρ and τ. Accordingly, we write

$$w = e^{-\lambda\tau}\phi(\rho), \tag{22}$$

where λ is, for the present, an unspecified constant; we then obtain for ϕ the differential equation

$$\frac{d}{d\rho}\left[\nu(\rho)\left\{\tfrac{1}{2}\rho\frac{d\phi}{d\rho}+(\rho^2-\tfrac{1}{2})\phi\right\}\right]+\lambda\rho\phi=0. \tag{23}$$

If we now let

$$\phi = e^{-\rho^2/2}\psi, \tag{24}$$

equation (23) reduces to

$$\frac{d^2\psi}{d\rho^2}+\frac{d\log\nu}{d\rho}\frac{d\psi}{d\rho}+\left[2\frac{\lambda}{\nu(\rho)}+3-\rho^2-\frac{d\log\nu}{d\rho}\left(\frac{1}{\rho}-\rho\right)\right]\psi=0. \tag{25}$$

It is now seen that, in order that a solution of the foregoing equation may vanish both at $\rho = 0$ and at $\rho = \rho_\infty$, it is necessary that λ take one of an infinite enumerable set of discrete values

$$\lambda_1,\ \lambda_2,\ \ldots,\ \lambda_n,\ \ldots, \tag{26}$$

which may properly be called the "characteristic values" of the problem. Further, if

$$\psi_1,\ \psi_2,\ \ldots,\ \psi_n,\ \ldots \tag{27}$$

denote the solutions of equation (25) which satisfy the boundary conditions (20) at $\rho = 0$ and at $\rho = \rho_\infty$ and belong, respectively, to the values $\lambda_1, \lambda_2, \ldots, \lambda_n, \ldots$, then it can be readily verified that these solutions form a complete set of orthogonal functions. Without loss of generality we can therefore suppose that these functions are all properly normalized. Consequently, in terms of the fundamental solutions

$$w_n = e^{-\lambda_n\tau}e^{-\rho^2/2}\psi_n(\rho) \tag{28}$$

which satisfy the boundary conditions (20) we can construct solutions which will satisfy any further arbitrary boundary condition for $\tau = 0$. Thus, the solution

$$w = \frac{1}{4\pi\rho_0}e^{-(\rho^2-\rho_0^2)/2}\sum_{n=1}^{\infty}e^{-\lambda_n\tau}\psi_n(\rho)\psi_n(\rho_0) \tag{29}$$

clearly satisfies the boundary condition (21) for $\tau = 0$. Corresponding to the solution (29) for w, we have

$$W = \frac{1}{4\pi\rho\rho_0}e^{-(\rho^2-\rho_0^2)/2}\sum_{n=1}^{\infty}e^{-\lambda_n\tau}\psi_n(\rho)\psi_n(\rho_0). \tag{30}$$

Using the foregoing solution for W, we can write down the probability function $p(\rho_0, \tau)$. For, since

$$p(\rho_0,\tau) = -2\pi\rho_\infty^2\nu(\rho_\infty)\left(\frac{\partial W}{\partial\rho}\right)_{\rho=\rho_\infty}, \tag{31}$$

we have

$$p(\rho_0,\tau) = \frac{\rho_\infty}{2\rho_0}\nu(\rho_\infty)e^{-(\rho_\infty^2-\rho_0^2)/2}\sum_{n=1}^{\infty}e^{-\lambda_n\tau}\left(-\frac{d\psi_n}{d\rho}\right)_{\rho=\rho_\infty}\psi_n(\rho_0). \tag{32}$$

To obtain the total probability $Q(\rho_0, \tau)$ that a star having initially a velocity corresponding to ρ_0 will have acquired during the time τ a velocity corresponding to ρ_∞, we have simply to integrate equation (32) from 0 to τ. Thus,

$$Q(\rho_0, \tau) = \int_0^\tau p(v_0, \tau)\, d\tau ; \tag{33}$$

or, using equation (32), we have

$$Q(\rho_0, \tau) = \frac{\rho_\infty}{2\rho_0} \nu(\rho_\infty)\, e^{-(\rho_\infty^2 - \rho_0^2)/2} \sum_{n=1}^{\infty} \frac{1}{\lambda_n} (1 - e^{-\lambda_n \tau}) \left(-\frac{d\psi_n}{d\rho} \right)_{\rho=\rho_\infty} \psi_n(\rho_0) . \tag{34}$$

Finally, to obtain the expectation, $Q(\tau)$, that an "average" star will have acquired the necessary velocity for escape during a time τ, we must average the foregoing expression over all ρ_0. The final result can therefore be expressed in the form

$$Q(\tau) = \sum_{n=1}^{\infty} Q_n(\tau) , \tag{35}$$

where

$$Q_n(\tau) = A_n (1 - e^{-\lambda_n \tau}) \tag{36}$$

and

$$A_n = \frac{1}{2\lambda_n} \rho_\infty \nu(\rho_\infty)\, e^{-\rho_\infty^2/2} \left(-\frac{d\psi_n}{d\rho} \right)_{\rho=\rho_\infty} \overline{\left[\frac{e^{\rho_0^2/2}}{\rho_0} \psi_n(\rho_0) \right]} . \tag{37}$$

3. *Numerical results.*—Now, since in a star cluster the root mean square velocity of escape is twice the root mean square velocity of the stars in the system,[2] it is clear that the values of ρ_∞ which come under discussion are in the general neighborhood of

$$\rho_\infty = \sqrt{6} \sim 2.45 . \tag{38}$$

As we shall see presently, for these values of ρ_∞, $Q(\tau)$ can be represented with ample accuracy by the first term on the right-hand side of equation (35). Accordingly, it would be sufficient to specify the lowest characteristic value of λ (for a given ρ_∞) and the normalized characteristic function ψ_1 belonging to it. For this purpose the following procedure appears suitable:

First we assign a value for λ and look for a solution $\Psi(\rho)$ of equation (25) whose behavior near the origin can be described by a series expansion of the form

$$\Psi = \rho + a_3 \rho^3 + a_5 \rho^5 + \dots . \tag{39}$$

For any prescribed value of λ the coefficients a_3, a_5, etc., can be successively determined from the differential equation (25) for Ψ. Thus a_3 and a_5 are found to be

$$\left. \begin{aligned} a_3 &= -\tfrac{1}{6}(3 + 2\lambda) , \\ a_5 &= \tfrac{1}{20}[2.2 - 1.2\lambda + \tfrac{1}{6}(3 + 2\lambda)(0.6 + 2\lambda)] . \end{aligned} \right\} \tag{40}$$

The higher coefficients can be similarly found, but the explicit formulae in terms of λ have no particular interest. However, it is clear that, starting a solution near the origin with a series expansion of the form (39), we can continue it for larger values of ρ by

[2] Cf. e.g., S.Chandrasekhar, *Principles of Stellar Dynamics*, pp. 206-207.

standard numerical methods until we reach the first zero $\rho_\infty(\lambda)$ of Ψ. Conversely, for the value of ρ_∞ thus determined, the solution Ψ satisfies the necessary boundary conditions at the origin and at $\rho = \rho_\infty$. The initially assigned value of λ is therefore the lowest characteristic value of λ for this value of ρ_∞. If we now let a denote the normalizing factor for the solution Ψ determined in this fashion, we can express A_1 (cf. eq. [37]) alternatively in the form

$$A_1 = \frac{a^2}{2\lambda} \rho_\infty \nu(\rho_\infty) e^{-\rho_\infty^2/2} \left(- \frac{d\Psi}{d\rho} \right)_{\rho=\rho_\infty} \overline{\left[\frac{e^{\rho_0^2/2}}{\rho_0} \Psi(\rho_0) \right]} . \quad (41)$$

Now, it is found that, for the values of ρ_∞ in the neighborhood of 2.45, λ is very small and A_1 is very close to unity. Thus, for $\lambda = 0.0075$, a numerical integration of equation (25) gave

$$\rho_\infty = 2.4518 ; \qquad A_1 = 0.9966 \quad (\lambda_1 = 0.0075) . \quad (42)$$

Accordingly, for this case, equation (35) takes the explicit form

$$Q(\tau) = 0.9966 (1 - e^{-0.0075\tau}) + \sum_{n=2}^{\infty} A_n (1 - e^{-\lambda_n \tau}) \quad (\rho_\infty = 2.4518) . \quad (43)$$

Since $Q(\tau)$ must, by definition, approach unity as $\tau \to \infty$, it is clear that

$$\sum_{n=2}^{\infty} A_n = 0.0034 \qquad (\rho_\infty = 2.4518) . \quad (44)$$

Again, since λ_2 must be in the neighborhood of 2 (cf. II, p. 266) and the higher characteristic values still larger, it is evident that, for $\tau > 5$, sufficient accuracy will be provided by

$$Q(\tau) = 1 - e^{-0.0075\tau} \qquad (\tau \gtrsim 5) . \quad (45)$$

The situation for other values of ρ_∞ is quite similar, as is apparent from Table 2, where the results for a few values of λ are collected together.

TABLE 2

THE RATE OF ESCAPE OF STARS FROM CLUSTERS INCLUDING DYNAMICAL FRICTION AND ALLOWING FOR ITS DEPENDENCE ON $|u|$

λ	ρ_∞	$\nu(\rho_\infty)$	$-\Psi'(\rho_\infty)$	a^2	$\overline{[e^{\rho_0^2/2}\rho_0^{-1}\Psi(\rho_0)]}$	$Q_1(\tau)$
0.0025	2.6642	0.07011	0.4077	2.3083	0.9891	$1.0000\,(1-e^{-0.0025\tau})$
.0050	2.5320	.08148	.5183	2.3458	.9813	$0.9978\,(1-e^{-0.0050\tau})$
.0075	2.4518	.08954	.5932	2.3787	.9748	$0.9966\,(1-e^{-0.0075\tau})$
.0100	2.3936	.09601	.6503	2.4089	.9689	$0.9941\,(1-e^{-0.0100\tau})$
0.0125	2.3476	0.10156	0.6969	2.4373	0.9634	$0.9921\,(1-e^{-0.0125\tau})$

4. *The half-life of a cluster.*—From our results of § 3 it follows that for $\tau \gtrsim 5$ we can write

$$Q(\tau) = 1 - e^{-\lambda_1 \tau} \qquad (\tau = \eta_0 t) \quad (46)$$

for the values of ρ_∞ which come under discussion. Since $Q(\tau)$ gives the expectation that an average star will have escaped during a time τ (in units of η_0^{-1}), we can properly regard $1/\lambda_1\eta_0$ as a measure of the half-life of the cluster. Thus,

$$\text{Half-life of the cluster} = (\lambda_1\eta_0)^{-1}, \tag{47}$$

where η_0 is defined in equation (10). The precise value of λ_1 will depend, of course, on circumstances; but it is clear that greatest interest attaches to a value of $\rho_\infty \simeq 2.45$. For this value of ρ_∞ we have found that $\lambda_1 \simeq 0.0075$, so that the half-life of the cluster may be defined by

$$\text{Half-life of the cluster} = 133\,\eta_0^{-1}. \tag{48}$$

For the Pleiades, η_0^{-1} is of the order of 2×10^7 years, so that its half-life is of the order of 3×10^9 years. In judging this value it should be remembered that, when dynamical friction is ignored, a half-life for the Pleiades of the order of only 5×10^7 years is predicted, while our own earlier calculations in II, in which we ignored the dependence of the coefficient of dynamical friction on $|\boldsymbol{u}|$, gave half-lives which are about seven to eight times shorter than those indicated by our present calculations. More explicitly, we have found that (cf. II, eqs. [28] and [62])

$$\left.\begin{aligned}
&Q(\tau) \simeq 1.3\,(1 - e^{-0.82\tau}) && \text{(dynamical friction ignored)},\\
&Q(\tau) = (1 - e^{-0.059\tau}) && \text{(dynamical friction included, but the dependence of } \eta \text{ on } |\boldsymbol{u}| \text{ ignored)},\\
&Q(\tau) = (1 - e^{-0.0075\tau}) && \text{(dynamical friction included and the dependence of } \eta \text{ on } |\boldsymbol{u}| \text{ allowed for)}.
\end{aligned}\right\} \tag{49}$$

There can thus be hardly any doubt that dynamical friction provides the principal mechanism for the continued existence of the galactic clusters like the Pleiades for times of the order of 3×10^9 years. But, even with dynamical friction properly allowed for, it will be hard to account for such clusters' half-lives of the order of 10^{10} years. This, in turn, provides another strong argument in favor of the "short-time scale."

The results of Table 2 allow us also to infer something about the relative rates of escape of stars of different masses: for stars with masses appreciably different from the average value, ρ_∞ may be expected to change according to [3]

$$\rho_\infty(m) = \left(6\,\frac{m}{\overline{m}}\right)^{1/2}. \tag{50}$$

From Table 2 we now see that even a 10 per cent increase of ρ_∞ prolongs the half-lives by a factor of the order 3, while a similar decrease in ρ_∞ shortens the half-life by a factor of the order 2. The general conclusion to be drawn from this is simply that a cluster loses its less massive members rather more rapidly than the average ones, while the more massive members continue to remain, on the average, for longer times. We hope to return to these questions in greater detail on a later occasion.

In conclusion, I wish to record my indebtedness to Mrs. T. Belland, who undertook most of the numerical work involved in the preparation of this paper, and in particular for the care with which she performed the necessary numerical integrations.

[3] *Ibid.*, pp. 209–213.

NEW METHODS IN STELLAR DYNAMICS

BY

S. CHANDRASEKHAR

Copyright © 1943 by The New York Academy of Sciences

New Methods in Stellar Dynamics was originally published in 1943 in the *Annals of the New York Academy of Sciences*, Volume XLV, Article 3. It is reprinted by the kind permission of the New York Academy of Sciences.

TABLE OF CONTENTS

PREFACE

The present paper gives a condensed version of certain new methods which the author has recently been developing for investigating the dynamics of stellar systems. In presenting the subject, it was thought desirable that the emphasis be placed throughout on the physical aspects of the problems and whenever this has required the suppression of the mathematical details I have not avoided doing so. This is particularly true in the more technical parts of the subject.

Since the original version of this paper was submitted to the New York Academy of Sciences in September, 1942, the subject has advanced along several directions. The author is therefore greatly indebted to the Council of the Academy for permission to drastically revise and recast the entire article.

S. C.

July, 1943.

I. THE STATISTICS OF THE GRAVITATIONAL FIELD ARISING FROM A RANDOM DISTRIBUTION OF STARS

The Outline of the Statistical Method

One of the principal problems of stellar dynamics is concerned with the analysis of the nature of the force acting on a star which is a member of a stellar system.[1] In a general way, it is clear that we may broadly distinguish between the influence of the system as a whole and the influence of the immediate neighborhood. The former will be a smoothly varying function of position and time while the latter will be subject to relatively rapid fluctuations (see below).

Considering first the influence of the system as a whole, it appears that we can express it in terms of the gravitational potential $\mathbf{V}(\boldsymbol{r}; t)$ derived from the function $n(\boldsymbol{r}, M; t)$ which governs the average spatial distribution of the stars of different masses at time t. Thus

$$\mathbf{V}(\boldsymbol{r};t) = -G\int_{-\infty}^{+\infty}\int_{0}^{\infty}\frac{Mn(\boldsymbol{r}_1,M,t)dMd\boldsymbol{r}_1}{|\boldsymbol{r}_1 - \boldsymbol{r}|}, \tag{1}$$

where G denotes the constant of gravitation. The potential $\mathbf{V}(\boldsymbol{r}; t)$ derived in this manner may be said to represent the "smoothed out"

[1] See for example, **Chandrasekhar, S.**, "Principles of Stellar Dynamics." Chapter II.

distribution of matter in the stellar system. The force per unit mass acting on a star due to the "system as a whole" is therefore given by

$$\boldsymbol{K} = - \operatorname{grad} \mathbf{V}(\boldsymbol{r}; t). \tag{2}$$

However, the fluctuations in the *complexion* of the local stellar distribution will make the instantaneous force acting on a star to deviate from the value given by (2). To elucidate the nature and origin of these fluctuations we surround the star under consideration by an element of volume σ which we shall suppose is small enough to contain, on the average, only a relatively few stars. The actual number of stars, which will be found in σ at any given instant of time, will not in general be the average number that will be expected to be in it, namely, $n\sigma$; it will be subject to fluctuations. These fluctuations will naturally be governed by a Poisson distribution with variance $n\sigma$. It is in direct consequence of this changing complexion of the local stellar distribution that the influence of the near neighbors on a star is variable. The average period of such a fluctuation is readily estimated. The order of magnitude of the time involved is evidently that required for two stars to separate by a distance D equal to the average distance between the stars. We may therefore expect that the influence of the immediate neighborhood will fluctuate with an average period of the order of

$$T \backsimeq \frac{D}{\sqrt{\overline{|\mathbf{V}|^2}}}, \tag{3}$$

where $[\overline{|V|^2}]^{1/2}$ denotes the root mean square relative velocity between two stars.

In the neighborhood of the sun, $D \sim 3$ parsecs, $[\overline{|V|^2}]^{1/2} \sim 50$ km/sec. Hence,

$$T \text{ (near the sun)} \sim 6 \times 10^4 \text{ years}. \tag{4}$$

When we compare this time with the period of galactic rotation (which is about 2×10^8 years), we observe that, in conformity with our earlier remarks, the fluctuations in the force acting on a star due to the changing local stellar distribution does in fact occur with extreme rapidity compared to the rate at which any of the other physical parameters change. Accordingly, we may write for the force per unit mass acting on a star, the expression

$$\mathbf{F} = \boldsymbol{K}(\boldsymbol{r};t) + \boldsymbol{F}(t), \tag{5}$$

where $\boldsymbol{K}$ is derived from the smoothed out distribution, as in equations (1) and (2), and $\boldsymbol{F}$ denotes the fluctuating force due to the near neighbors. Moreover, if Δt denotes an interval of time, long compared to (3), we may write

$$\mathbf{F}\Delta t = \mathbf{K}\Delta t + \delta\boldsymbol{u}(t;t+\Delta t), \tag{6}$$

where

$$\delta\boldsymbol{u}(t;t+\Delta t) = \int_t^{t+\Delta t} \boldsymbol{F}(\xi)d\xi \qquad (\Delta t \gg T). \tag{7}$$

Under the circumstances stated ($\Delta t \gg T$), the accelerations $\delta\boldsymbol{u}(t;t+\Delta t)$ and $\delta\boldsymbol{u}(t+\Delta t; t+2\Delta t)$ suffered during two successive intervals $(t,t+\Delta t)$ and $(t+\Delta t, t+2\Delta t)$ will not be expected to show any correlation. We may therefore anticipate the existence of a definite law of distribution which will govern the probability of occurrence of the different values of $\delta\boldsymbol{u}(t;t+\Delta t)$. We thus see that the acceleration which a star suffers during an interval $\Delta t \gg T$ can be formally expressed as the sum of two terms: a *systematic* term, $\mathbf{K}\Delta t$, due to the action of the gravitational field of the smoothed out distribution and a *stochastic* term, $\delta\boldsymbol{u}(t; t+\Delta t)$, representing the influence of the near neighbors. Stated in this fashion, we recognize the similarity between our present problems in stellar dynamics with those which occur in the modern theories of Brownian motion.[2]

We proceed now to the outline of a general method which appears suitable for analyzing the statistical properties of $\boldsymbol{F}(t)$. The force $\boldsymbol{F}$ acting on a star, per unit mass, is given by

$$\boldsymbol{F} = G\sum_i \frac{M_i}{|\boldsymbol{r}_i|^3}\boldsymbol{r}_i, \tag{8}$$

where M_i denotes the mass of a typical "field" star and $\boldsymbol{r}_i$ its position vector relative to the star under consideration; further, in equation (8) the summation is to be extended over all the neighboring stars. The actual value of $\boldsymbol{F}$ given by equation (8) at any particular instant of time will depend on the instantaneous complexion of the local stellar distribution. It is in consequence subject to fluctuations. We can therefore ask only for the probability of occurrence

$$W(\boldsymbol{F})dF_x dF_y dF_z = W(\boldsymbol{F})d\boldsymbol{F} \tag{9}$$

of $\boldsymbol{F}$ in the range $\boldsymbol{F}$ and $\boldsymbol{F} + d\boldsymbol{F}$. In evaluating this probability distribution we shall suppose, consistent with the physical situations we have in view, that fluctuations subject only to the restriction of a constant average density occur. However, the specification of $W(\boldsymbol{F})$ does *not* provide us with all the necessary information concerning the fluctuating force $\boldsymbol{F}$. An equally important aspect of the problem concerns the *speed of fluctuations*.

[2] See a forthcoming article by the author in the "Reviews of Modern Physics."

According to equation (8) the rate of change of $\boldsymbol{F}$ with time is given by

$$\boldsymbol{f} = \frac{d\boldsymbol{F}}{dt} = G \sum_i M_i \left\{ \frac{\boldsymbol{V}_i}{|\boldsymbol{r}_i|^3} - 3\boldsymbol{r}_i \frac{(\boldsymbol{r}_i \cdot \boldsymbol{V}_i)}{|\boldsymbol{r}_i|^5} \right\}, \tag{10}$$

where $\boldsymbol{V}_i$ denotes the velocity of a typical field star *relative* [3] to the star under consideration. It is now apparent that the speed of fluctuations in $\boldsymbol{F}$ can be specified in terms of the bivariate distribution

$$W(\boldsymbol{F}, \boldsymbol{f}), \tag{11}$$

which governs the probability of the simultaneous occurrence of prescribed values for both $\boldsymbol{F}$ and $\boldsymbol{f}$. It is seen that this distribution function $W(\boldsymbol{F}, \boldsymbol{f})$ will depend on the assignment of *a priori* probability in the *phase space* in contrast to the distribution $W(\boldsymbol{F})$ of $\boldsymbol{F}$, which depends only on a similar assignment in the *configuration space*. While it is possible by an application of a general method, due to Markoff, to write down a general formula for $W(\boldsymbol{F}, \boldsymbol{f})$, it does not appear feasible to obtain the required distribution function in an explicit form. However, it is possible to obtain explicit formulae for all the first and second moments of $\boldsymbol{f}$ for a given $\boldsymbol{F}$; and it appears possible to make some progress in the specification of the statistical properties of $\boldsymbol{F}$ in terms of these moments.

The Statistical Properties of F

We require the stationary distribution of $\boldsymbol{F}$ and its simultaneous rate of change $\boldsymbol{f}$ acting on a given star. Without loss of generality we can suppose that the point under consideration is at the origin, O, of our system of coordinates. About O describe a sphere of radius R and containing N stars. In the first instance we shall suppose that

$$\boldsymbol{F} = G \sum_{i=1}^{N} \frac{M_i}{|\boldsymbol{r}_i|^3} \boldsymbol{r}_i \tag{12}$$

and

$$\boldsymbol{f} = G \sum_{i=1}^{N} M_i \left\{ \frac{\boldsymbol{V}_i}{|\boldsymbol{r}_i|^3} - 3\boldsymbol{r}_i \frac{(\boldsymbol{r}_i \cdot \boldsymbol{V}_i)}{|\boldsymbol{r}_i|^5} \right\}; \tag{13}$$

but we shall later let R and N tend to infinity simultaneously in such a way that

$$\frac{4}{3}\pi R^3 n = N; \qquad (R \to \infty; \qquad N \to \infty; \qquad n = \text{constant}). \tag{14}$$

This limiting process is permissible, in view of the fact that the dominant contribution to $\boldsymbol{F}$ is made by the nearest neighbor [4]; consequently, the

[3] It is in this respect that the analysis which follows differs from that contained in **Chandrasekhar, S., & von Neumann, J.** Astrophysical Jour. **95**: 489, 1942, where the speed of fluctuations in **F** acting at some *fixed* point in space is considered.

[4] Cf. **Chandrasekhar, S.**, Astrophysical Jour. **94**: 511, 1941 (see particularly § 4).

formal extrapolation to infinity of the density of stars obtained only in a given region of stellar system can hardly affect the results to any appreciable extent.

Using a general method due to Markoff, we can readily write down a general formula for the distribution function $W(\boldsymbol{F}, \boldsymbol{f})$. We have [5]

$$W(\boldsymbol{F},\boldsymbol{f}) = \frac{1}{64\pi^6}\int_{|\boldsymbol{\rho}|=0}^{\infty}\int_{|\boldsymbol{\sigma}|=0}^{\infty} e^{-i(\boldsymbol{\rho}\cdot\boldsymbol{F}+\boldsymbol{\sigma}\cdot\boldsymbol{f})}\,A(\boldsymbol{\rho},\boldsymbol{\sigma})d\boldsymbol{\rho}d\boldsymbol{\sigma}, \tag{15}$$

where

$$A(\boldsymbol{\rho},\boldsymbol{\sigma}) = \underset{R\to\infty}{\text{Limit}}\left[\frac{3}{4\pi R^3}\int_{M=0}^{\infty}\int_{|\boldsymbol{V}|=0}^{\infty}\int_{|\boldsymbol{r}|=0}^{R} e^{i(\boldsymbol{\rho}\cdot\boldsymbol{\phi}+\boldsymbol{\sigma}\cdot\boldsymbol{\psi})}\,\tau d\boldsymbol{r}d\boldsymbol{V}dM\right]^{4\pi R^3 n/3}. \tag{16}$$

In equations (15) and (16) $\boldsymbol{\rho}$ and $\boldsymbol{\sigma}$ are two auxiliary vectors; n denotes the number of stars per unit volume;

$$\boldsymbol{\phi} = GM\frac{\boldsymbol{r}}{|\boldsymbol{r}|^3}; \quad \boldsymbol{\psi} = GM\left(\frac{\boldsymbol{V}}{|\boldsymbol{r}|^3} - 3\boldsymbol{r}\frac{(\boldsymbol{r}\cdot\boldsymbol{V})}{|\boldsymbol{r}|^5}\right). \tag{17}$$

Further,

$$\tau d\boldsymbol{V}dM = \tau(\boldsymbol{V};M)d\boldsymbol{V}dM \tag{18}$$

gives the probability that a star with a relative velocity in the range $(\boldsymbol{V}, \boldsymbol{V}+d\boldsymbol{V})$ and with a mass between M and $M+dM$ will be found. It should also be noted that in writing equations (15) and (16) we have supposed that the fluctuations in the local stellar distribution which occur are subject only to the restriction of a constant average density.

Since

$$\frac{3}{4\pi R^3}\int_{M=0}^{\infty}\int_{|\boldsymbol{r}|=0}^{R}\int_{|\boldsymbol{V}|=0}^{\infty}\tau d\boldsymbol{V}d\boldsymbol{r}dM = 1, \tag{19}$$

we can rewrite (16) as

$$A(\boldsymbol{\rho},\boldsymbol{\sigma}) = \underset{R\to\infty}{\text{Limit}}\left[1 - \frac{3}{4\pi R^3}\int_{M=0}^{\infty}\int_{|\boldsymbol{r}|=0}^{R}\int_{|\boldsymbol{V}|=0}^{\infty}[1 - e^{i(\boldsymbol{\rho}\cdot\boldsymbol{\phi}+\boldsymbol{\sigma}\cdot\boldsymbol{\psi})}]\tau d\boldsymbol{V}d\boldsymbol{r}dM\right]^{4\pi R^3 n/3}. \tag{20}$$

The integral over $\boldsymbol{r}$ which occurs in equation (20) is seen to be absolutely convergent when extended over all $|\boldsymbol{r}|$ i.e., also for $|\boldsymbol{r}| \to \infty$. Hence, we can write

[5] Cf. **Chandrasekhar, S., & von Neumann, J.,** Astrophysical Jour. **95:** 489. 1942. (§ 2).

$$A(\boldsymbol{\rho},\boldsymbol{\sigma}) = \underset{R\to\infty}{\text{Limit}}\left[1 - \frac{3}{4\pi R^3}\int\limits_{M=0}^{\infty}\int\limits_{|\boldsymbol{r}|=0}^{\infty}\int\limits_{|\boldsymbol{V}|=0}^{\infty}[1 - e^{i(\boldsymbol{\rho}\cdot\boldsymbol{\phi}+\boldsymbol{\sigma}\cdot\boldsymbol{\psi})}]\tau d\boldsymbol{V}d\boldsymbol{r}dM\right]^{4\pi R^3 n/3}, \tag{21}$$

or

$$A(\boldsymbol{\rho},\boldsymbol{\sigma}) = e^{-nC(\boldsymbol{\rho},\boldsymbol{\sigma})}, \tag{22}$$

where

$$C(\boldsymbol{\rho},\boldsymbol{\sigma}) = \int\limits_{0}^{\infty}\int\limits_{-\infty}^{+\infty}\int\limits_{-\infty}^{+\infty}[1 - e^{i(\boldsymbol{\rho}\cdot\boldsymbol{\phi}+\boldsymbol{\sigma}\cdot\boldsymbol{\psi})}]\tau d\boldsymbol{r}d\boldsymbol{V}dM. \tag{23}$$

This formally solves the problem. It does not, however, appear that the integral representing $C(\boldsymbol{\rho},\boldsymbol{\sigma})$ can be evaluated explicitly in terms of any of the known functions. But if we are interested only in the distribution $W(\boldsymbol{F})$ of $\boldsymbol{F}$ and in the moments of $\boldsymbol{f}$ for a given $\boldsymbol{F}$ then we need only the behavior of $A(\boldsymbol{\rho},\boldsymbol{\sigma})$, and therefore also of $C(\boldsymbol{\rho},\boldsymbol{\sigma})$, for $|\boldsymbol{\sigma}| \to 0$, for the distribution $W(\boldsymbol{F})$ is clearly given by

$$W(\boldsymbol{F}) = \int\limits_{-\infty}^{+\infty} W(\boldsymbol{F},\boldsymbol{f})d\boldsymbol{f}. \tag{24}$$

Similarly, the first and the second moments of the components f_ξ, f_η, and f_ζ of $\boldsymbol{f}$ along three directions ξ, η and ζ at right angles to each other are given by

$$W(\boldsymbol{F})\overline{f_\mu} = \int\limits_{-\infty}^{+\infty} W(\boldsymbol{F},\boldsymbol{f})f_\mu d\boldsymbol{f} \qquad (\mu = \xi,\eta,\zeta), \tag{25}$$

and

$$W(\boldsymbol{F})\overline{f_\mu f_\nu} = \int\limits_{-\infty}^{+\infty} W(\boldsymbol{F},\boldsymbol{f})f_\mu f_\nu d\boldsymbol{f} \qquad (\mu,\nu = \xi,\eta,\zeta). \tag{26}$$

Substituting now for $W(\boldsymbol{F},\boldsymbol{f})$ according to equation (15) in the foregoing equations we obtain

$$\left.\begin{aligned} W(\boldsymbol{F}) &= \frac{1}{64\pi^6}\int\limits_{-\infty}^{+\infty}\int\limits_{-\infty}^{+\infty}\int\limits_{-\infty}^{+\infty} e^{-i(\boldsymbol{\rho}\cdot\boldsymbol{F}+\boldsymbol{\sigma}\cdot\boldsymbol{f})}\,A(\boldsymbol{\rho},\boldsymbol{\sigma})d\boldsymbol{f}d\boldsymbol{\rho}d\boldsymbol{\sigma}, \\ W(\boldsymbol{F})\overline{f_\mu} &= \frac{1}{64\pi^6}\int\limits_{-\infty}^{+\infty}\int\limits_{-\infty}^{+\infty}\int\limits_{-\infty}^{+\infty} e^{-i(\boldsymbol{\rho}\cdot\boldsymbol{F}+\boldsymbol{\sigma}\cdot\boldsymbol{f})}\,A(\boldsymbol{\rho},\boldsymbol{\sigma})f_\mu d\boldsymbol{f}d\boldsymbol{\rho}d\boldsymbol{\sigma}, \\ W(\boldsymbol{F})\overline{f_\mu f_\nu} &= \frac{1}{64\pi^6}\int\limits_{-\infty}^{+\infty}\int\limits_{-\infty}^{+\infty}\int\limits_{-\infty}^{+\infty} e^{-i(\boldsymbol{\rho}\cdot\boldsymbol{F}+\boldsymbol{\sigma}\cdot\boldsymbol{f})}\,A(\boldsymbol{\rho},\boldsymbol{\sigma})f_\mu f_\nu d\boldsymbol{f}d\boldsymbol{\rho}d\boldsymbol{\sigma}. \end{aligned}\right\} \tag{27}$$

But

$$\left.\begin{aligned}
\frac{1}{8\pi^3}\int_{-\infty}^{+\infty} e^{-i\boldsymbol{\sigma}\cdot\boldsymbol{f}}d\boldsymbol{f} &= \delta(\sigma_\xi)\delta(\sigma_\eta)\delta(\sigma_\zeta), \\
\frac{1}{8\pi^3}\int_{-\infty}^{+\infty} e^{-i\boldsymbol{\sigma}\cdot\boldsymbol{f}}f_\xi d\boldsymbol{f} &= i\delta'(\sigma_\xi)\delta(\sigma_\eta)\delta(\sigma_\zeta), \\
\frac{1}{8\pi^3}\int_{-\infty}^{+\infty} e^{-i\boldsymbol{\sigma}\cdot\boldsymbol{f}}f_\xi^2 d\boldsymbol{f} &= -\delta''(\sigma_\xi)\delta(\sigma_\eta)\delta(\sigma_\zeta), \\
\frac{1}{8\pi^3}\int_{-\infty}^{+\infty} e^{-i\boldsymbol{\sigma}\cdot\boldsymbol{f}}f_\xi f_\eta d\boldsymbol{f} &= -\delta'(\sigma_\xi)\delta'(\sigma_\eta)\delta(\sigma_\zeta),
\end{aligned}\right\} \tag{28}$$

etc. In equations (28), δ denotes Dirac's δ-function and δ' and δ'' its first and second derivatives; and remembering also that

$$\left.\begin{aligned}
\int_{-\infty}^{+\infty} f(x)\delta(x)dx = f(0); \qquad \int_{-\infty}^{+\infty} f(x)\delta'(x)dx = -f'(0); \\
\int_{-\infty}^{+\infty} f(x)\delta''(x)dx = f''(0),
\end{aligned}\right\} \tag{29}$$

equations (27) reduce to

$$W(\boldsymbol{F}) = \frac{1}{8\pi^3}\int_{-\infty}^{+\infty} e^{-i\boldsymbol{\varrho}\cdot\boldsymbol{F}}\left[A(\boldsymbol{\varrho},\boldsymbol{\sigma})\right]_{|\boldsymbol{\sigma}|=0}d\boldsymbol{\varrho}, \tag{30}$$

$$W(\boldsymbol{F})\overline{f_\mu} = -\frac{i}{8\pi^3}\int_{-\infty}^{+\infty} e^{-i\boldsymbol{\varrho}\cdot\boldsymbol{F}}\left[\frac{\partial}{\partial\sigma_\mu}A(\boldsymbol{\varrho},\boldsymbol{\sigma})\right]_{|\boldsymbol{\sigma}|=0}d\boldsymbol{\varrho}, \tag{31}$$

and

$$W(\boldsymbol{F})\overline{f_\mu f_\nu} = -\frac{1}{8\pi^3}\int_{-\infty}^{+\infty} e^{-i\boldsymbol{\varrho}\cdot\boldsymbol{F}}\left[\frac{\partial^2}{\partial\sigma_\mu\partial\sigma_\nu}A(\boldsymbol{\varrho},\boldsymbol{\sigma})\right]_{|\boldsymbol{\sigma}|=0}d\boldsymbol{\varrho}. \tag{32}$$

We accordingly see that the distribution function $W(\boldsymbol{F})$ and all the first and the second moments of $\boldsymbol{f}$ for a given $\boldsymbol{F}$ can be evaluated from a series expansion of $A(\boldsymbol{\varrho},\boldsymbol{\sigma})$ [or of $C(\boldsymbol{\varrho},\boldsymbol{\sigma})$] which is correct up to the second order in $|\boldsymbol{\sigma}|$. The development of such a series is long and tedious.

Omitting, therefore, all the details of the calculations, we give only the final result. It is found that

$$\left.\begin{aligned} C(\boldsymbol{\rho},\boldsymbol{\sigma}) &= \frac{4}{15}(2\pi)^{3/2}G^{3/2}\overline{M^{3/2}}|\boldsymbol{\rho}|^{3/2} \\ &+ \frac{2}{3}\pi i G_1(\sigma_1\overline{MV_1} + \sigma_2\overline{MV_2} - 2\sigma_3\overline{MV_3}) \\ &+ \frac{3}{28}(2\pi)^{3/2}G^{1/2}|\boldsymbol{\rho}|^{-3/2}[(5\sigma_1^2 + 4\sigma_2^2 - 2\sigma_3^2)\overline{M^{1/2}V_1^2} \\ &+ (4\sigma_1^2 + 5\sigma_2^2 - 2\sigma_3^2)\overline{M^{1/2}V_2^2} \\ &+ (4\sigma_3^2 - 2\sigma_1^2 - 2\sigma_2^2)\overline{M^{1/2}V_3^2} - 8\sigma_2\sigma_3\overline{M^{1/2}V_2V_3} \\ &- 8\sigma_1\sigma_3\overline{M^{1/2}V_1V_3} + 2\sigma_1\sigma_2\overline{M^{1/2}V_1V_2}] + O(|\boldsymbol{\sigma}|^3), \quad (|\boldsymbol{\sigma}|\to 0), \end{aligned}\right\} \tag{33}$$

where a bar indicates that the corresponding quantity has been averaged with the weight function $\tau(\boldsymbol{V};M)$ (see equation [18]); further, in equation (33), $(\sigma_1,\sigma_2,\sigma_3)$ and (V_1,V_2,V_3) are the components of $\boldsymbol{\sigma}$ and $\boldsymbol{V}$ in a system of coordinates in which the Z-axis is in the direction of $\boldsymbol{\rho}$.

In equation (33) $\boldsymbol{V} = (V_1,V_2,V_3)$ denotes of course the velocity of a field star relative to the one under consideration. If we now let $\boldsymbol{u}$ and $\boldsymbol{v}$ denote respectively the velocities of the field star and the star under consideration in an appropriately chosen local standard of rest, then

$$\boldsymbol{V} = \boldsymbol{u} - \boldsymbol{v}. \tag{34}$$

In our further discussion we shall introduce the assumption that the distribution of the velocities $\boldsymbol{u}$ among the stars is *spherical*; i.e., the distribution function $\Psi(\boldsymbol{u})$ has the form

$$\Psi(\boldsymbol{u}) \equiv \Psi[j^2(M)|\boldsymbol{u}|^2], \tag{35}$$

where Ψ is an arbitrary function of the argument specified and the parameter j (of the dimensions of [velocity]$^{-1}$) can be a function of the mass of the star. This assumption for the distribution of the peculiar velocities $\boldsymbol{u}$ implies that the probability function $\tau(\boldsymbol{V};M)$ must be expressible as

$$\tau(\boldsymbol{V};M) = \Psi[j^2(M)|\boldsymbol{u}|^2]\chi(M) \tag{36}$$

where $\chi(M)$ governs the distribution over the different masses. For a function τ of this form we clearly have

$$\left.\begin{aligned} \overline{MV_i} = -\overline{M}v_i; \qquad \overline{M^{1/2}V_i^2} = \frac{1}{3}\overline{M^{1/2}|\boldsymbol{u}|^2} + \overline{M^{1/2}}v_i^2 \qquad (i = 1,2,3) \\ \overline{M^{1/2}V_iV_j} = \overline{M^{1/2}}v_iv_j, \qquad [i,j = 1,2,3; \qquad i \neq j)]. \end{aligned}\right\} \tag{37}$$

Substituting these values in equation (33) we find, after some minor reductions, that

$$\left.\begin{aligned} C(\boldsymbol{\varrho},\boldsymbol{\sigma}) &= \frac{4}{15}(2\pi)^{3/2}G^{3/2}\overline{M^{3/2}}|\boldsymbol{\varrho}|^{3/2} - \frac{2}{3}\pi i G\overline{M}(\sigma_1 v_1 + \sigma_2 v_2 - 2\sigma_3 v_3) \\ &+ \frac{1}{4}(2\pi)^{3/2}G^{1/2}\overline{M^{1/2}|\boldsymbol{u}|^2}|\boldsymbol{\varrho}|^{-3/2}(\sigma_1^2 + \sigma_2^2) \\ &+ \frac{3}{28}(2\pi)^{3/2}G^{1/2}\overline{M^{1/2}}|\boldsymbol{\varrho}|^{-3/2}\{\sigma_1^2(5v_1^2 + 4v_2^2 - 2v_3^2) \\ &+ \sigma_2^2(4v_1^2 + 5v_2^2 - 2v_3^2) + \sigma_3^2(4v_3^2 - 2v_1^2 - 2v_2^2) \\ &- 8\sigma_2\sigma_3 v_1 v_3 - 8\sigma_3\sigma_1 v_3 v_1 + 2\sigma_1\sigma_2 v_1 v_2\} + O(|\boldsymbol{\sigma}|^3),\ (|\boldsymbol{\sigma}|\to 0). \end{aligned}\right\} \quad (38)$$

With a series expansion of this form, we can, as we have already remarked, evaluate the distribution $W(\boldsymbol{F})$ and all the first and the second moments of $\boldsymbol{f}$ for a given $\boldsymbol{F}$.

THE DISTRIBUTION $W(\boldsymbol{F})$

According to equations (30) and (38) we have

$$W(\boldsymbol{F}) = \frac{1}{8\pi^3}\int_{-\infty}^{+\infty} e^{-i\boldsymbol{\varrho}\cdot\boldsymbol{F} - a|\boldsymbol{\varrho}|^{3/2}}d\boldsymbol{\varrho}, \quad (39)$$

where we have written

$$a = \frac{4}{15}(2\pi G)^{3/2}\overline{M^{3/2}}n. \quad (40)$$

From equation (39) we derive the formula[6]

$$W(\boldsymbol{F}) = \frac{1}{4\pi a^2}\frac{H(\beta)}{\beta^2}, \quad (41)$$

where

$$H(\beta) = \frac{2}{\pi\beta}\int_0^\infty e^{-(x|\beta)^{3/2}}x \sin x\, dx, \quad (42)$$

and β measures $|\boldsymbol{F}|$ in units of Q_H where

$$Q_H = a^{2/3} = 2.6031G(M^{3/2}n)^{2/3}. \quad (43)$$

The function $H(\beta)$ has been numerically evaluated and tabulated in Chandrasekhar and von Neumann's paper.

THE FIRST MOMENT OF $\boldsymbol{f}$: DYNAMICAL FRICTION

Turning next to the first moment of $\boldsymbol{f}$ it is found after some lengthy calculations that

$$\bar{\boldsymbol{f}} = \overline{\left(\frac{d\boldsymbol{F}}{dt}\right)}_{\boldsymbol{F},\boldsymbol{v}} = -\frac{2}{3}\pi G\overline{M}nB\left(\frac{|\boldsymbol{F}|}{Q_H}\right)\left(\boldsymbol{v} - 3\frac{\boldsymbol{v}.\boldsymbol{F}}{|\boldsymbol{F}|^2}\boldsymbol{F}\right), \quad (44)$$

where Q_H is the normal field defined in equation (43) and

[6] Cf. **Chandrasekhar, S., & von Neumann, J.** Astrophysical Jour. **95**: 489, 1942. (§ 7).

$$B(\beta) = 3\frac{\int_0^\beta H(\beta)d\beta}{\beta H(\beta)} - 1. \tag{45}$$

The function $B(\beta)$ has the following asymptotic forms:

$$\left.\begin{aligned} B(\beta) &\to \frac{1}{15}\Gamma\left(\frac{10}{3}\right)\beta^2 \qquad (\beta \to 0), \\ B(\beta) &\to \frac{8}{5}\sqrt{\frac{\pi}{2}}\,\beta^{3/2} \qquad (\beta \to \infty). \end{aligned}\right\} \tag{46}$$

We shall first examine certain formal consequences of equation (44).

Multiplying equation (44) scalarly with $\boldsymbol{F}$ we obtain

$$\overline{\boldsymbol{F}.\left(\frac{d\boldsymbol{F}}{dt}\right)}_{\boldsymbol{F},\boldsymbol{\nu}} = \frac{4}{3}\pi G\overline{M}nB\left(\frac{|\boldsymbol{F}|}{Q_H}\right)(\boldsymbol{\nu}.\boldsymbol{F}) \tag{47}$$

but

$$\overline{\boldsymbol{F}.\left(\frac{d\boldsymbol{F}}{dt}\right)}_{\boldsymbol{F},\boldsymbol{\nu}} = |\boldsymbol{F}|\,\overline{\left(\frac{d|\boldsymbol{F}|}{dt}\right)}_{\boldsymbol{F},\boldsymbol{\nu}}. \tag{48}$$

Hence,

$$\overline{\left(\frac{d|\boldsymbol{F}|}{dt}\right)}_{\boldsymbol{F},\boldsymbol{\nu}} = \frac{4}{3}\pi G\overline{M}nB\left(\frac{|\boldsymbol{F}|}{Q_H}\right)\frac{\boldsymbol{\nu}.\boldsymbol{F}}{|\boldsymbol{F}|}. \tag{49}$$

On the other hand, if F_j denotes the component of $\boldsymbol{F}$ in an arbitrary direction at right angles to the direction of $\boldsymbol{\nu}$ then, according to equation (44),

$$\overline{\left(\frac{dF_j}{dt}\right)}_{\boldsymbol{F},\boldsymbol{\nu}} = 2\pi G\overline{M}nB\left(\frac{|\boldsymbol{F}|}{Q_H}\right)\frac{\boldsymbol{\nu}.\boldsymbol{F}}{|\boldsymbol{F}|^2}F_j. \tag{50}$$

Combining equations (49) and (50) we have

$$\frac{1}{F_j}\overline{\left(\frac{dF_j}{dt}\right)}_{\boldsymbol{F},\boldsymbol{\nu}} = \frac{3}{2}\frac{1}{|\boldsymbol{F}|}\overline{\left(\frac{d|\boldsymbol{F}|}{dt}\right)}_{\boldsymbol{F},\boldsymbol{\nu}}. \tag{51}$$

Equation (51) is clearly equivalent to

$$\overline{\left[\frac{d}{dt}\left(\log F_j - \frac{3}{2}\log|\boldsymbol{F}|\right)\right]}_{\boldsymbol{F},\boldsymbol{\nu}} = 0. \tag{52}$$

We have thus proved that

$$\overline{\left[\frac{d}{dt}\left(\frac{F_j}{|\boldsymbol{F}|^{3/2}}\right)\right]}_{\boldsymbol{F},\boldsymbol{\nu}} = 0. \tag{53}$$

We shall now examine the physical consequences of equation (44) more closely. In words, the meaning of this equation is that the component of

$$-\frac{2}{3}\pi G\overline{M}nB\left(\frac{|\boldsymbol{F}|}{Q_H}\right)\left(\boldsymbol{v}-3\frac{\boldsymbol{v}\cdot\boldsymbol{F}}{|\boldsymbol{F}|^2}\boldsymbol{F}\right) \tag{54}$$

along any particular direction gives the average value of the rate of change in the force $\boldsymbol{F}$ per unit mass acting on a star that is to be expected in the specified direction, when the star is moving with a velocity $\boldsymbol{v}$ in an appropriately chosen local standard of rest. Stated in this manner, we at once see the essential difference in the stochastic variations of $\boldsymbol{F}$ with time in the two cases $|\boldsymbol{v}| = 0$ and $|\boldsymbol{v}| \neq 0$. In the former case, $\overline{\dot{\boldsymbol{F}}} \equiv 0$; but this is not generally true when $|\boldsymbol{v}| \neq 0$. Or expressed differently, when $|\boldsymbol{v}| = 0$ the changes in $\boldsymbol{F}$ occur with equal probability in all directions, while this is not the case when $|\boldsymbol{v}| \neq 0$. The true nature of this difference is brought out very clearly when we consider

$$\overline{\left(\frac{d|\boldsymbol{F}|}{dt}\right)}_{\boldsymbol{F},\boldsymbol{v}} \tag{55}$$

according to equation (49). Remembering that $B(\beta) \geq 0$ for $\beta \geq 0$, we conclude from equation (49) that

$$\overline{\left(\frac{d|\boldsymbol{F}|}{dt}\right)}_{\boldsymbol{F},\boldsymbol{v}} > 0 \quad \text{if} \quad \boldsymbol{v}\cdot\boldsymbol{F} > 0, \tag{56}$$

and

$$\overline{\left(\frac{d|\boldsymbol{F}|}{dt}\right)}_{\boldsymbol{F},\boldsymbol{v}} < 0 \quad \text{if} \quad \boldsymbol{v}\cdot\boldsymbol{F} < 0. \tag{57}$$

In other words, if $\boldsymbol{F}$ has a positive component in the direction of $\boldsymbol{v}$, $|\boldsymbol{F}|$ increases on the average, while if $\boldsymbol{F}$ has a negative component in the direction of $\boldsymbol{v}$, $|\boldsymbol{F}|$ decreases on the average. This essential asymmetry introduced by the direction of $\boldsymbol{v}$ may be expected to give rise to the phenomenon of dynamical friction.

The characteristic aspects of the situation governed by equation (44) are best understood when we contrast it with the case $|\boldsymbol{v}| = 0$. Under these circumstances, we can visualize the motion of the representative point in the velocity space somewhat as follows.[7] The representative point suffers small random displacements in a manner that can be adequately described by the problem of random flights or more generally as Brownian motion. More specifically, the star may be assumed to suffer a large number of discrete increases in velocity of amounts $T(|\boldsymbol{F}|)\boldsymbol{F}$, where T denotes the mean life of the state $|\boldsymbol{F}|$ (see subsection below). Moreover, these increases may be assumed to take place in

[7] Cf. **Chandrasekhar, S.**, Astrophysical Jour. **94**: 511. 1941. (§§ 2 and 7.)

random directions. Accordingly, we may conclude that the mean square increase $\overline{|\Delta \boldsymbol{v}|^2}$ in the velocity to be expected in time t is given by

$$\overline{|\Delta \boldsymbol{v}|^2} = \overline{|\boldsymbol{F}|^2 T} t. \tag{58}$$

An alternative way of describing the same situation is that if we denote by $W(\boldsymbol{v};t)$ the probability that the star has a velocity $\boldsymbol{v}$ at time t when the velocity at $t = 0$ is $\boldsymbol{v}_0$, then W satisfies the *diffusion equation*

$$\frac{\partial W}{\partial t} = q\left(\frac{\partial^2 W}{\partial v_1{}^2} + \frac{\partial^2 W}{\partial v_2{}^2} + \frac{\partial^2 W}{\partial v_3{}^2}\right), \tag{59}$$

with the "*coefficient of diffusion*" q having the value

$$q = \frac{1}{6}\overline{|\boldsymbol{F}|^2 T}. \tag{60}$$

The solution of equation (59) for our purposes then is

$$W(\boldsymbol{v},t;\boldsymbol{v}_0) = \frac{1}{(4\pi q t)^{3/2}} e^{-|\boldsymbol{v}-\boldsymbol{v}_0|^2/4qt}. \tag{61}$$

The formula (58) is seen to be an immediate consequence of the solution (61).

Returning to the discussion of the case governed by equations (44) and (49), it is at once clear that the idealization of the motion of the representative point in the velocity space, as a problem in random flights, can no longer be valid. For, according to (56) and (57), during a given state of fluctuation of $\boldsymbol{F}$ a star is likely to suffer a greater absolute amount of acceleration if $(\boldsymbol{v}\cdot\boldsymbol{F})$ is negative than if $(\boldsymbol{v}\cdot\boldsymbol{F})$ is positive. But the *a priori* probability for $(\boldsymbol{v}\cdot\boldsymbol{F})$ to be positive or negative is equal. Hence, when integrated over a large number of fluctuations the star must suffer cumulatively a larger absolute amount of acceleration in a direction opposite to its own direction of motion than in the direction of motion. In other words we may expect a net tendency for the star to be relatively decelerated in the direction of its motion; further, this tendency is proportional to $|\boldsymbol{v}|$. But these are exactly what are implied by the existence of dynamical friction. (See Part II where the question of dynamical friction is considered in greater detail.)

THE SECOND MOMENT OF $[f]$ AND THE MEAN LIFE OF THE STATE $[F]$

According to equation (32)

$$W(F)\overline{|\boldsymbol{f}|^2} = -\frac{1}{8\pi^3}\int_{-\infty}^{+\infty} e^{-i\boldsymbol{\varrho}\cdot\boldsymbol{F}}\left[\nabla_{\boldsymbol{\sigma}}{}^2 A(\boldsymbol{\varrho},\boldsymbol{\sigma})\right]_{|\boldsymbol{\sigma}|=0} d\boldsymbol{\varrho}. \tag{62}$$

Using the expansion (33) for $C(\boldsymbol{\varrho},\boldsymbol{\sigma})$ we find after some lengthy calculations that

$$\left.\begin{aligned}\overline{|\boldsymbol{f}|^2}_{\boldsymbol{F},\boldsymbol{v}} = 2ab\,\frac{\beta^{1/2}}{H(\beta)}\Big\{2G(\beta) + 7k[\sin^2\alpha G(\beta) - (3\sin^2\alpha - 2)I(\beta)]\Big\} \\ + \frac{g^2}{\beta H(\beta)}\Big\{(4 - 3\sin^2\alpha)\beta H(\beta) + 3(3\sin^2\alpha - 2)K(\beta)\Big\}.\end{aligned}\right\} \tag{63}$$

where α denotes the angle between the directions of $\boldsymbol{F}$ and $\boldsymbol{v}$,

$$\left.\begin{aligned} a &= \frac{4}{15}(2\pi G)^{3/2}\overline{M^{3/2}}n, & b &= \frac{1}{4}(2\pi)^{3/2}G^{1/2}\overline{M^{1/2}|\boldsymbol{u}|^2}n, \\ g &= \frac{2}{3}\pi G\overline{M}|\boldsymbol{v}|n, & k &= \frac{3}{7}\frac{\overline{M^{1/2}|\boldsymbol{v}|^2}}{\overline{M^{1/2}|\boldsymbol{u}|^2}},\end{aligned}\right\} \tag{64}$$

and

$$\left.\begin{aligned} H(\beta) &= \frac{2}{\pi\beta}\int_0^\infty e^{-(x/\beta)^{3/2}}x\sin x\,dx, \\ G(\beta) &= \frac{3}{2}\int_0^\beta \beta^{-3/2}H(\beta)d\beta, \\ I(\beta) &= \beta^{-3/2}\int_0^\beta \beta^{1/2}G(\beta)d\beta, \\ K(\beta) &= \int_0^\beta H(\beta)d\beta.\end{aligned}\right\} \tag{65}$$

Averaging equation (63) for all possible mutual orientations of the two vectors $\boldsymbol{F}$ and $\boldsymbol{v}$ we readily find that

$$\overline{\overline{|\boldsymbol{f}|^2}}_{|\boldsymbol{F}|,|\boldsymbol{v}|} = 4ab\left\{\frac{\beta^{1/2}G(\beta)}{H(\beta)}\left(1 + \frac{7}{3}k\right) + \frac{g^2}{2ab}\right\}, \tag{66}$$

or substituting for k and $g^2/2ab$ from (64), we find that

$$\overline{\overline{|\boldsymbol{f}|^2}}_{|\boldsymbol{F}|,|\boldsymbol{v}|} = 4ab\left\{\frac{\beta^{1/2}G(\beta)}{H(\beta)}\left(1 + \frac{\overline{M^{1/2}|\boldsymbol{v}|^2}}{\overline{M^{1/2}|\boldsymbol{u}|^2}}\right) + \frac{5}{12\pi}\frac{\overline{M}^2|\boldsymbol{v}|^2}{\overline{M^{3/2}}\,\overline{M^{1/2}|\boldsymbol{u}|^2}}\right\}. \tag{67}$$

In terms of equation (67) we can define an approximate formula for the mean life of the state $|\boldsymbol{F}|$ according to [8]

$$T_{|\boldsymbol{F}|,|\boldsymbol{v}|} = \frac{|\boldsymbol{F}|}{\sqrt{\overline{\overline{|\boldsymbol{f}|^2}}_{|\boldsymbol{F}|,|\boldsymbol{v}|}}}. \tag{68}$$

[8] Cf. **Chandrasekhar, S., & von Neumann, J.** Astrophysical Jour. **95**: 489. 1942. Equation (167).

Combining equations (67) and (68) we find that

$$T_{|\boldsymbol{F}|,|\boldsymbol{v}|} = T_{|\boldsymbol{F}|,0} \frac{1}{\left[1 + \dfrac{\overline{M^{1/2}|\boldsymbol{v}|^2}}{\overline{M^{1/2}|\boldsymbol{u}|^2}} + \dfrac{5}{12\pi} \dfrac{\overline{M^2}\,|\boldsymbol{v}|^2}{\overline{M^{3/2}}\;\overline{M^{1/2}|\boldsymbol{u}|^2}} \dfrac{H(\beta)}{\beta^{1/2}G(\beta)}\right]^{1/2}}, \tag{69}$$

where $T_{|\boldsymbol{F}|,0}$ denotes the mean life when $|\boldsymbol{v}| = 0$:

$$T_{|\boldsymbol{F}|,0} = \sqrt{\frac{a^{1/3}}{4b} \cdot \frac{\beta^{3/2}H(\beta)}{G(\beta)}}. \tag{70}$$

Equation (70) suggests that we measure T in terms of the following unit, t_0, which appears natural to this problem:

$$t_0 = \sqrt{\frac{a^{1/3}}{4b}}. \tag{71}$$

Substituting for a and b from equation (64), we find that

$$\left.\begin{aligned} t_0 &= \frac{1}{(30)^{1/6}\pi^{1/2}} \left(\frac{[\overline{M^{3/2}}]^{1/3}}{[\overline{M^{1/2}|\boldsymbol{u}|^2}]}\right)^{1/2} \frac{1}{n^{1/3}} \\ &= \frac{0.3201}{n^{1/3}} \left(\frac{[\overline{M^{3/2}}]^{1/3}}{\overline{M^{1/2}|\boldsymbol{u}|^2}}\right)^{1/2}. \end{aligned}\right\} \tag{72}$$

And, finally, if we denote by $\tau(\beta;|\boldsymbol{v}|)$ the mean life expressed in this unit, we have

$$\tau(\beta;|\boldsymbol{v}|) = \tau(\beta;0) \frac{1}{\left[1 + \dfrac{\overline{M^{1/2}|\boldsymbol{v}|^2}}{\overline{M^{1/2}|\boldsymbol{u}|^2}} + \dfrac{5}{12\pi} \dfrac{\overline{M^2}|\boldsymbol{v}|^2}{\overline{M^{1/2}|\boldsymbol{u}|^2}} \dfrac{H(\beta)}{\beta^{1/2}G(\beta)}\right]^{1/2}}. \tag{73}$$

From equation (73) we derive the asymptotic formulae

$$\tau \to \beta \frac{1}{\left[1 + \dfrac{\overline{M^{1/2}|\boldsymbol{v}|^2}}{\overline{M^{1/2}|\boldsymbol{u}|^2}} + \dfrac{5}{12\pi} \dfrac{\overline{M^2}|\boldsymbol{v}|^2}{\overline{M^{3/2}}\,\overline{M^{1/2}|\boldsymbol{u}|^2}}\right]^{1/2}} \quad (\beta \to 0), \tag{74}$$

and

$$\tau \to \sqrt{\frac{15}{8}} \frac{1}{\left[1 + \dfrac{\overline{M^{1/2}|\boldsymbol{v}|^2}}{\overline{M^{1/2}|\boldsymbol{u}|^2}}\right]^{1/2}} \beta^{-1/2} \qquad (\beta \to \infty). \tag{75}$$

The function $\tau(\beta;0)$ is tabulated in Chandrasekhar and von Neumann's paper. Our present results show that approximately

$$\tau(\beta;|\boldsymbol{v}|) \sim \tau(\beta;0) \frac{1}{\left[1 + \dfrac{\overline{M^{1/2}|\boldsymbol{v}|^2}}{\overline{M^{1/2}|\boldsymbol{u}|^2}}\right]^{1/2}}. \tag{76}$$

According to equations (74) and (75), the approximate formula (76) may be expected to give values of τ correct to within 15 per cent over the entire range of β.

We may particularly draw attention to the very short lives of the weak fields.

II. DYNAMICAL FRICTION AND THE PRINCIPLES OF STATISTICAL DYNAMICS

General Considerations

As we have seen in Part I, in a first approximative discussion of the fluctuating part of the gravitational field acting on a star, we may suppose that the probability function $W(\boldsymbol{u},t)$ governing the occurrence of the velocity $\boldsymbol{u}$ at time t satisfies the diffusion equation (see equation [59]),

$$\frac{\partial W}{dt} = q\nabla_u{}^2 W\cdot \tag{77}$$

According to this equation, the probability distribution of the velocities $\boldsymbol{u}$ at time t when it is known with certainty that the star had the velocity $\boldsymbol{u}_0$ at time $t = 0$ is given by

$$W(\boldsymbol{u},t;\boldsymbol{u}_0) = \frac{1}{(4\pi qt)^{3/2}}\, e^{-|\boldsymbol{u}-\boldsymbol{u}_0|^2/4qt}. \tag{78}$$

We shall now indicate why the considerations outlined above cannot be valid for times which are long compared to $|\boldsymbol{u}|^2/q$ where $|\boldsymbol{u}|^2$ denotes the mean square velocity of the stars in an appropriately chosen local standard of rest. For, if $W(\boldsymbol{u},t;\boldsymbol{u}_0)$ according to equation (78) were valid for all times, then the probability that a star may have suffered any arbitrarily assigned large acceleration can be made as close to unity as we may choose by letting t approach infinity. This is, however, contrary to what we should expect on general grounds, namely, that $W(\boldsymbol{u},t;\boldsymbol{u}_0)$ approaches a Maxwellian distribution independently of $\boldsymbol{u}_0$ as $t \to \infty$. Expressed somewhat differently, we should strictly suppose that the stochastic variations in the velocity which a star experiences must be such as to leave an initial Maxwellian distribution of the velocities invariant. This is evidently not the case with the process described by equation (77). And the question now arises as to how we can generalize our earlier approximate considerations leading to equation (77) so that the underlying stochastic process may satisfy the criterion stated above. We shall now show how this can be achieved by the introduction of *dynamical friction*. More specifically, we shall suppose that the acceleration $\Delta\boldsymbol{u}$ which a star experiences in an interval of time Δt (long compared to the periods of the elementary fluctuations in $\boldsymbol{F}$ but short compared to the intervals during which $\boldsymbol{u}$ may be expected to change appreciably) can be expressed as the sum of two terms in the form

$$\Delta \boldsymbol{u} = \delta \boldsymbol{u}(\Delta t) - \eta \boldsymbol{u} \Delta t \tag{79}$$

where the first term on the right-hand side is governed by the probability distribution

$$\psi(\delta \boldsymbol{u}[\Delta t]) = \frac{1}{(4\pi q \Delta t)^{3/2}} e^{-|\delta \boldsymbol{u} - \text{grad}_{\boldsymbol{u}} q\, \Delta t|^2/4q\Delta t}. \tag{80}$$

and where the second term $-\eta \boldsymbol{u} \Delta t$ represents a *deceleration* of the star in the direction of its motion by an amount depending on $|\boldsymbol{u}|$. The constant of proportionality η can therefore be properly called the *coefficient of dynamical friction.*

With the underlying stochastic process defined as in equations (79) and (80), the probability distribution $W(\boldsymbol{u},t + \Delta t)$ of $\boldsymbol{u}$ at time $t + \Delta t$ can be derived from the distribution $W(\boldsymbol{u},t)$ at the earlier time t by means of the integral equation

$$W(\boldsymbol{u},t+\Delta t) = \int_{-\infty}^{+\infty} W(\boldsymbol{u}-\Delta \boldsymbol{u},t)\psi(\boldsymbol{u}-\Delta \boldsymbol{u};\Delta \boldsymbol{u})d(\Delta \boldsymbol{u}), \tag{81}$$

where $\psi(\boldsymbol{u};\Delta \boldsymbol{u})$ denotes the transition probability (see equation [80])

$$\psi(\boldsymbol{u};\Delta \boldsymbol{u}) = \frac{1}{(4\pi q \Delta t)^{3/2}} e^{-|\Delta \boldsymbol{u} - \text{grad}_{\boldsymbol{u}} q\Delta t + \eta \boldsymbol{u} \Delta t|^2/4q\Delta t} \tag{82}$$

Expanding $W(\boldsymbol{u},t + \Delta t)$, $W(\boldsymbol{u} - \Delta \boldsymbol{u},t)$ and $\psi(\boldsymbol{u} - \Delta \boldsymbol{u};\Delta \boldsymbol{u})$ which occur in equation (81) in the form of Taylor series, evaluating the various moments of $\Delta \boldsymbol{u}$ according to equation (82) and passing finally to the limit we obtain the following equation

$$\frac{\partial W}{\partial t} = \text{div}_{\boldsymbol{u}}\, (q\, \text{grad}_{\boldsymbol{u}}\, W + \eta W \boldsymbol{u}). \tag{83}$$

Finally, the condition that the Maxwellian distribution

$$\left(\frac{3}{2\pi \overline{|\boldsymbol{u}|^2}}\right)^{3/2} e^{-3|\boldsymbol{u}|^2/2\overline{|\boldsymbol{u}|^2}} \tag{84}$$

satisfy equation (83) *identically* requires that q and η be related according to

$$q = \frac{1}{3}\, \overline{|\boldsymbol{u}|^2} \eta. \tag{85}$$

Summarizing the conclusion reached, we may say that *general considerations, such as the invariance of the Maxwellian distribution to the underlying stochastic process, require that stars experience dynamical friction during their motion.*

The Resolution of Certain Fallacies and an Elementary Derivation of the Coefficient of Dynamical Friction

The conclusion we have reached in the preceding paragraph appears contrary to what might be expected on first sight. For we *might* argue in the following manner:

(a) Suppose we consider a star with a velocity $|\boldsymbol{u}|$ appreciably less than the root mean square velocity $(\overline{|\boldsymbol{u}|^2})^{1/2}$. We would then expect it to encounter oftener stars with velocities greater than its own than stars with velocities less than its own. And, consequently, we might be led to believe that stars with velocities less than the average would be systematically accelerated and, similarly, that stars with velocities greater than the average would be systematically decelerated.

How then does dynamical friction come to operate on *all* stars? Before we answer this question we shall state the second paradox.

(b) We might go farther and even argue that the conclusion reached in (a) is "reasonable." For, it might be supposed that systematically different effects on stars with relatively large, respectively small velocities, are required for the statistical maintenance of the average (i.e., normal) conditions.

In view of the great importance of dynamical friction for statistical dynamics, we shall analyze the questions raised above in some detail and expose the fallacies involved in (a) and (b).

First, it is easy to show that (b) is a plain misunderstanding. For, there is nothing obvious in the requirement that for the statistical maintenance of the average conditions stars differing from the average conditions should be affected differently according to the *sense* of their departure from the normal state. Indeed, the requirement that the normal conditions are self perpetuating is to state in a different form one of two things: Either, that starting from any arbitrary initial state we approach the normal state (e.g., the Maxwellian distribution of the velocities) as $t \to \infty$; or, that once the normal state has been attained it continues to be maintained. It is now apparent that these conditions can be met only if a given star behaves at later times in a manner less and less dependent on an initial state as time goes on; or expressing the same thing somewhat differently, we should much rather expect a star to gradually lose all trace of its initial state as the time progresses. Such a gradual loss of "memory" can be achieved only by the operation of a dissipative force like dynamical friction which will gradually damp out any given initial velocity. Thus, if we assume for the sake of simplicity, that η is independent of $|\boldsymbol{u}|$, then the *average* velocity at later times will tend to zero according as

$$\bar{\boldsymbol{u}} = \boldsymbol{u}_0 e^{-\eta t}. \tag{86}$$

But this is not to imply that the mean square velocity tends to zero. Indeed, the restoration of a Maxwellian distribution of velocities from an arbitrary initial state requires that

$$\bar{\boldsymbol{u}} \to 0 \qquad \text{and} \qquad \overline{|\boldsymbol{u}|^2} \to \text{a constant as } t \to \infty. \tag{87}$$

To achieve the first of the two foregoing conditions we need dynamical friction. Thus, the conclusions reached in (a), if valid, are contrary to the requirement for the restoration and maintenance of the normal state. It is therefore necessary to show wherein the argumentation of (a) is in error, and this we now proceed to do.

The way to refute arguments such as (a) is, of course, to actually verify directly whether or not a star with a given initial velocity is decelerated on the average independent of the magnitude of its velocity. For this purpose, it is perhaps simplest and most instructive to examine the problem on an approximation in which the fluctuations in $\boldsymbol{F}$ are analyzed in terms of single encounters each idealized as a two-body problem. On this approximation the increments in velocity $\Delta u_{||}$ and $\Delta u_{\perp}$ which a star with a velocity $u = |\boldsymbol{u}|$ and mass m suffers as the result of an encounter with another star, in directions which are respectively parallel to and perpendicular to the direction of motion, can be specified in terms of the parameters defining the encounter. We have[9]

$$\Delta u_{||} = -\frac{2m_1}{m_1 + m}[(u - v_1 \cos\theta)\cos\psi + v_1 \sin\theta\cos\Theta\sin\psi]\cos\psi, \tag{88}$$

and

$$\left.\begin{aligned} \Delta u_{\perp} = \pm\frac{2m_1}{m_1 + m}&[v_1^2 + u^2 - 2uv_1\cos\theta \\ &- \{(u - v_1\cos\theta)\cos\psi + v_1\sin\theta\cos\Theta\sin\psi\}^2]^{1/2}\cos\psi \end{aligned}\right\} \tag{89}$$

where m_1 and v_1 denote the mass and velocity of a typical field star and the rest of the symbols have the same meanings as in "Stellar Dynamics," Chapter ii (see particularly, pp. 51–64).

According to equation (89), and as can indeed be expected on general symmetry grounds, $\Delta u_{\perp}$ when summed over a large number of encounters vanishes identically. But this is not the case with $\Delta u_{||}$, for the net increase in the velocity which the star suffers in the direction of its motion during a time Δt (long compared to the periods of the elementary fluctuations in $\mathbf{F}$, but short compared to the time intervals during which $|\boldsymbol{u}|$ may be expected to change appreciably) is given by

[9] Cf. **Chandrasekhar, S.**, "Principles of Stellar Dynamics," p. 229 (equation 5.721). This monograph will be referred to hereafter as "Stellar Dynamics."

$$\Sigma \Delta u_{||} = \Delta t \int_0^\infty dv_1 \int_0^\pi d\theta \int_0^{2\pi} d\varphi \int_0^{D_0} dD \int_0^{2\pi} d\Theta N(v_1,\theta,\varphi) V D \Delta u_{||}, \quad (90)$$

when V denotes the relative velocity between the two stars, D the impact parameter, and where, further, the various integrations are, with respect to the different parameters, defining the single encounters. We shall not go into the details here of the evaluation of the multiple integral (90),[10] but only state that on carrying out the various integrations the remarkable result emerges that *to a sufficient accuracy only stars with velocities less than the one under consideration contribute to* $\Sigma \Delta u_{||}$. This result conclusively establishes the fallacy in the assertions made in (a) and, moreover, accounts for the appearance of dynamical friction on our present analysis. Omitting then the details of the analysis we find that

$$\Sigma \Delta u_{||} = -4\pi N m_1(m_1 + m) \frac{G^2}{|\boldsymbol{u}|^2} \left(\log_e \left[\frac{D_0 \overline{|\boldsymbol{u}|^2}}{G(m_1 + m)} \right] \right) \times [\Phi(j|\boldsymbol{u}|) - j|\boldsymbol{u}|\Phi'(j|\boldsymbol{u}|)]\Delta t, \quad (91)$$

where N denotes the number of stars per unit volume, D_0 the average distance between the stars, Φ and Φ' the error function

$$\Phi(x) = \frac{2}{\pi^{1/2}} \int_0^x e^{-x^2} dx, \quad (92)$$

and its derivative, respectively, and j the parameter which occurs in the assumed Maxwellian distribution of the velocities

$$\frac{j^3}{\pi^{3/2}} e^{-j^2|\boldsymbol{u}|^2} du; \qquad j = \left(\frac{3}{2\overline{|\boldsymbol{u}|^2}} \right)^{1/2}. \quad (93)$$

Remembering that $\Sigma \Delta u_\perp = 0$ we can write

$$\Sigma \Delta \boldsymbol{u} = -\eta \boldsymbol{u} \Delta t \quad (94)$$

where the coefficient of dynamical friction η has now the value

$$\eta = 4\pi N m_1(m_1 + m) \frac{G^2}{|\boldsymbol{u}|^3} \left(\log_e \left[\frac{D_0 \overline{|\boldsymbol{u}|^2}}{G(m_1 + m)} \right] \right) \times [\Phi(j|\boldsymbol{u}|) - j|\boldsymbol{u}|\Phi'(j|\boldsymbol{u}|)]. \quad (95)$$

In order next to verify directly the existence of a relation of the form (85) we evaluate the sum

$$\Sigma \Delta u_{||}{}^2. \quad (96)$$

We find that [11]

---

[10] The details have since been published in Astrophysical Jour. 97: 255, 1943. See p. 251 of this volume.

[11] "Stellar Dynamics," Equations (2.356) and (5.724).

$$\Sigma \Delta u_{||}^2 = \frac{8}{3}\pi N m_1^2 \frac{G^2}{|\boldsymbol{u}|^3}\left(\log_e\left[\frac{D_0\overline{|\boldsymbol{u}|^2}}{G(m_1+m)}\right]\right)$$
$$\times\,[\Phi(j|\boldsymbol{u}|) - j|\boldsymbol{u}|\Phi'(j|\boldsymbol{u}|)]\widehat{|\boldsymbol{u}|^2}\Delta t. \quad (97)$$

Hence,

$$\frac{\Sigma \Delta u_{||}^2}{\eta \Delta t} = \frac{2}{3}\frac{m_1}{m+m_1}\overline{|\boldsymbol{u}|^2}, \quad (98)$$

which is to be compared with equation (85). It is thus seen that a detailed analysis of the fluctuating field of the nearby stars in terms of individual stellar encounters idealized, as two body problems, fully confirms the conclusions reached earlier on the basis of certain general principles. In addition we now have an explicit evaluation of the coefficients q and η.

The Principles of Statistical Dynamics

In the two preceding sections we have seen how we can take into account the effect of the near neighbors on the motion of a star statistically through the two coefficients q and η. In thus representing the effect of the near neighbors in terms of the diffusion coefficient q (in the velocity space) and the frictional coefficient η we have abandoned all attempts to describe in detail the motion of any single star and have agreed instead to follow its motion through the distribution function $W(\boldsymbol{u},t)$ governing the probability of occurrence of the velocity $\boldsymbol{u}$ at time t. And as we have already shown, this probability function $W(\boldsymbol{u},t)$ satisfies the equation

$$\frac{\partial W}{\partial t} = \text{div}_{\boldsymbol{u}}\,(q\,\text{grad}_{\boldsymbol{u}}\,W + \eta W\boldsymbol{u}), \quad (99)$$

where it may be recalled that q and η are related according to equation (85). This differential equation satisfied by W leads to an important interpretation of the stochastic process which takes place in the velocity space. For, according to equation (99) we can visualize the motion of the representative points in the velocity space as a *process of diffusion* in which the rate of flow across an element of surface $d\sigma$ is given by

$$-\,(q\,\text{grad}_{\boldsymbol{u}}\,W + \eta W\boldsymbol{u})\cdot\mathbf{1}_{d\sigma}d\sigma, \quad (100)$$

where $\mathbf{1}_{d\sigma}$ is a unit vector normal to the element of surface considered. We shall find that this interpretation of the stochastic process which takes place in the velocity space as a diffusion process has important consequences for the applications of the theory (see Part III).

So far, we have restricted ourselves to what happens in the velocity space. We have, moreover, assumed that no external forces were acting. The question now arises as to how we can incorporate in a rational system of dynamics the stochastic variations in the velocity which a star suffers on account of the fluctuating force acting on it. It is evident that to build such a system of dynamics what we need is essentially a differential equation which will be appropriate for discussing the probability distribution in the six dimensional phase space in contrast to equation (99) which operates only in the velocity space. In other words, we require a proper generalization of Liouville's equation of classical dynamics to include terms corresponding to the stochastic variations in $\boldsymbol{u}$. Such a generalization can be readily found.

Quite generally we may write

$$\left.\begin{aligned} \Delta\boldsymbol{u} &= \boldsymbol{K}\Delta t + \delta\boldsymbol{u}(\Delta t) - \eta\boldsymbol{u}\Delta t \\ \Delta\boldsymbol{r} &= \boldsymbol{u}\Delta t \end{aligned}\right\} \qquad (101)$$

where $\boldsymbol{K}$ denotes the external force per unit mass acting on the star and $\Delta\boldsymbol{u}$ and $\Delta\boldsymbol{r}$ the increments in the velocity and position experienced by the star in a time Δt. The interval which is chosen must again be such that it is long compared to the periods of the elementary fluctuations but short compared to the intervals during which $\boldsymbol{u}$ and $\boldsymbol{r}$ may be expected to change appreciably. Then analogous to the integral equation (81) we now have

$$W(\boldsymbol{r},\boldsymbol{u},t+\Delta t) = \int_{-\infty}^{+\infty}\int_{-\infty}^{+\infty} W(\boldsymbol{r}-\Delta\boldsymbol{r},\boldsymbol{u}-\Delta\boldsymbol{u},t) \Psi(\boldsymbol{r}-\Delta\boldsymbol{r},\boldsymbol{u}-\Delta\boldsymbol{u};\Delta\boldsymbol{r},\Delta\boldsymbol{u})d(\Delta\boldsymbol{r})d(\Delta\boldsymbol{u}), \qquad (102)$$

where $\Psi(\boldsymbol{r},\boldsymbol{u};\Delta\boldsymbol{r},\Delta\boldsymbol{u})$ denotes the transition probability in the phase space. According to equations (82) and (101) we now have

$$\Psi(\boldsymbol{r},\boldsymbol{u};\Delta\boldsymbol{r},\Delta\boldsymbol{u}) = \frac{1}{(4\pi q\Delta t)^{3/2}} e^{-|\Delta\boldsymbol{u}-\boldsymbol{K}\Delta t - q\,\mathrm{grad}_{\boldsymbol{u}}\Delta t + \eta\boldsymbol{u}\Delta t|^2/4q\Delta t} \times \delta(\Delta x - u_x\Delta t)\delta(\Delta y - u_y\Delta t)\delta(\Delta z - u_z\Delta t). \qquad (103)$$

Expanding the various terms in equation (102) in the form of Taylor series and proceeding as in the derivation of equation (83) we obtain

$$\frac{\partial W}{\partial t} + \boldsymbol{u}\cdot\mathrm{grad}_r\, W + \boldsymbol{K}\ \mathrm{grad}_u\, W = \mathrm{div}_u\,(q\ \mathrm{grad}_u\, W + \eta W\boldsymbol{u}). \qquad (104)$$

The foregoing equation represents the complete generalization of Liouville's theorem of classical dynamics for a single particle. On the left-hand side we have the usual Stokes' operator D/Dt operating on W while on the right-hand side we have the terms incorporating the fluctuations caused by the neighboring stars. It should, however, be noticed that the Liouville equation now operates in the six dimensional phase space. This is because we have taken into account the effect of the neighboring stars statistically through the terms involving q and η. Further, it should be noticed, too, that the relation (85) between q and η ensures that the Maxwell-Boltzmann distribution in the phase space is invariant to the stochastic process considered (see the section below).

Analytical Dynamics versus Statistical Dynamics

In the preceding sections we have outlined the general principles of a statistical theory of stellar dynamics. In order that we may emphasize and further amplify the basic ideas which are involved, we shall contrast the outlook of statistical dynamics with the point of view familiar in analytical dynamics.

ANALYTICAL DYNAMICS	STATISTICAL DYNAMICS
1. In analytical dynamics we follow in *detail* the motion of each of the degrees of freedom of the dynamical system.	1. In statistical dynamics we follow instead the motion of each of the particles *statistically* when under the fluctuating influence of a large number of other particles belonging also to the system.
2. The notion of acceleration is fundamental to analytical dymanics.	2. For the success of the methods of statistical dynamics it is essential that time intervals Δt exist with the property that they are long compared to the periods of the elementary fluctuations but which are at the same time short compared to the times necessary for $\boldsymbol{u}$ to change appreciably. Moreover, during such an interval Δt the mean square increment in $\boldsymbol{u}$ is given by $\overline{\lvert\Delta \boldsymbol{u}\rvert^2} = 2q\Delta t.$ Accordingly $\frac{\sqrt{\overline{\lvert\Delta \boldsymbol{u}\rvert^2}}}{\Delta t} \rightarrow \infty \quad \text{as} \quad \Delta t \rightarrow 0.$ In other words, we cannot properly define acceleration within the framework of statistical dynamics.

3. The equations of motion governing a conservative dynamical system can be thrown into the canonical forms

$$\dot{p}_r = -\frac{\partial H}{\partial q_r}; \qquad \dot{q}_r = \frac{\partial H}{\partial p_r} \qquad (r = 1, \cdots, N),$$

where H is the Hamiltonian function. These equations can be interpreted by the statement that the development of a conservative dynamical system represents "the gradual unfolding of a contact transformation" (Whittaker).

3. In statistical dynamics the fundamental assumption is generally made that the stochastic process which takes place can be described as a *Markoff chain.* More explicitly, we suppose that the probability distribution

$$W(\boldsymbol{r}, \boldsymbol{u}, t + \Delta t)$$

at the time $t + \Delta t$ can be derived from the distribution ($W(\boldsymbol{r}, \boldsymbol{u}, t)$ at the slightly earlier time t through an integral equation of the form

$$W(\boldsymbol{r}, \boldsymbol{u}, t + \Delta t) = \int_{-\infty}^{+\infty}\int_{-\infty}^{+\infty} W(\boldsymbol{r} - \Delta\boldsymbol{r}, \boldsymbol{u} - \Delta\boldsymbol{u}, t) \times \Psi(\boldsymbol{r} - \Delta\boldsymbol{r}, \boldsymbol{u} - \Delta\boldsymbol{u}; \Delta\boldsymbol{r}, \Delta\boldsymbol{u}) \times d(\Delta\boldsymbol{r})d(\Delta\boldsymbol{u})$$

where $\Psi(\boldsymbol{r}, \boldsymbol{u}; \Delta\boldsymbol{r}, \Delta\boldsymbol{u})$ denotes the transition probability. (The foregoing integral relation connecting $W(\boldsymbol{r}, \boldsymbol{u}, t + \Delta t)$ and $W(\boldsymbol{r}, \boldsymbol{u}, t)$ can be regarded as defining a Markoff chain.) Analogous to the interpretation of the canonical equations in analytical dynamics we may describe a Markoff process as "the gradual unfolding of a transition probability."

4. In the $2N$ dimensional phase space the hydrodynamical flow which can be set up by following each point in this space according to the canonical equations is described by Liouville's theorem. According to this theorem, an initially assigned density

$$W(q_1, \cdots, q_N, p_1, \cdots, p_N)$$

in the phase space varies according to the equation

$$\frac{\partial W}{\partial t} + \sum_{r=1}^{N} \left(\frac{\partial H}{\partial p_r}\frac{\partial W}{\partial q_r} - \frac{\partial H}{\partial q_r}\frac{\partial W}{\partial p_r} \right) = 0.$$

4. The probability distribution in the 6-dimensional phase space (i.e., the phase space of a *single* particle) is governed by the equation

$$\frac{\partial W}{\partial t} + \boldsymbol{u} \cdot \operatorname{grad}_r W + \boldsymbol{K} \cdot \operatorname{grad}_{\boldsymbol{u}} W = \operatorname{div}_{\boldsymbol{u}}(q \operatorname{grad}_{\boldsymbol{u}} W + \eta W \boldsymbol{u}),$$

where $\boldsymbol{K}$ denotes the external force per unit mass acting on the particle, and q and η the diffusion and the frictional coefficients describing the stochastic process which takes place in the velocity space (see 5 below).

5. The order of the system of equations governing the development of a dynamical system equals twice the number of degrees of freedom of the system.

5. In statistical dynamics *almost all* the coordinates are ignored. This ignoration of the coordinates of all the neighboring particles becomes possible only because we are able to represent their influence on the statistical motion of any single particle through the two coefficients q and η. More particularly, the stochastic variations which take place in the velocity space can be described as a general process of diffusion in which the rate of flow across an element of surface $d\sigma$ is given by

$$-\left(q \operatorname{grad}_{\boldsymbol{u}} W + \eta W \boldsymbol{u} - \boldsymbol{K} W\right) . \mathbf{1}_{d\sigma} d\sigma,$$

where $\mathbf{1}_{d\sigma}$ is a unit vector normal to the element of surface considered.

6. The equations of motion of a conservative dynamical system possess the energy integral

$$H = \text{Constant}.$$

6. The generalized Liouville equation in the 6-dimensional phase space governing the probability distribution $W(\boldsymbol{r}, \boldsymbol{u}, t)$ is satisfied identically by the Maxwell-Boltzmann distribution

$$W = \text{Constant } e^{-3(|\boldsymbol{u}|^2 + 2\mathbf{V})/2\overline{|\boldsymbol{u}|^2}}$$

where

$$\boldsymbol{K} = -\operatorname{grad} \mathbf{V}.$$

It is this circumstance which enables the restoration of a Maxwell-Boltzmann distribution from any arbitrary initial state.

7. When dealing with conservative dynamical systems, dissipative forces are foreign to the notions of analytical dynamics. However, dissipative forces may appear in the discussion of dynamical systems in their *non-natural* forms, i.e., when the system is considered in a reduced number of coordinates after the process of the ignoration of coordinates (Whittaker, *Analytical Dynamics*, p. 57).

7. The occurrence of dissipative forces like dynamical friction in the stochastic variations in the velocity experienced by a particle is essential for the success of statistical dynamics. For, it is precisely on account of the occurrence of the term involving dynamical friction that the restoration and maintenance, for example, of a Maxwellian distribution of the velocities among the particles is made possible. Alternatively, we may express the same thing by saying that the operation of a dissipative force like dynamical friction is exactly what is needed to conserve the energy of the assembly as a whole. This may sound paradoxical at first sight, but it is intimately connected with the fact that in statistical dynamics we have essentially performed an ignoration of the coordinates of the neighboring particles.

III. THE RATE OF ESCAPE OF STARS FROM CLUSTERS AND THE EVIDENCE FOR THE OPERATION OF DYNAMICAL FRICTION

The General Theory of the Rate of Escape of Stars from Clusters

One of the most important factors in the evolution of the galactic and the globular clusters is their gradual impoverishment due to the escape of stars.[12] Essentially, the mechanism underlying this escape of stars is as follows:

On account of the fluctuating gravitational field acting on a star we should expect that there exists a finite probability for a star to acquire a velocity sufficient to escape from the cluster during any specified length of time t. And if a star should acquire the necessary velocity it would naturally escape from the cluster. We shall now show how, on the basis of the statistical theory developed in Part II, we can evaluate this factor in the evolution of clusters quite rigorously.

To be specific, we shall suppose that in order that a star may escape from a cluster it is only necessary that it acquire a velocity greater than or equal to a certain critical velocity which we shall denote by v_∞. On this assumption the probability that a star will have acquired the necessary velocity for escape during a certain time t can be evaluated quite simply from the probability $p(v_0,t)\Delta t$ that a star having initially a velocity $|\boldsymbol{u}| = v_0$ at time $t = 0$ will acquire for the *first time* the velocity $|\boldsymbol{u}| = v_\infty$ during t and $t + dt$. For, on integrating $p(v_0,t)$ over t from 0 to t we shall obtain the total probability $Q(v_0,t)$ that the star will have acquired the velocity v_∞ during the entire interval from 0 to t. And finally averaging $Q(v_0,t)$ over the relevant range of the initial velocities, we shall obtain the *expectation* $Q(t)$ that a star will have acquired the velocity v_∞ during the time t.

The advantage of formulating the problem in the manner described above is that the function $p(v_0,t)$ can be determined in terms of a solution of the equation (see equation [99])

$$\frac{\partial W}{\partial t} = \text{div}_{\boldsymbol{u}}\,(q\,\text{grad}_{\boldsymbol{u}}\,W + \eta W\boldsymbol{u}) \tag{105}$$

which satisfies certain appropriate boundary conditions. For, remembering that the stochastic process described by the foregoing equation has a simple interpretation in terms of general type of diffusion process, it is evident that $p(v_0,t)$ will be given by

[12] This fact was first clearly recognized by Ambarzumian and Spitzer. For an account of these earlier discussions see "Stellar Dynamics," §§ 5.3 and 5.4, pp. 250–213.

$$p(v_0,t) = -\left(4\pi q|\boldsymbol{u}|^2 \frac{\partial W(|\boldsymbol{u}|,t)}{\partial|\boldsymbol{u}|}\right)_{|\boldsymbol{u}|=v_\infty}, \tag{106}$$

where $W(|\boldsymbol{u}|,t)$ denotes a spherically symmetric solution of equation (105) which satisfied the boundary conditions

$$W(|\boldsymbol{u}|,t) = 0 \text{ for } |\boldsymbol{u}| = v_\infty \text{ for all } t > 0, \tag{107}$$

and

$$W(|\boldsymbol{u}|,t) \rightarrow \frac{1}{4\pi v_0^2}\,\delta(|\boldsymbol{u}| - v_0) \quad \text{as} \quad t \rightarrow 0, \tag{108}$$

where δ stands for the δ-function of Dirac. We shall now show how we can obtain such a solution.

For the case under discussion we have (see equation [95])

$$\eta = 8\pi N m^2 G^2\left(\log_e\left[\frac{D_0\overline{|\boldsymbol{u}|^2}}{2Gm}\right]\right)\frac{1}{|\boldsymbol{u}|^3}[\Phi(j|\boldsymbol{u}|) - j|\boldsymbol{u}|\Phi'(j|\boldsymbol{u}|)]. \tag{109}$$

This formula for η can be written more conveniently as

$$\eta = \eta_0\nu(j|\boldsymbol{u}|) \tag{110}$$

where

$$\eta_0 = 8\pi N m^2 G^2\left(\log_e\left[\frac{D_0\overline{|\boldsymbol{u}|^2}}{2Gm}\right]\right)\left(\frac{3}{2\overline{|\boldsymbol{u}|^2}}\right)^{3/2}\frac{4}{3\pi^{1/2}} \tag{111}$$

and

$$\nu(\rho) = \frac{3\pi^{1/2}}{4}\,\rho^{-3}[\Phi(\rho) - \rho\Phi'(\rho)]; \tag{112}$$

with $\nu(\rho)$ defined in this manner

$$\left.\begin{aligned} &\nu(\rho) \rightarrow 1 \quad \text{as} \quad \rho \rightarrow 0,\\ &\nu(\rho) \rightarrow \frac{3\pi^{1/2}}{4}\,\rho^{-3} \quad \text{as} \quad \rho \rightarrow \infty. \end{aligned}\right\} \tag{113}$$

Again, since q and η are generally related according to equation (85), we have

$$q = \frac{1}{3}\,\overline{|\boldsymbol{u}|^2}\eta_0\nu(j|\boldsymbol{u}|). \tag{114}$$

Returning to equation (105) we introduce the following change of the independent variables:

$$\tau = \eta_0 t; \qquad \boldsymbol{u} = \left(\frac{2}{3}\,\overline{|u|^2}\right)^{1/2}\boldsymbol{\varrho}. \tag{115}$$

Equation (105) now takes the dimensionless form

$$\frac{\partial W}{\partial\tau} = \text{div}_{\boldsymbol{\varrho}}\left[\frac{1}{2}\,\nu(|\boldsymbol{\varrho}|)\,\text{grad}_{\boldsymbol{\varrho}}\,W + \nu(|\boldsymbol{\varrho}|)W\boldsymbol{\varrho}\right]. \tag{116}$$

For a spherically symmetric solution $W(|\mathbf{\varrho}|,\tau)$ equation (116) reduces to

$$\rho \frac{\partial w}{\partial \tau} = \frac{\partial}{\partial \rho}\left[\nu(\rho)\left\{\frac{1}{2}\rho \frac{\partial w}{\partial \rho} + \left(\rho^2 - \frac{1}{2}\right)w\right\}\right] \tag{117}$$

where we have written

$$\rho = |\mathbf{\varrho}|; \qquad w = Wp. \tag{118}$$

According to equations (107) and (108) we require a solution of equation (117) which satisfies the boundary conditions

$$w(\rho,\tau) = 0 \text{ for both } \rho = 0 \text{ and } \rho = \rho_\infty \text{ for all } \tau > 0, \tag{119}$$

and

$$w(\rho,\tau) \rightarrow \frac{1}{4\pi\rho_0}\,\delta(\rho - \rho_0) \quad \text{as} \quad \tau \rightarrow 0. \tag{120}$$

Now equation (117) is separable in the variables ρ and τ. Accordingly we write

$$w = e^{-\lambda\tau}\phi(\rho) \tag{121}$$

where λ is for the present an unspecified constant; we then obtain for ϕ the differential equation

$$\frac{d}{d\rho}\left[\nu(\rho)\left\{\frac{1}{2}\rho \frac{d\phi}{d\rho} + \left(\rho^2 - \frac{1}{2}\right)\phi\right\}\right] + \lambda\rho\phi = 0 \tag{122}$$

If we now let

$$\phi = e^{-\rho^2/2}\psi \tag{123}$$

we obtain

$$\frac{d^2\psi}{d\rho^2} + \frac{d \log \nu}{d\rho}\frac{d\psi}{d\rho} + \left[2\frac{\lambda}{\nu(\rho)} + 3 - \rho^2 - \frac{d \log \nu}{d\rho}\left(\frac{1}{\rho} - \rho\right)\right]\psi = 0. \tag{124}$$

It is now seen that in order that a solution of the foregoing equation may vanish at $\rho = 0$ and at $\rho = \rho_\infty$, it is necessary that λ take one of an infinite enumerable set of discrete values

$$\lambda_1, \lambda_2, \cdots, \lambda_n, \cdots \tag{125}$$

which we may properly call the "characteristic values" of the problem. Further if

$$\psi_1, \psi_2, \cdots, \psi_n, \cdots \tag{126}$$

denote the solutions of equation (124) which satisfy the boundary conditions (119) at $\rho = 0$ and $\rho = \rho_\infty$ and belong, respectively, to the values $\lambda_1, \lambda_2, \cdots, \lambda_n, \cdots$ then it can be readily verified that these solutions form a complete set of orthogonal functions. Without loss of generality we can therefore suppose that these functions are all properly normalized. Consequently, in terms of the fundamental solutions

$$w_n = e^{-\lambda_n\tau}e^{-\rho^2/2}\psi_n(\rho) \tag{127}$$

which satisfy the boundary conditions (119) we can construct solutions which will satisfy any further arbitrary boundary condition for $\tau = 0$. Thus, remembering that a δ-function can always be constructed in terms of any complete set of orthogonal functions according to

$$\delta(\rho - \rho_0) = \sum_{n=1}^{\infty} \psi_n(\rho)\psi_n(\rho_0), \tag{128}$$

it is evident that

$$w = \frac{1}{4\pi\rho_0} e^{-(\rho^2-\rho_0^2)/2} \sum_{n=1}^{\infty} e^{-\lambda_n\tau} \psi_n(\rho)\psi_n(\rho_0) \tag{129}$$

satisfies all the boundary conditions of our problem. Corresponding to the solution (129) for w we have

$$W = \frac{1}{4\pi\rho\rho_0} e^{-(\rho^2-\rho_0^2)/2} \sum_{n=1}^{\infty} e^{-\lambda_n\tau} \psi_n(\rho)\psi_n(\rho_0). \tag{130}$$

Using the foregoing solution for W we can write down the probability function $p(\rho_0,\tau)$. For, since

$$p(\rho_0,\tau) = -2\pi\rho_\infty^2\nu(\rho_\infty)\left(\frac{\partial W}{\partial \rho}\right)_{\rho=\rho_\infty}, \tag{131}$$

we have

$$p(\rho_0,\tau) = \frac{\rho_\infty}{2\rho_0}\nu(\rho_\infty)e^{-(\rho_\infty^2-\rho_0^2)/2} \sum_{n=1}^{\infty} e^{-\lambda_n\tau}\left(-\frac{\partial\psi_n}{\partial\rho}\right)_{\rho=\rho_\infty}\psi_n(\rho_0). \tag{132}$$

To obtain the probability $Q(\rho_0,\tau)$ that a star having an initial velocity corresponding to ρ_0 will have acquired a velocity corresponding to ρ_∞ during the time τ we have simply to integrate equation (132) from 0 to τ. Thus we find that

$$\left.\begin{aligned} Q(\rho_0,\tau) = \frac{\rho_\infty}{2\rho_0}\nu(\rho_\infty)e^{-(\rho_\infty^2-\rho_0^2)/2} \sum_{n=1}^{\infty} \frac{1}{\lambda_n}(1 - e^{-\lambda_n\tau}) \\ \left(-\frac{d\psi_n}{d\rho}\right)_{\rho=\rho_\infty}\psi_n(\rho_0). \end{aligned}\right\} \tag{133}$$

Finally to obtain, $Q(\tau)$, that an average star will have acquired the necessary velocity for escape during a time τ, we must average the foregoing expression over all ρ_0. The final result can therefore be expressed in the form

$$Q(\tau) = \sum_{n=1}^{\infty} Q_n(\tau), \tag{134}$$

where

$$Q_n(\tau) = A_n(1 - e^{-\lambda_n\tau}), \tag{135}$$

and

$$A_n = \frac{1}{2\lambda_n}\rho_\infty\nu(\rho_\infty)e^{-\rho_\infty^2/2}\left(-\frac{d\psi_n}{d\rho}\right)_{\rho=\rho_\infty}\left[\overline{\frac{e^{\rho_0^2/2}}{\rho_0}\psi_n(\rho_0)}\right]. \tag{136}$$

The Evidence for the Operation of Dynamical Friction

We shall now illustrate with some numerical results the theory developed in the preceding section.

Now, since in a star cluster the root mean square velocity of escape is twice the mean square velocity of the stars in the system,[13] it is clear that the values of ρ_∞ which come under discussion are in the general neighborhood of

$$\rho_\infty = \sqrt{6} \sim 2.45. \tag{137}$$

For values of ρ_∞ in this neighborhood it was found that $Q(\tau)$ can be represented with ample accuracy by the first term on the right-hand side of equation (134). Accordingly it was sufficient to specify the lowest characteristic value λ_1 (for a given ρ_∞) and the normalized characteristic function ψ_1 belonging to it. In this manner it was found that

$$Q(\tau) = 1 - e^{-0.0075\tau} \qquad (\rho_\infty = 2.4518). \tag{138}$$

(The foregoing equation provides sufficient accuracy for $\tau > 5$).

Since $Q(\tau)$ gives the expectation that an average star will have escaped during a time τ (in units of η_0^{-1}) we can properly regard $(0.0075\eta_0)^{-1}$ as a measure of the half-life of the cluster. Thus

$$\text{Half-life of a cluster} \backsimeq 133\ \eta_0^{-1}. \tag{139}$$

For the Pleiades η_0^{-1} is of the order of 2×10^7 years, so that its half-life is of the order of 3×10^9 years. In judging this value it should be remembered that (as may be readily verified) when dynamical friction is ignored, a half-life for the Pleiades of the order of only 5×10^7 years is predicted. There can thus be hardly any doubt that dynamical friction provides the principal mechanism for the continued existence of the galactic clusters like the Pleiades for times of the order of 3×10^9 years. But, even with dynamical friction properly allowed for (as we have done), it will be hard to account for such clusters half-lives of the order 10^{10} years. This, in turn, provides another strong argument in favor of the now currently adopted "short time scale" of the order of 3×10^9 years.

In concluding this essay, we might draw attention to the far reaching analogy which exists between these newer methods in stellar dynamics and methods long familiar in the theory of Brownian movement. However, while parts of the theory of Brownian motion are heuristic and appeal to intuitive considerations, it appears that in stellar dynamics the entire problem can be analyzed explicitly in all its phases.

[13] Cf. "Stellar Dynamics," pp. 206–207.

SUBJECT INDEX

This index covers *Principles of Stellar Dynamics* and its appendixes. It does not cover the later papers, *Dynamical Friction* and *New Methods in Stellar Dynamics.*